GOLDEN EAGLE. ¼ NAT SIZE

PLATE I.

BRITISH BIRDS

BY

W. H. HUDSON, C.M.Z.S.

WITH A CHAPTER ON STRUCTURE AND CLASSIFICATION
BY FRANK E. BEDDARD, F.R.S.

*With 8 Coloured Plates from Original Drawings by A. Thorburn
and 8 Plates and 100 Figures in black and white from Original Drawings by G. E. Lodge
and 3 Illustrations from Photographs from Nature by R. B. Lodge*

NEW IMPRESSION

LONGMANS, GREEN, AND CO.
39 PATERNOSTER ROW, LONDON
FOURTH AVENUE & 30TH STREET, NEW YORK
BOMBAY, CALCUTTA, AND MADRAS

1921

CONTENTS.

Order STEGANOPODES.

Order HERODIONES.

Order ANSERES.

LIST OF ILLUSTRATIONS.

———◆◇◆———

INTRODUCTION.

THE plan followed in the descriptive portion of this work has, I trust, the merit of simplicity. A brief account is given of the appearance, language, and life-habits of all the species that reside permanently, or for a portion of each year, within the limits of the British Islands. The accidental stragglers, with the irregular or occasional visitors, have been included, but not described, in the work. To have omitted all mention of them would, perhaps, have been to carry the process of simplification too far. And as much may be said of the retention in this book of Latin, or 'science' names. The mass of technical matter with which ornithological works are usually weighted is scarcely wanted in a book intended for the general reader, more especially for the young. Nor was there space sufficient to make the work at the same time a technical and a popular one : the briefest description that could possibly be given of the characters of genera would have occupied thirty to forty pages. The student must, in any case, go to the large standard works on the subject, especially to those of Yarrell (fourth edition), Seebohm, and Howard Saunders, which are repositories of all the most important facts relating to our bird life, gathered from the time of Willughby, the father of British ornithology, down to the present.

The order in which I have placed the species, beginning with the thrushes and ending with the auks, is that of

Sclater, based on Huxley's classification, and is the arrangement adopted in the official list of the British Ornithologists' Union (1883). The B.O.U. list enumerates 376 species; and of this number 211 species are counted as residents and regular visitants; the remaining 165 being loosely described as 'Occasional Visitants.' About these aliens, which are claimed as citizens, something requires to be said.

It has long been the practice of our ornithologists to regard as 'British' any species of which one specimen has been found in a wild state within the limits of the United Kingdom. As a result of this excessive hospitality we find in the list about forty-three species of which not more than three specimens have been obtained; in a majority of cases only one. We also find that there are not fewer than forty-five exclusively American species in the list; but by what means, or by what series of extraordinary accidents, these lost wanderers have been carried thousands of miles from their own region, across the Atlantic, and have succeeded in reaching our shores alive, it is impossible to imagine. It is highly probable that some of the American, Asiatic, and European waifs that have been picked up in these islands were birds that had escaped from confinement; but whether brought by man or borne on the wings of the tempest to our shores, the fact remains that they are not members of our avifauna, and the young reader should clearly understand that only by a pleasing fiction are they called 'British.'

I have spoken at some length on this subject, because it is one that appears to interest a great many persons who are not ornithologists. How many British species are there? is a question that is continually being asked of those who are supposed to know. I should say that, in round numbers, there are 200; at the very outside, 210. Seebohm, in the introduction to his great work, gives 222 as the number of species 'fairly entitled to be considered British birds'; but he probably counted some that are usually regarded as irregular visitors, and perhaps others which have been exterminated in recent times. Of the 165 species set down in the

'British' list as occasional visitors, about 55 or 60 deserve
that description, since they do, as a fact, visit the British
Islands at irregular intervals. All the others are accidental
stragglers.

It only remains to add something on another subject—the
little life-histories of the two hundred and odd species described in this volume. Although this is in no sense a con-
troversial subject, the apologetic tone must be still used. I
wish that these sketches had been better done, but I do not
greatly regret that they had to be brief. The longest history
of a bird ever written, the most abounding in facts and
delightful to read, when tested in the only sure way—
namely, by close observation of its subject—is found to be
scarcely more complete or satisfactory than the briefest,
which contains only the main facts. This is because birds
are not automata, but intelligent beings. Seebohm has well
said, 'The real history of a bird is its *life*-history. The
deepest interest attaches to everything that reveals the little
mind, however feebly it may be developed, which lies behind
the feathers.' It has been remarked more than once that
we do not rightly appreciate birds because we do not see
them well. In most cases persecution has made them
fearful of the human form ; they fly from us, and distance
obscures their delicate harmonious colouring and blurs the
exquisite aërial lines on which they are formed. When we
look closely at them, we are surprised at their beauty and
the indescribable grace of their varied motions. An analogous
effect is produced by a close observation of their habits
or actions, which, seen from afar, may appear few and monotonous. Canon Atkinson, in his ' Sketches in Natural History '
(1865), has a chapter about the partridge, prefaced by Yarrell's
remark, that of a bird so universally known there was little
that was new to be said. While admitting the general truth
of this statement, the author goes on to say : ' Still, I have
from time to time observed some slight peculiarity in the
habits of the partridge that I have not seen noticed in any
professed description of the bird, forming certain passages, as

it were, of its minute history.' It is precisely this 'minute history' that gives so great and enduring a fascination to the study of birds in a state of nature. But it cannot be written, on account of the infinity of 'passages' contained in it, or, in other words, of that element of mind which gives it endless variety.

Let us imagine the case of a youth or boy who has read and re-read half a dozen long histories of some one species ; and, primed with all this knowledge, who finally goes out to observe it for himself. It will astonish him to find how much he has not been told. He will begin to think that the writers must have been hasty or careless, that they neglected their opportunities, and missed much that they ought not to have missed ; and he may even experience a feeling of resentment towards them, as if they had treated him unfairly. But after more time spent in observation he will make the interesting discovery that, so long as they are watched for, fresh things will continue to appear. The reflection will follow that there must be a limit to the things that can be recorded ; that the life-history of a bird cannot be contained in any book, however voluminous it may be ; and, finally, that books have a quite different object from the one he had imagined. And in the end he will be more than content that it should be so.

W. H. H.

BRITISH BIRDS.

THE ANATOMY OF A BIRD.

IT is very important that every one who studies birds should have some acquaintance with their insides as well as with their outsides. To have a proper appreciation of the mechanism of flight, the most distinctive attribute of a bird, we must explore the air reservoirs and muscles, which combine, with other organs, to form a complicated, but exquisitely adjusted, system. It is true that other animals show a similar adaptation to their several modes of life, but in a bird the necessities of life seem to have produced a more obvious and striking harmony between structure and habit. Furthermore, the young ornithologist should not be content with gaining the ability to recognise the different kinds of birds : he should understand their mutual relations, and the place of a bird in Nature. To form an opinion about these matters needs more than an acquaintance with the colours and outward form, and with the eggs and nest. A great deal can be learnt from these characters, but they are at most only useful in linking together closely related species. All the members of the extensive tribe of parrots, for example, are bound together by their hooked bills, their white eggs, their grasping feet, &c. But we want to go further, and determine what are the relations of the parrots to other birds which differ totally from them in all outward and visible signs. To solve, or rather to attempt to solve, broader questions of this kind we must have recourse to the scalpel, and even to the microscope. Besides, there not only *are* birds, but there *were* birds, which have now passed away utterly, leaving behind only a few bones embedded in the rocks. Nothing of an external

nature will avail us in considering what these birds were like in
their day, and which of existing kinds they most resembled. We
must have a knowledge of bones, of osteology, to grapple with
the problems which they present. For these reasons I have dealt in
the following pages principally with the organs of flight, and with
those internal and external characters which are admitted to be of
most use in classificatory questions. I have paid less attention to
those organs which are not of importance from these points of view.

Feathers and Feathering.

It is only a very few birds that have a complete and continuous
covering of feathers. The penguins are in this condition; and
some of the ostrich-like birds are so, more than most others. But
in other birds the feathers are arranged in tracts, between which
are patches of quite, or nearly, bare skin. The technical name for
the feathered districts is 'Pterylia'; that for the bare patches, 'Apteria.' If two birds, belonging to different families, are compared,
it will often be discovered that they present considerable unlikeness
in the mutual arrangement of the feathered and unfeathered tracts.
In fact, it was pointed out not far from the beginning of this century
that the dispersal of the feathers over the body was one of the very
best characters for classifying birds upon. But when the author of
this discovery, Professor Nitzsch, of Halle, first published his book
on the matter, it was received with some ridicule, and the pictures
of birds denuded of their feathers in order to show up clearly the
feather tracts were ironically compared to a portion of a poulterer's
shop. This ridicule, however, did not do away with the fact that
the character is often of great use in settling the mutual relation-
ships of birds. When a bird is carefully skinned, it will be seen
that the feather tracts have their own special slips of muscle inserted
into the roots of the feathers. These muscles, when they contract,
serve to raise the feathers slightly, and must be of at least subsidiary importance in flying. This is, perhaps, why the feather
tracts are so well marked in birds that fly, and explains the reason
for their unmarked character in birds that do not. We can easily
understand that the movement of the feathers, if the covering were
continuous, would be much more difficult and less pronounced than
when there were separate patches far enough away from each other
to allow of free and independent movement. In the Penguin, which

glides smoothly and rapidly under water in pursuit of its fishy prey, a continuous coating of feathers is not only a source of additional warmth, but offers less resistance to the water ; so, too, with a running bird like the Emu or Ostrich. But in the case of the latter, at any rate, the young nestling has quite distinct tracts and apteria, thus showing that, although nowadays it is incapable of flight, it has descended from an ancestor that could fly—at least, that is the way in which it is customary to interpret such differences in structure between young animals and their parents. The Apteryx also, of New Zealand, is quite analogous. The old bird has a nearly continuous covering of feathers, but the unhatched young show perfectly distinct patches of feathers with bare spaces between. We shall show on another page that there are other arguments which appear to prove that all these flightless birds have been gradually derived in the course of time from birds that could fly perfectly well. They are an instance, so far, of what is termed degeneration.

The examination of any bird will show that it has several kinds of feathers. They are all constructed upon the same plan, but some are larger than others, and the smallest are soft instead of firm to the touch.

The biggest feathers of all are a set which fringe the wing (see fig. 1) and another set at the end of the tail. These are called respectively the ' Remiges ' and ' Rectrices,' or the ' rowing ' feathers and the . ' steering ' feathers. Their principal use, as may be imagined, is in flight. The remaining feathers are also to some extent used in flight, but their main use appears to be to keep the body warm. An eider-down quilt, as everybody knows, is the warmest kind of coverlet ; the reason being that the feathers are very bad conductors of heat, and do not, therefore, allow the heat of the body to escape. Birds are the hottest of all animals, which is in part due to their covering of feathers. To understand the structure of a typical feather is perhaps a little difficult ; but possibly the accompanying figures (figs. 1, 2, 3, 4) will render the explanation easier to follow. The feather consists of a stem which is technically called the rhachis, the word simply signifying stem. From each side of this a row of parallel rodlets arise which are called barbs. These in their turn give rise to another set of processes which are the barbules. This, however, is not all ; the barbules are firmly locked together by other processes, so that the entire feather is quite firm, and can be used as a kind of oar with which to row

through the air. It does not give when the wings are flapped. The
barbules are of two sorts, those nearest to the root of the barb being
different from those which are nearest to its tip. The former, as
is shown in fig. 2, are shaped something like a knife-blade;
they are thickened above and bent in the middle; they gradually
taper away to a fine point. Just in the middle, where the bend
is, are two or three small teeth (2, fig. 2) on the upper margin.
By means of these teeth-like processes the successive barbules are
attached to one another. At the end of each barb, as already mentioned, the barbules are of a different structure. A few of them are

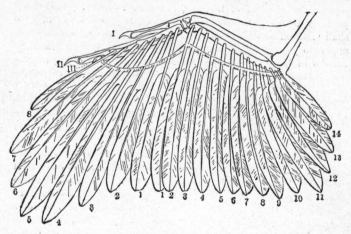

FIG. 1.—Skeleton of Wing of Archæopteryx with Remiges attached.
(Restoration after Pycraft, 'Natural Science,' vol. v.)

I, II, III, digits.

illustrated in fig. 4. The end is frayed out into a number of
delicate spines, of which those farthest from the actual tip are
hooked, while those at the tip are only curved and not hook-like.
All these spines are called barbicels. They are upon the lower edge
of the barbule; but upon the upper edge are a few shorter and
stouter spinelets. As the barbules come off in an oblique direction,
it follows that each one of them overlaps a considerable number, in
fact five, barbules of the opposite barb. The attachment is by these
hooklets, or hamuli, as they are usually termed. The stiff feathers

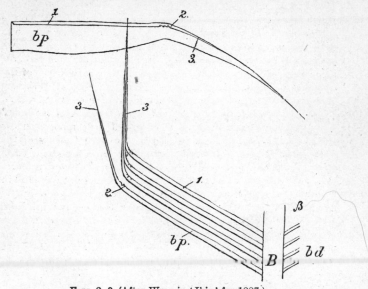

Figs. 2, 3. (After Wray in 'Ibis' for 1887.)

B, Barbs; *bp*, proximal barbules; 1, flange; 2, 'dog-tooth,' part of flange; 3, overlapping portion.

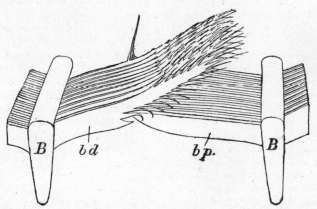

FIG. 4.—PORTION OF TWO ADJACENT BARBS. (After Wray in 'Ibis' for 1887.)

B, barbs; *bd*, *bp*, barbules (distal and proximal).

which have this elaborate structure are not found at all in the ostrich-like birds; in them there is no need for a firm surface to catch the air; on the contrary, it would be, if anything, disadvantageous to swift runners, as those birds are. The feathers, therefore, are much reduced in complexity, and in some they consist only of the stem and the barbs. Even in flying birds there are plenty of feathers of a simple structure lying between the stronger contour feathers. These are the soft feathers which are generally spoken of as ' down.' Some of them are so reduced as to consist of little more than the stem. The same reduction is seen in the wing feathers of the Cassowary. Along the margin of the wing are a few strong black spines, which are really the quills of the wing feathers with no barbs at all; they consist merely of the stem, which has not dwindled in the least, but is quite as strong as it would be in a feather of use for flying. In a good many birds the contour feathers and the down feathers also have a kind of appendix, known as the aftershaft. This is a sort of supplementary feather arising from the stem just at the point where the barbs begin, and having precisely the structure of a small feather. In the Emu and the Cassowary this aftershaft is fully as large as the main feather; from each stem in these birds arise as it were two feathers.

The most curious modification, however, of the feather is into that structure known as a ' powder-down.' These feathers have, as their name denotes, a powdery appearance, which is due to the continual breaking off of the fine ends of the barbs; the feathers themselves are soft, and belong to the variety of feathers which have been described as down feathers. The dusty matter which they give off has been described as ' dry and yet fatty to the touch.' They are found in various birds; they do not characterise any one particular group, except the Heron tribe; some Parrots have them, a few Hawks, and certain other genera. It has been said that they are phosphorescent; and it has been suggested that their presence in the heron is of use to it in its fishing. The light, it is thought, attracts the small fishes within reach of the heron's long bill. But this appears to be one of those exaggerations founded upon actual fact which are so common in natural history.

Another important fact about a feather is its colour. There is no purely white bird in this country and not very many that are chiefly white. But there are some, like the Gulls and the Storks. The nearest approach to an absolutely white bird is the beautiful little Egret, whose plumes are, unfortunately, so much used in feminine adornment. As concerns its feathers, this bird is absolutely white, but other parts of the body are black. A bird that is purely white, not only in the feathers but in the legs and beak, is called an albino. This state of affairs is not commonly met with, but it sometimes occurs; everybody has heard of that contradiction in terms, but actually existent creature, the ' white blackbird.' In all these cases there is something wanting in the feather; for white is not a colour—it is the negation of colour, and is due in nearly every case to the scattering of the rays of light which fall upon the object. This happens when the material that is coloured white is broken up into minute fragments separated by air. The froth of the sea or of a brimming tankard is simply due to the entangling of bubbles of air, which scatter the rays of light. The stems of the feathers contain bubbles of air, which bring about a like effect. But the majority of birds are coloured, and, as a rule, perhaps, brightly coloured. We have not in this country many birds which can compare with the gaudy parrots of the East; but brilliancy of hue is by no means wanting in the birds of this and of other countries which enjoy a temperate climate. It used to be said that brilliancy of colour was a characteristic of the tropics. But it is always pointed out, by way of a refutation of that statement, that the Golden Pheasant of China is as gorgeous a bird as any which exists. There are few small birds which are really more brilliant in hue than our Yellow-hammers, Goldfinches, Bullfinches, and some others. We have, it is true, nothing to seriously compete with the Humming-birds; but these birds are found not only in the tropical forests of Brazil, but also in North America and upon the snowy summits of the Andes, and can therefore hardly be used as an instance of the exclusive restriction of brilliant colour to a tropical climate.

The hues of the feathers are due to two causes. In every case where there is colour at all the feathers contain a certain amount of dye, or pigment, as it is more usually termed; this pigment may be alone responsible for the colour of the feather, or it may be only a part of the cause. If the bright blue feather from a Macaw's wing be roughly pressed so as to injure the surface, the blue colour will disappear from the rubbed place, and will be apparently replaced by a brownish black. The reason for this is that the blue colour is the result of the actual structure of the feather, which requires the underlying black pigment for its manifestation. The crushing destroys that structure and leaves only the dark pigment. The brilliant and varying hues of the soap-bubble and of mother-of-pearl

are examples of substances which owe their colour to their
structure; and the hues of the bird's feather are produced by a
similar kind of structure. Finely ruled lines engraved upon the
feather just below a clear and transparent outer skin are responsible
for the tints of different colours. But there are many birds whose
colours are entirely due to the pigments. The most interesting
instance of this in many ways is an African bird, the Touraco.
This bird is green for the most part, but the feathers of the wings
are of a magnificent crimson. When the birds take to the wing
this gorgeous colour is displayed; before, it is concealed by the
overlying feathers. The colouring matter can be easily extracted
from the wing, and it forms a solution of a splendid crimson as
bright as the substance called cochineal, which is the product of an
insect. It was once said that this colour could be, and was as a
matter of fact, washed out from the wings of the bird during heavy
storms of rain, and that when a touraco was shot and fell into the
water it stained the water red, not with its blood, but with the dye
from its feathers. This is, however, an exaggerated way of putting
the fact that even very feebly alkaline water will dissolve out the
colour. Some of the yellows of the woodpeckers and the browns
and reds of other birds are solely brought about by the presence of
pigments.

In speaking of birds as 'feathered songsters' or as 'feathered
bipeds,' we are a little apt to lose sight of the fact that they are also
scaly—an error which is occasionally rectified by the view of an
obtrusive pair of legs belonging to the fowl upon the dinner-table.
The legs of birds are nearly always scaly; there are a few exceptions or nearly exceptions. For instance, there is a special breed
of pigeons with feathered legs; and the sand-grouse, which makes
those remarkable and periodical invasions, has legs which are more
covered with feathers than with scales.

The possession of scales is one of the most striking points of
resemblance between birds and reptiles. At first sight it seems to
be almost absurd to attempt to draw any parallel between the active,
feathered, hot-blooded bird and the scaly, cold-blooded reptile; yet
there are many resemblances, some others of which will be indicated
in the following pages. In the meantime we are concerned with
the scales. These are flat plates, produced by a horny alteration of
the soft underlying skin, which are precisely like those of the lizards
and snakes. No other animals possess scales; those of the
armadillo appear to be not unlike the scales of reptiles and birds,

but they really are not, nor are those of the scaly manis, which are more comparable to closely matted tufts of hair. The scales of a fish are totally different, since they are not formed by the true skin, the epidermis, at all, but by the underlying dermis. In no bird, however, are there scales upon any part of the body except the legs. But one bird makes a near approach to having scales elsewhere. This is the Penguin, the feathers of whose wings are flattened and very scale-like. But the characteristic fringing of the feather can be detected on a careful examination. The penguin uses its wings as paddles to fly under water. A branching and delicate feather would be worse than useless under such circumstances; hence the superfluous fringing of the stem of the feather has been got rid of, and the feather itself has become flattened and lies close to the skin.

Beak.

The beak is simply a horny tract of skin which has become hardened for its special uses. It is not even distinctive of the bird; for turtles, particularly the snapping turtles, have beaks which are not only precisely like those of birds, but are equally effectual when turned to aggressive ends. It is a commonplace of knowledge that the bill or beak presents an almost endless variety of form, which is associated with an equally diversified use. The remarkable shovel-shaped bill of the duck is suitable for dabbling in soft mud, just as is the hooked beak of the hawk or owl for tearing living prey. The most prevalent form of bill is that possessed by most passerine birds, a conical longer or shorter bill. The relatively enormous beak of the toucan is serrated along the free edge, which enables its possessor to obtain a firmer grasp of the fruits upon which it feeds. The ridges upon the inner surface of the beak in the ducks serve an analogous purpose; the same structure is seen in the bill of the Flamingo, though the outline of the bill is unlike that of the duck, and gave rise to the idea, or at any rate had something to do with the former impression, that the flamingo was a long-legged duck. But, as a matter of fact, there is a stork in which there is precisely the same ridging of the beak, and it is more usual now to place the flamingo among the storks, or near to them. The Spoonbill, as its name denotes, has a beak which is at the extreme of the series of beaks which are useful for sifting the mud at the bottom of pools and rivers; the extremity is widened and flattened out.

Most singular is the recurved bill of the Avocet, and equally so the under-jawed Rhynchops, the terms used implying the peculiarities in each case. There is no living bird which lacks a beak; but in some of the extinct and toothed birds, which are again referred to later, the beak was absent. Its place was taken in them by the teeth.

Feet.

Hardly less diversified in form are the feet of birds. The skeleton of this part of the body is dealt with on another page; here we are concerned only with the external form of the feet and legs. Aquatic

FIG. 5.—FOOT OF PELICAN.

FIG. 6.—FOOT OF PERCHING BIRD.

birds often have webbed feet, but not always. The Dipper, for example, is a bird which lives largely on and under the water, but

FIG. 7.—FOOT OF KINGFISHER.

its feet are not in the least like those of a Duck or Grebe. The webbed foot presents us with at least two varieties. In the Pelican tribe (fig. 5) the extreme of web-footedness is to be seen. Here all the toes (four) are connected by a webbing. In the Duck only three of the toes are webbed Another kind of webbed foot is termed palmate. In the Coots, for example. each toe is fringed with a broad membrane, but there is no connection between the fringes of successive toes. The toes of birds are apt to be differently disposed. In most birds (fig. 6) there are three toes which are turned forwards, and one, the great toe (hallux), which is turned backwards. But in the Trogons and others two toes are turned forwards and two backwards, thus producing a very efficient mechanism for holding on tightly to the bough of a tree, a mechanism which is shared by that, in some other respects, bird-like lizard, the chameleon. A foot of this kind is technically called 'zygodactyle.' A singular modification of the foot is seen in the Kingfisher (fig. 7) where the two middle toes are enclosed in the same fold of skin ; this is called syngenesious.'

Skeleton.

A bird's skeleton is wonderfully light and spongy in texture. It is full of air (see below, p. 27), but deficient in marrow. Its entire structure is pre-eminently suited to a flying creature, not only for the above reasons, but because the heaviest part (the sternum) lies in the middle, in the centre of gravity, and thus assists in preserving the balance, like Blondin's pole.

The Skull.

The skull of a bird is composed of a large number of separate bones, which are very closely united in the adult bird, so much so that it is next to impossible to recognise that they are distinct bones. The bones are also thin and light, for to a flying animal any weight forward would be most disadvantageous. The weight of the bird should be, and is, concentrated in the middle of the body. We can divide the skull into two regions : behind is the smooth, rounded brain-case or cranium ; in front is the face, which is largely ensheathed by the beak. It is chiefly formed by the maxillary and nasal bones above, and by the palatine and pterygoids below. The length of this part of the skull is subject to great variation in different birds. In the Storks, for instance, the face is extremely long, while in the Parrots it is comparatively short.

Professor Huxley, about thirty years ago, proposed to classify birds by the form of the bones of the palate. In the skull of the Hawk, it will be seen that two bones lying in the front region of the palate are fused with each other in the middle line, and to the type of skull which is thus characterised the name ' desmognathous ' was given. It is found not only in the Hawks, but in a quantity of other birds ; for instance, in the Stork tribe, and in the Hornbills and Toucans. The second form of skull distinguishes the gallinaceous birds ; in them the two maxillo-palatines remain unconnected, and the palate is therefore in a way cleft ; this is termed the ' schizognathous ' skull. In the finch tribe there is a slight modification of this, called, from the Greek word for a finch, ' ægithognathous.' In these birds a median bone, called the vomer, from the fact that the bone to which it corresponds in the human skull is shaped somewhat like a plough-share, is truncated in front, instead of tapering, as it does in the schizognathous skull of the common fowl. There is a fourth variety, which marks out the Ostrich tribe and the American Tinamous, in which the two pairs of bones called the pterygoids and palatines do not, as they do in the types of skull that have been hitherto considered, reach the middle line of the skull, but are kept off from it by the vomers, which extend backwards. The term ' dromæognathous,' or emu-like, is applied to this form of skull. If the back of any bird's skull be examined, it will be noticed that just below the great hole or foramen, through which the medulla passes to join the spinal cord in the canal of the vertebral column, is a rounded, rather kidney-shaped boss. This is the occipital condyle, by means of which the skull articulates with the first vertebra. If you look at the same region in a mammal, you will find that there are two of these, one on each side, though also below the foramen magnum. This is one of the many points of structure that distinguish a bird from a mammal and ally it to the reptiles ; but it must be remembered that in some reptiles there is a commencing division of the single condyle into two.

The Vertebral Column.

Like all other backboned animals, birds have a chain of small bones running along the back, and enclosing a canal in which runs the spinal marrow. In most vertebrates some of the individual vertebræ in the region of the hind limb, the sacral region, are some-what intimately fused together, forming a more solid structure for the support of the pelvis. In birds the strong coupling of the vertebræ is more marked, and extends to the dorsal region. The mechanical value of this to a flying animal is clear ; it is analogous to the tight coupling of an express train, and prevents the back from bending from side to side under the strain produced by the powerful movements of the muscles in flight. The tail vertebræ show some curious modifications in different birds. In the typical carinate bird, the last few vertebræ are fused into a piece which is called the ' plough-share bone,' or ' pygostyle.' The name of this bone sufficiently indicates its shape; the expanded end of the bone serves as a firm base, upon which rest the strong tail feathers. Now, in the ostrich tribe there are no rectrices comparable in size to those of the flying carinates. Here there is no pygostyle, but the individual vertebræ are small and disconnected. They are, however, few in number, whereas in the Archæopteryx they are numerous, though, oddly enough, not so numerous altogether as are the tail vertebræ of some flying birds. Each individual vertebra in the Archæopteryx supports a pair of rectrices, which are thus arranged in a series, and not in one row. A very distinctive peculiarity of the vertebræ of birds is the saddle-shaped centrum. The centrum of the vertebra is the solid piece which underlies the canal of the spinal cord, the walls of the latter being formed by the neural arches, which unite above to form a neural spine. In other vertebrates the centra are flat (mammals), or proccœlous (the concavity being forward), or opisthocœlous (the concavity posterior), or amphicœlous (concave on both sides). This latter form of vertebra is frequently met with in archaic forms belonging to various groups. It occurs, for example, in many fishes. Such reptiles as Hyperodapedon and the Geckos have the same kind of vertebræ. Among birds there is no existing genus or species which is to be thus characterised; but the extinct Ichthyornis had clearly biconcave vertebræ.

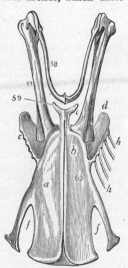

FIG. 8.—STERNUM OF
SHRIKE.

h, ribs ; 58, furcula ; 52, coracoid ; 59, anterior end of sternum.

Shoulder Girdle.

This series of bones serves as the intermediary between the fore limb and the vertebral column. It consists of three distinct elements. There is, first of all, a sword-blade-like bone with sharp edges, which lies along the vertebral column— the scapula. To the end of this is firmly attached a somewhat shorter bone, which approaches its fellow as it joins the sternum below; this bone is known as the coracoid (52. fig. 8,). The angle between these two bones is, in flying birds, a considerable one, but in the ostrich tribe they are almost in the same straight line; this is really connected with the power of flight, for it has been shown by careful measurements that, in birds which still have wings that bear every appearance of being functional, and yet are not used for their legitimate purpose, the angle tends to approach the obtusity of the scapula and coracoid of the Ostrich. Birds have, besides these two bones, the merry-thought, or clavicle (58, fig. 8), which corresponds to our collar-bone. Its two halves are generally closely united to form one U-shaped or V-shaped bone; but sometimes they are separate, and then more or less rudimentary.

· Wing.

We must enter into the matter of wing a little more closely—it is so important a feature of bird organisation. The wing, of course, although it performs so different a *rôle*, is the exact equivalent of the fore limb of mammals. We can easily recognise precisely the same bones, though they are diminished in number, and often of a different form. It will be noticed that in each case we can distinguish the three bones forming the arm, and which are known as the humerus, the radius, and ulna. The rest of the limb in the bird is not quite so obviously like the hand of the mammal; but a little attention will show that it is constructed upon a perfectly similar plan. The flexible wrist of the mammal is made up of many small bones; the hand itself is made up of a larger series still, of which those nearest to the wrist are technically termed the metacarpals, and those which follow, the phalanges. In many mammals there are five fingers; but there are many which have less, and the extreme is reached in the horse, which has to put up with a single finger and small rudiments of two others. Now the bird is better off in the way of fingers than the horse, as it has three fairly well-developed fingers, or rather two well developed and one less perfect. The shortest finger corresponds to the thumb of our hand. It is more freely movable than the others. The metacarpal bones of the second and third fingers are firmly welded together, and are long; each finger (as will be seen from a look at fig. 1, p. 4) has one or two phalanges, as the case may be. Now in mammals the end phalanx of each finger is tipped with a nail, or with a hoof. The powerful claws of the tiger, used for tearing, and the solid hoof of the ox or horse, upon which the creature walks, are one and the same thing. It might be supposed that the hand of the bird, which is not an organ of offence or meant to walk with, might be shorn of these appendages. But this is not the case: every bird has at least two nails (fig. 9), of a long and rather claw-like form when well developed, and sometimes three nails, that is, one to each of its fingers. It looks, therefore, very much as if the wing of the bird had been formed out of a limb that was once an organ for climbing or walking with. There is a curious bird, found in British Guiana, which is known as the Hoatzin (figs. 9, 11). In the very young nestlings of the hoatzin the claws of the fingers are so conspicuous that they are actually used by the callow chick to climb with, before the feathers of the wings have grown sufficiently to enable them to use their wings in the proper way in which a bird should ; it has been said also, that

FIG. 9.—WING OF NESTLING OPISTHOCOMUS. (After Pycraft in ' Natural Science.')

The second digit (II) is free, being prolonged beyond ala membrane (P.m.), and remiges 8–10 are not developed.

other birds scramble about and use their claws when they are young. In the case of the hoatzin, it is stated that the thumb and the first finger can be brought together so as to lay hold definitely of an object. A very important thing to notice about the wing bones is that they are capable of but little movement upon each other. There are two hinges, one at the elbow, and the other at the wrist ; but the radius and ulna cannot move round each other, as they can in our arms, and the fingers are fixed and rigid. This would be most unfortunate if the wing had to be used as a walking or climbing limb ; but it is most useful in relation to the function which the wing has to perform—that of flight. The strength of the downward stroke would be enfeebled if the bones were in a limp condition and moved upon each other. They offer, too, a firm foothold for the thick quills of the big feathers of the wing. It has been mentioned that

all the evidence at our disposal points to the view that the wing
has become gradually moulded into an organ of flight, from a condition in which it played a different part. The earliest bird of which
we have any record had wings which were much less perfect as
flying organs than those of modern birds. It seems pretty plain
that the bones in that antique bird were much less rigidly fixed
together, and it is equally clear that the fingers were very much
more loosely attached to one another. They were also more on an
equality as regards size; the great disparity evident in fig. 12 is
not to be seen in the Archæopteryx. All this, of course, shows that the
Archæopteryx could not have possessed the ample pinion of its more
vigorous descendants of to-day. The fossil Archæopteryx looks a
little like a crow would look after receiving at close quarters a charge
of duck shot; but a closer examination will show that in reality all

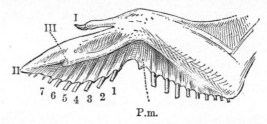

FIG. 10.—Wing of Young Fowl of same Age as Fig. 9 (of Wing of
Opisthocomus).   (After Pycraft in 'Natural Science.')
The hand is shorter, and not fitted to be a grasping organ.

the bones are there, on one side at least. Out of the disjecta membra
of the fossil numerous 'restorations' have been put together; which
are as diverse as the minds which imagined them. We cannot
really say with certainty what were the precise relations of the
hand to the feathers.   It seems most probable that the hand of this
'mediæval' bird still retained the ordinary functions of a hand;
that it served its possessor to lay hold of convenient branches, from
which it fluttered feebly to others. One bold speculator has insisted
upon the probability that the Archæopteryx had the requisite five
fingers of the presumed ancestral type; but there are no traces of
them, except in so far as the lie of the feathers enables a hint to be
gathered. Boring operations, or at least prospecting in the interior
of the stony slab on which the fossil lies, might reveal some
additional fingers; but the operation would be fraught with too

obvious perils to a nearly unique object. There are a good many
birds which do not, and some which cannot, fly. To the first category belong such birds as the domestic ducks and fowls, and some
of the rails. These birds, when put to it—when chased by a dog, for
example—can often fly ; but as a rule they do not, or at most only

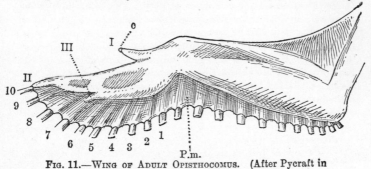

FIG. 11.—WING OF ADULT OPISTHOCOMUS. (After Pycraft in
'Natural Science.')

The hand is smaller relatively to the forearm ; *c,* the claw of digit I, much reduced.

flutter along. The Ostrich tribe and a few other birds have totally
lost the power of flight. But though this is the case, the bony
structure of the hand remains the same in the Ostrich and in the
American Rhea ; in the Cassowary, however, and the Apteryx of New
Zealand, the fingers are reduced to one. The last stage in the
atrophy of the organ of flight is seen in the giant and extinct birds

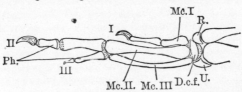

FIG. 12.—WING OF HALF-GROWN OSTRICH. (After Parker.)

I, II, III, digits ; R., U., D.c.f., carpal bones ; Mc., metacarpals.

of New Zealand, the Moa or Dinornis, in which no trace of a wing has
been so far discovered. But in some of these birds in which the wing
is reduced in size, or so simplified in structure that it can no longer
serve its legitimate purpose, it is made use of for other purposes.
When the Ostrich skims along the surface of the sandy deserts

where it is often found, it holds out both wings, which are compared to sails; they possibly serve rather as the pole of the tight-rope walker, to preserve the balance of the bird when hurrying along at full speed. In the Secretary Vulture of Africa the wings can be used for flying, but they are also used as weapons wherewith to combat the poisonous snakes upon which the bird so usefully feeds. It strikes down the venomous serpent when the latter is attempting to strike the bird. The Chauna of South America has strong spurs upon its wings, which are used for fighting as well as for flying. But the most curious use to which wings are put is afforded by the Penguin. If the reader has never seen the 'diving birds' fed at the Zoological Gardens, let him go there on the first opportunity, and see how rapidly and gracefully the Penguin 'flies' under water by the flapping of its wings. They are shorter than those of most birds, and the feathers have become flattened and almost scale-like, so as to offer no resistance to the water; at the same time the bones of the wing are flattened, so that a broad surface is provided, which of course acts like an oar. With this oar-like wing the Penguin can outswim a small fish.

Sternum and Ribs.

The breast-bone or sternum (fig. 8, **p.** 13) of birds shows the same relation to the power of flight that is shown by so many, if not by all, parts of the skeleton. It is relatively a very large bone, and is in all perfectly flying birds furnished in the middle line, below, with a strongly marked keel, the presence of which has given its name to the great group of birds called carinates. The ostrich tribe, from whose sterna the keel is absent, are termed 'ratite,' or 'raftlike.' The reason for the keel is the attachment of the great pectoral muscle, which is the most important muscle of flight. The sternum often offers useful characters to the systematist. The surface of the bone is sometimes in various degrees fenestrate, or more or less deeply incised, the one condition being an exaggeration of the other, and both the conditions being due to defective ossification. The sternum is attached to the vertebral column by the ribs, which are well developed in all birds, but vary very much in number. A highly characteristic feature of the ribs of birds is a small bony projection of the hinder margin of a certain number of them, called the uncinate processes. These are present in all birds, with the single and remarkable exception of the South American Screamers (*Chauna, Palamedea*), a group of birds occupying a rather isolated position, and showing resemblances to a great many different groups.

Pelvis.

The hind limbs are attached to the vertebral column by means of a considerable bony structure known as the pelvic girdle (fig. 13).

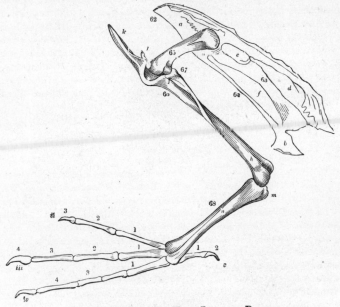

FIG. 13.—PELVIS AND HIND LIMB OF DIVER.

a, d, ilium ; 63, ischium ; 64, pubis ; 65, femur ; 66, tibia ; 67, fibula; 68, tarsometatarsus ; i.–iv. digits with phalanges numbered.

This mass of bone is in reality composed of three pairs of elements, though they are in the adult strongly compacted together. The main bone, which is firmly attached to the vertebral column, is the ilium ; with this is almost completely fused the ischium ; the very slender pubis is to a large extent free from these bones. The pelvis is in its form one of the most characteristic of the bones of the bird's skeleton. In other animals the three bones are present, but they are directed away from each other ; in the bird, as already described, the pubis is directed backwards, parallel to the ischium ; in correspondence, perhaps, with its position it has become a feeble bone, and has but few muscles attached to it. The interest of the matter, however, is mainly in the fact that among the extinct Dinosaurs, a race of mesozoic reptiles, there were some in which the pelvis had a very bird-like structure, with the same feeble and recurrent pubis. This has been urged as a mark of affinity between the Dinosaurs and birds. The several bones of the pelvis are free from each other at the extremity, or almost so, in all the Ratites, and in the Tinamous, which are supposed to bear some relationship to the Ratites. The fact is interesting as being an example of the retention of a character by one group of birds which is only transitional and embryonic in another, for in all young birds the bones of the pelvis are separate ; it is not until some time before hatching that they become fused together as we see them in the adult.

Hind Limb.

At first sight there appears to be a considerable difference between the fore limb and the hind limb. In both there is a long proximal bone, called humerus in the one case and femur in the other, followed by a pair of bones—the tibia and fibula—corresponding to the radius and ulna of the fore limb. But in the hind limb (fig. 13), the foot proper, consisting of metatarsals and phalanges, appears to come immediately after the tibia and fibula. In a sufficiently young bird, what is the apparent lower end of the tibia, and what is equally apparently the upper end of the metatarsus, are detachable ; these two halves which are thus detachable are the tarsus, which is the equivalent of the carpus of the wing. The lower bone of the leg is on this account usually spoken of as the tarso-metatarsus. The lower part of this bone is made up of three fused elements, the separation of which from each other is clearly apparent at the lower end of the bone, where the phalanges are attached. In the Penguins the three bones are separated by grooves of a very marked character throughout. In some birds there is a fourth toe, the hallux ; in these cases there is a small separate metatarsal loosely fixed to the lower end of the large conjoint metatarsals.

Gizzard and Alimentary Canal.

The gizzard (fig. 14) of the fowl is simply a part of the stomach which has especially hard and muscular walls, the other half remaining soft in texture; this latter is termed the proventriculus, and into it open the mouths of glands which secrete the digestive juice of the stomach. But the muscular part of the stomach —the gizzard—has to grind down the frequently hard food of the bird, so it has not merely a strong wall made of muscle, but also a very tough lining; the whole organ, therefore, forms a highly efficient mechanism for crushing and grinding the seeds and other hard vegetable food which is swallowed. It is rendered more useful still for this purpose by the pebbles which every bird takes care to swallow. The true and singular stories about the varied contents of an Ostrich's stomach are

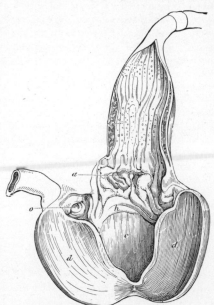

FIG. 14.—GIZZARD OF SWAN.
o, orifice of duodenum ;
a, end of proventriculus ; *cd*, muscular part of gizzard.

founded upon the fact that, like other birds, it picks up stones, and with them occasionally other objects. But all birds do not possess a hard gizzard ; in Hawks and fish-eating birds the walls are thinner, and the organ is flaccid instead of being rigid. By a very curious and unique exception certain Tanagers, a race of large, often bright-coloured, American, finch-like birds, have nothing at all that can be compared to the gizzard of other birds · this part of the alimentary canal is totally wanting. Now the difference between the gizzard of the grain-eating fowl and the flesh-eating hawk is chiefly a matter of diet. The celebrated anatomist, John Hunter, who lived in the last century, and wrote so much about the anatomy of all kinds of animals, including birds, found that he could feed a soft-stomached bird into one with a hard gizzard, and *vice versâ*.

We can pass briefly over the rest of the alimentary system, which does not vary a great deal in different birds. The intestines are always rather short, and are diversely coiled, the method of coiling being often characteristic of a particular group. A good way down the intestine are a pair of cæca, which may be entirely absent, as in the Hornbills, for example ; and if present may be extremely short, as in the Sparrow, or very long, as in the Ostrich ; various intermediate degrees exist. As in all vertebrated animals, two glands pour their secretion into the intestine ; these are the pancreas and the liver. The secretion of the liver is the bile ; this fluid is accumulated as it is formed in a largish bag—the gall-bladder, in those birds which possess one. Shakespeare used the epithet pigeon-livered,' which meant literally the absence of a gall-bladder ; but, oddly enough, there are some kinds of pigeons which have a gall-bladder, while others, like the common pigeon, have not. The intestine ends in the cloaca, which is the common chamber into which the urinary and generative organs also open.

Tongue and Teeth.

In the inside of a bird's mouth we find only one of the two things that we might expect to find : there is a tongue, but no teeth. We shall come back to the teeth immediately. The tongue is not so useful among the majority of birds as it is in most mammals. But some do make use of it to a great extent. If you watch a parrot eating its food, you will observe that its thick and fleshy tongue is of the greatest assistance in helping it to manipulate the pieces of food—to extract, for instance, the kernel from a seed or nut. It plays exactly the same part as it does with us. In one kind of parrot, called the ' Brush-tongued Parrakeet,' the tongue is frayed out at the free end into a brush-like extremity. And there are some small birds, which peck at flowers and live upon honey, in which the tongue is thin and delicate, and frayed out in the same way ; this allows them to suck up the juices of the flower. In the Humming-bird the tongue is rolled up so as to form two tubes running side by side, and the same power of sucking up juices is acquired by this means, which, curiously enough, is exactly paralleled by the proboscis of the butterfly. In other birds the tongue is sometimes merely a thin, flat, horny projection, and in others, again, it is just not absent altogether.

A little reflection about the habits of birds will show that they really do not want teeth ; and we know that Nature is a most rigid economist : nothing superfluous is allowed in the body. Even rapacious birds like Owls and Hawks have no teeth, because they have a powerful beak and claws, with which the food may be as effectually torn to pieces. Birds such as the Pigeon, which feed upon grain, possess a gizzard—which we have had something to say about already—that performs effectually the function of a mill, grinding into a powder the hard grains of wheat and other seeds which the bird swallows. Nevertheless birds once did possess teeth. In earlier times of the history of this earth there were some birds whose jaws had as formidable a range of teeth as the mouth of many reptiles. They were fish-eaters, and have been named *Hesperornis* and *Ichthyornis*. The first was something like a Diver in shape, the latter more like a Gull. A still more ancient bird, the oldest form of bird known to us, the *Archæopteryx*, had also toothed jaws. In fact, in the old days it was the rule for birds to have teeth, whereas now it is the rule, without a single exception, for birds to be toothless. Perhaps these ancient and extinct forms had some corresponding disadvantage when compared with their modern representatives ; their teeth and claws, for example, may have been less effective. But although there is no bird now living which has real teeth, traces of these organs have been discovered in the young embryos of certain birds, which seems to be an absolute proof that they, at any rate, had for their first parents toothed birds. But although modern birds have no teeth, with enamel, dentine, and so forth, all complete, the horny beak has occasionally ridges which to some extent play the part of teeth. The inside of the Duck's mouth is rough with such ridges, which occur also in some other birds. The large Flamingo was for some time regarded as a long-legged and awkward Duck that had partially adopted the habits of a Stork, partly on account of the fact that the inner edges of the beak were ridged in a fashion exactly like that of the Duck. But it happens that there is a Stork, a true Stork, in India, whose scientific name is *Anastomus*, which has similar ridges. Ducks feed to some

extent upon shellfish, which the roughened edges of the beak are
well suited to crush.　The replacement in the course of ages of true
teeth by horny teeth is seen—a curiously parallel case—in the Duck-
billed Platypus of Australia, which has when adult horny plates
instead of teeth, but when young has real teeth.

Heart.

As with all vertebrated animals, birds have a centrally placed
heart, with which are connected arteries and veins, the two systems
of tubes being connected at the ends farthest away from the heart
by minute vessels—the capillaries.　In relation, no doubt, to the
intelligence and activity of birds, as compared with their slower
relatives, the reptiles, we find a heart of much more perfect organisation.　There are four distinct chambers, as in the mammal, so
that the arterial and venous blood are separate, and do not com-
mingle.　The two sides of the heart are only in indirect communication by way of the arteries and veins and capillaries.　The left
ventricle gives rise to the aorta, which is the great arterial trunk of
the heart; this divides into the carotid and other arteries, which
supply the entire body, with the exception of the lungs.　The blood,
which is sent out through this vessel by the contractions of the ventricle, permeates the system generally, and is then collected into a
series of veins, which ultimately unite into two great veins, he
venæ cavæ in front, and a large vein situated posteriorly, the inferior vena cava.　These pour the blood back into the right auricle,
whence it passes at once to the right ventricle.　From the right
ventricle it is driven into the lungs, whence it is returned to the left
auricle, and so into the left ventricle to renew the circulation.　The
two chambers of each half of the heart are guarded from each other
by valves, which only allow the blood to flow in the proper direction,
as stated in the above brief description of the course of the circulation.
It is a curious fact that the valve which separates the right auricle
and ventricle is a completely muscular structure, while the other is
membranous.　Moreover, it does not form a complete circle, but is
deficient upon one side of the orifice.　The interest of this fact is
not merely in its abnormality, its divergence from what one would
expect, but in the resemblance which is thus shown to a group of
mammals, the Monotremata.　This group includes only the Duck-
billed Platypus of Australia and the spiny Anteater (Echidna) of the

same continent and New Guinea. In both of these animals the heart valve in question is also largely muscular, and does not entirely encircle the opening from the auricle. These two mammals also, as everyone knows by this time, have the strange habit for a mammal of laying eggs, which is one among some other reasons which once led naturalists to place them in the neighbourhood of birds. The egg-laying, of course, is not distinctive, since reptiles have the same way of bringing forth their young; and as to the heart valve, it is rather to be explained by the fact that both types of animals are low in the scale of their respective groups, and therefore both approach a common ancestral form.

Voice Organ.

By their voice, too, birds are distinguished from the rest of the animal creation. Though there may be legends of singing serpents and of talking monkeys, a harsh scream or a growl is the only manifestation of the emotions through the voice which exists until we arrive at man. Among birds, the possession of a melodious voice is limited to that group which we term the Passeres. Other birds can scream or utter a dull note, while many are mute. So flexible is the voice organ of these creatures that they are the only animals that can imitate human speech. Here, however, it is not only the Passeres which can imitate the essential attribute of man. The Parrots, of course, are always supposed to be *the* birds which can talk, but this is far from being the truth. The hoarse utterances of most Parrots are left far behind in clearness of sound and correctness of imitation by the little Indian Mynah, which may be usually seen at the Zoological Gardens, and heard to speak. But the Parrot cannot sing. These are the only two groups of birds which have so elaborate and flexible an organ of voice. From this it might be inferred that some peculiarities of mechanism would distinguish the organ in question of these birds, and that is what we actually find to be the case. But, oddly enough, it is not only those birds which have a beautiful voice whose voice organs are so elaborate in structure. The harsh croak of the Raven issues from a syrinx which is as delicately fashioned as that which allows of the exquisitely varied tones of the Nightingale. The word 'syrinx' has been mentioned ; that is the technical term for the voice organ of the bird, which is formed from a part of the windpipe, as in man and the mammalia, but from a different part of that tube. In man and in mammals the voice organ is placed in the throat just a little way down, at the prominence often spoken of as 'Adam's apple.' This is a wider part of the tube, with larger rings of cartilage, which contains a pair of tightly stretched membranes that can be made to vibrate and cause a sound. In the bird, the voice organ is situated farther down, at the very point where the trachea forks into the two bronchi, one for each lung. Here are figures which illustrate the voice organ of a singing-bird (figs. 15, 16, 17). At

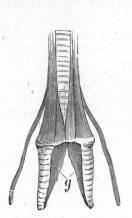 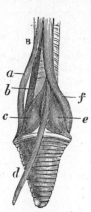 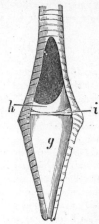

FIG. 15.—SYRINX OF RAVEN (Posterior Surface).

*, tympaniform membrane.

FIG. 16.—SYRINX OF RAVEN (LATERAL VIEW).

a, b, c, e, f, intrinsic muscles; *d,* sternotracheal muscle.

FIG. 17.—SYRINX OF RAVEN CUT OPEN LONGITUDINALLY.

t, pessulus; *h,* vibrating membrane; *g,* membrana tympaniformis.

this forking of the trachea the rings of the tube, which are of gristle or cartilage, become somewhat different in form. In the middle is a piece, which is often converted into bone, like the 'three-way' piece used to fix together the stick and the hoop of cane of a butterfly-net. To the upper side of this, and therefore within the tube, and directed upwards, is a little crescent-shaped piece of membrane (*h,* fig. 17); this can be set vibrating by the stream of air passing up and down the windpipe. At the sides of the syrinx there are shown in the figure (fig. 16) three pairs of muscles; these when they contract shorten the syrinx, and of course produce alterations in the note, just as the shortening of the tube in a cornet alters the sound. In many passerine birds, and in most other birds, there is only one pair of these muscles; but the Parrots agree with the passerines in having several pairs of muscles, and therefore a more easily alterable syrinx. In a good many birds there are no muscles at all in this place; for example, in the Storks, which have not by any means a flexible voice. The syrinx, in fact, is one of those organs which show a great deal of difference in different kinds of birds. But it is never entirely absent, though rather rudimentary in the Ostrich. The Australian Emu has a curious way of producing its sounds which is not found in any other bird. The cock and hen Emus can only be recognised by their voice, which is duller in the hen and sharper in the cock. When the bird is uttering its note, it seems almost to come from some-where else, and not from the throat of the bird; the bird is some-thing of a ventriloquist. The sound, which is a low bellow, is pro-duced by a bag of skin opening into the windpipe some way up the neck; a current of air passing down the tube is believed to set the air in this bag in vibration, just as the air in a key may be caused to vibrate by blowing over its edge. Generally speaking, the windpipes of birds are straight tubes running to the lungs by the shortest route; but in the Cranes, and in a few other birds, the pipe is coiled upon itself once or twice, and the coils are even hidden in an excavation of the breast-bone. The increased length of tube gives a louder and more resonant note, such as we know character-ises the Crane.

Lungs and Air-sacs.

It is not only by virtue of their powerful muscles and stiffened fore limbs that birds can fly. The body is rendered lighter in pro-portion to its bulk by air-cavities, which permeate everywhere, even into the substance of the bones. So thorough is this aëration in the Screamer of South America, that when the skin of the recently dead bird is roughly pressed it crackles. Curiously enough, there seems to be no very definite relation between the degree of thoroughness to which the aëration of the body is carried out and the capacity for flight. The Screamer, that has just been mentioned, is fuller of air-cavities than the Frigate-bird, in which the art of flying is carried to the highest extreme—the 'triumph of the wing,' as Michelet says in 'L'Oiseau.' Anyone who has the opportunity of dissecting a Hornbill will be struck by the large and abundant air-spaces between the muscles. This applies even to the Ground Hornbill of Abyssinia; and yet the latter, as its name denotes, lives upon the ground, while the flight of other hornbills is heavy and most unsuggestive of lightness of body. These air-spaces are in direct communication with the windpipe. It is much easier to understand their arrangement by the actual dissection of a bird. We must first get a notion of the position and form of the lungs, which differ very much from the lungs of other animals. In a rabbit, for example, or any other mammal, the lungs lie freely on each side of the heart, and are capable of being pushed here and there after the body is opened, and of much expansion and diminution of volume during the movements of respiration. But the lungs of all birds are tightly fixed to the wall of the chest cavity, being, as it were, moulded on to the ribs and vertebræ; when they are carefully picked away from their place, they retain the impressions of the bones which they touch. There is no great possibility here of independent movements on the part of the lungs. Respiration is effected in a totally different manner; it is, in fact, bound up with the mechanical filling of the air-spaces. Each of the two lungs is contained within a large compartment, which is bounded externally by an obliquely disposed septum, often spoken of, on account of its direction, as the 'oblique septum.' Others call it the diaphragm, imagining that it is the equivalent of the diaphragm in the mammal, that partly fleshy, partly tendinous plate which shuts off the cavity of the chest, in which lie the heart and lungs, from the cavity of the abdomen, in which lie the intestines, stomach, and liver. Now, this oblique septum does not by any means closely invest the lungs; on the contrary, a deep space is thereby shut off, at the bottom of which are the lungs. This cavity is subdivided by two partitions into three separate compartments. It requires a very skilful manipulation to show the fact, but it can, with care, be demonstrated that each of these compartments is lined by a delicate membrane, which is continuous with the lung, and is actually a kind of bubble, as it were, blown out of the lung; these delicate sacs are the air-sacs. There are altogether nine of them, but all these sacs do not lie within the cavity bounded by the oblique septa. The largest pair of all the abdominal air-sacs project into the body cavity far behind the gizzard. Now these sacs are fairly easy to see in a dissection; but it is not so easy to make out that they are all of them, except the middle two, connected with a system of ramified air-spaces which, as already said, permeates the body generally, lying among the viscera, between the muscles below the skin, and deep into the actual interior of the bones. But though it is difficult to see this by a dissection, it is easy enough to prove it by inflating them. If a syringe is passed down the windpipe and tied carefully into it, so that no air can escape at the sides, and air is blown down the tube, the passage of the air into the skin and other parts can be followed ; if a bone be cut across, the air can be noticed to issue from the cut surface ; and if the experiment be varied by using a coloured fluid instead of air—which is pumped in by a syringe— the fluid can be seen to ooze from the end of any bone or muscle that has been cut across. A bird, therefore, when it takes in a deep breath, not only supplies its lungs with fresh air, but fills its whole body with the superfluous air. It has been proved that a bird can continue to breathe if it be held under water, and only the end of a broken limb allowed above the surface ; for, as all the spaces of air are in communication with the lungs, they (the lungs) can obviously be as conveniently filled from one end as from the other. When you are bathing, and take a very deep breath as you are swimming, you can detect a sensible increase in the buoyancy of the body ; in a bird, of course, the difference is enormous, after the sacs are filled, from a condition of comparative emptiness. The way in which a bird breathes is different from the way in which a human being breathes. There is, of course, the essential resemblance that is shown between all animals that have definite organs which are set apart for respiration : the feathery gills of the marine worms, the closely set branchiæ of the fish, the lungs of the bird and of the mammal, are all constructed upon one plan, so far as essentials are concerned. In all of them blood-vessels are brought into close relation, though not into actual contact, with water or air containing oxygen. The blood-vessels are separated from the water or air by the thin membranes of the lungs or gills, through which the oxygen can pass in to the blood, and the carbonic acid and effete gases can pass out ; it is this exchange which is the essential act of respiration. We cannot, however, in this book pretend to go into general matters of this kind, which would take us too far from the subject at hand ; but anyone who would pursue this further can consult Professor Huxley's ' Elementary Physiology,' or any other elementary text-book upon physiology. When a mammal—a human being, for example—breathes certain muscles are called into play. If a person is watched, it will

D

be seen that the chest expands during inspiration, and that its calibre diminishes during expiration. What happens is this. The lungs are contained in a cavity which contains no air. This cavity can be increased in size in two directions. When the ribs are moved out—which they can be by the movements of the muscles called intercostal, which lie between them—the cavity of the chest from before backwards is evidently enlarged. On the other hand there is the diaphragm, which we have already spoken of as bounding the chest cavity below. Now this diaphragm is muscular, with a tendinous centre. When the muscles contract, like all muscles do, the surface of the diaphragm, which was before rather convex towards the chest cavity, becomes more flat; hence the cavity lying above it, *i.e.* the chest cavity, becomes larger in a downward direction also. When it is increased in this way by the action of the two separate sets of muscles, some space—more space than before—is left between its walls and the lungs which lie within it; it follows, therefore, that, as there is no air in the cavity, the pressure of air outside the body forces more air into the lungs, because there is no counterbalancing pressure to prevent this. The principle is the same in the bird, but the details are different. If you will turn again to the bird's skeleton, you will see that the backbone and ribs and sternum form a bony box, which is jointed in the middle ; this acts precisely like a pair of bellows : the bones at top and bottom represent the wood, and the soft intervening leather of the bellows is represented by the muscles which lie between, and which connect the sternum with the abdomen and with the ribs. When these muscles contract, the sternum is obviously brought nearer to the backbone, and air is expelled from the inside ; when they are relaxed, a vacuum is created and air rushes in. The air-spaces, then, are really ramified tags of lung which have no blood-vessels in their walls, and are therefore not meant for respiration, but serve as reservoirs of air, lightening the body of the creature. It is curious that birds are not the only animals which possess expansions of lung that are apparently useless for breathing purposes. The lungs of the Chameleon have quite similar sacs appended to them. There is, it is true, no such complicated a ramification as that which we find in the bird, but still there is no doubt that the structure is of the same nature. It looks almost like a first step in the path towards a bird. Very possibly the extinct Pterodactyles, which flew through the woods of the middle ages of the earth, had bodies lightened in the same or a similar way ; for we know that their bones have thin walls, the large cavity of which in all probability contained air-sacs. Even some of the jumping Dinosaurs, to which reference has already been made, seem to have possibly had lungs constructed on the bird type. We see, therefore, that even where a bird is, so to speak, most characteristically a bird—in the subsidiary mechanisms of flight—it betrays a likeness to the comparatively grovelling reptile, letting alone the aërial and more bird-like Pterodactyles.

Brain.

The brain of birds is large in proportion to the body, thus contrasting with that of the unintelligent reptile. From some tables on the matter which have been published, it appears that, if weight of brain goes for anything, the goldfinch is one of the most intelligent of birds. The weight of its brain is one-fourteenth of the entire weight of the body. The most unintelligent of all is the domestic fowl, whose body is 412 times heavier than its brain. The size of brain, however, seems to be largely a matter of the size of the bird : generally speaking, the smaller birds have heavier brains, and *vice versâ*. One might have expected something from the apparently intelligent Parrot ; but the brain of the ' Amazon ' is only one forty-second part of the weight of its body. Even the cruel and bloodthirsty Hawk, which one associates with brutality and ignorance, has a brain which is but little heavier.

The front part of the organ, known as the cerebral hemispheres, or, more briefly, as the cerebrum, is that part of the brain which is associated with intelligence. Now among the mammals this part of the brain is generally much furrowed, the brain surface being, therefore, increased without any actual increase in the skull-space required. This furrowing is met with in most mammals, but not always in the smaller and in the less intelligent kinds. But in the bird's brain there are no convolutions : the surface is as smooth as in the reptile. Not even in the artful Raven, which some hold as the most highly developed of birds, is there a trace of the furrowing which one rightly associates, so far as the mammalia are concerned, with a high position in the series. The hinder part of the brain is known as the cerebellum ; between this and the cerebrum are the optic lobes, of which there are only two, the mammals having four. From the brain arises the spinal cord, or marrow, which runs in the canal formed by the vertebræ, just as the brain lies in the brain-case. The nerves of the body come off either from the brain or the marrow, but it is not important to enumerate them. They show no difference in different kinds of birds.

The Muscles.

The muscles of a bird are what is popularly known as its flesh. When the skin is removed, the bones are seen to be covered by a mass of this flesh, which is of a red colour, darker in some birds than in others. For instance, in a Duck the colour is a dark red; in a Pigeon, quite a pale brown. The flesh is not, however, merely a thick sheet covering the bones: it can be separated into layers which are themselves made up of a number of separate pieces of muscle. These individual muscles are very commonly of a spindle-like shape, being thickest in the middle and dwindling towards both ends, where they often end in a tough substance called the tendon, which has a glistening and very characteristic appearance. All muscles are not of this form—sometimes they are strap-shaped; and not all of them end in tendons. As the most important act of the bird's life that depends upon its muscles is flying, it is not surprising to find that the muscle which effects the downward stroke of the wing is the largest. This muscle is known as the great pectoral, and it is said to be almost as large as all the other muscles of the body put together. The way in which a muscle effects the movements of the bones to which it is attached is by contracting. All muscles are able to contract; they shorten, and, accordingly, the ends, with whatever they happen to be attached to, are brought closer together. The contraction is governed by the nerves, and it has been discovered that the nerves actually end in communication with the fibres of which the muscle is composed. This pectoral muscle lies on the breast-bone, and nearly completely covers it; indeed, only the edge of the keel appears, and a very little tract at the sides. When this muscle is dissected away another muscle, not nearly so large, comes into view underneath it; this is called the pectoralis secundus, or the second pectoral. Its action is precisely the reverse of that of the great pectoral: it pulls the wing up instead of down. Between them, these two muscles do most of the work in flying. Naturally, in the ostrich tribe, which do not fly, they are much reduced in bulk. But they are never absent altogether, even in the

Apteryx, which is, perhaps, further removed from the possibilities of flight than any other bird.

A very curious muscle runs into the patagium of the wing, which is that fold of skin which lies between the shoulder and the hand. This muscle is called the patagial muscle. It starts from the shoulder as a fleshy band, but soon ends in two long tendons : one of these follows the upper margin of the patagium, and finally ends in the wrist; the other passes down over the patagium, and ends below in connection with some of the muscles of the arm, and also by being attached in a fan-shaped way to the skin itself. The function of this muscle is to assist in the folding up of the wing when it is, so to speak, put away after use. The tendons in which the latter part of this muscle ends often show a most complicated branching in the patagium; they frequently offer characteristic differences in different birds, and are made some use of by the systematist. The bird has got a biceps to its arm just as we have. It sometimes happens that this biceps gives off a muscular slip, which runs into the patagium and becomes attached to the upper of the two tendons of the patagial muscle. A good deal of stress is laid by certain ornithologists as to whether this biceps slip is absent or present. Several of the common British birds will afford material to the beginner to ascertain for himself some of the chief variations in these and the other muscles of the body. It will be a good exercise to get a few birds, and to carefully dissect two of them, belonging to as widely different kinds as possible, side by side. You might select, for instance, a Crow and a Pigeon, which are fairly extreme types. To revert to our account of the muscular anatomy of a bird, it will be impossible to attempt any comprehensive account of this branch of the subject, because the facts are so appallingly numerous. We shall content ourselves, therefore, with the mention of a highly characteristic bird muscle which occurs in the leg. This muscle is known as the ambiens. This muscle is thin and ribbon-like. It takes its origin from a little process of the pubic bone usually called the prepubic process. From this point it runs along the inside of the thigh until it reaches the knee; it then bends over the knee and comes out on the other side, where it runs down the leg to join the deep flexor muscle of the foot. When this ambiens muscle contracts it pulls upon the flexor muscle, already referred to; the effect of this is that the toes are brought together by the tendons in which the last-mentioned muscle ends. The ambiens is far from being universally present among birds. It is notably absent from the passerine birds (the Sparrows, Crows, Rooks, and small perching birds generally), and from the Hornbills, Toucans, Woodpeckers, and that varied assemblage known as picarian birds. On the other hand, the Storks, Hawks, and most of the larger birds, have the muscle. But among some of these it is absent ; thus, the Owls on the one hand, and the Herons on the other, have no ambiens; but from their general resemblance in other particulars to birds which have an ambiens, it was thought by Professor Garrod that the loss in them was a recent event, and that they might be fairly placed in one great group of birds with an ambiens which he termed, somewhat lengthily, the ' homalogonatæ,' or normal-kneed birds, reserving the name ' anomalogonatæ,' or abnormal-kneed birds, for the passerines, &c., without an ambiens.

CLASSIFICATION.

ONE great advantage of the study of birds is that the amount of facts to be learnt in anatomy is far less than with some other groups. They are wonderfully uniform in structure. There is less difference in structure between an ostrich and a humming-bird than between, say, a lizard and a crocodile. Though this may be gratifying to the student of birds who is content with a broad knowledge of anatomical fact, it has its disadvantages—very distinct disadvantages —to those who want to arrange and classify the species. As there are computed to be over eleven thousand different kinds of birds, it is clear that an arrangement of some kind is wanted ; we must have an artificial brain in which to store the characters of each bird in their proper place. But before we can consider this it is necessary to consider first what place birds as a whole occupy in Nature. It used to be thought that warm-blooded birds ought to be put near to the warm-blooded mammals. But it is now the general opinion that, as we have before pointed out in relation to certain details of structure, their proper place is in the neighbourhood of the reptiles. In fact they are regarded as a separate division of an order of vertebrated animals which has received the name of Sauropsida, which signifies ' lizard-like ' animals.

Now, as to these eleven thousand, how are they to be divided ? To this simple question innumerable answers have been given—it is hardly an exaggeration to say as many answers as there are ornithologists. Every part of the body has had its turn in affording a base for a classificatory scheme. At first, and with the older generation, it was bill and claw; then came a period of bones; later the muscles were held to be all-important; at present the fashion is in favour of taking all characters into consideration, which is clearly a more reasonable way of looking at the matter. The reason for the divergences of opinion—which implies great difficulty in the subject —is that birds are so modern a race. They are now at their heyday of development. By-and-by, when gaps appear in the now serried ranks, classification will be an easier matter; for classification, after all, is an artificial, unnatural sort of thing, if we believe in a gradual modification of species out of pre-existing species. It is not too much to say that, the more perfect our scheme of classification, the greater our ignorance of the group classified. If the only birds known to science were a Hornbill, a Duck, and a Crow, together with a few of the immediate allies of each, we could easily sort them. But there are so many intermediate forms which absolutely decline to fit accurately into any system. Then the would-be systematist has to distinguish between those characters which imply a deep-seated relationship and those which are only due to similar needs. The aim of classification is, of course, to indicate real relationship, not merely to pigeon-hole in a convenient way. Real relationship is often masked by superficial differences. For instance, the common blindworm of our hedgerows is not, as might be thought, a snake, but a lizard; it appears to be unlike the lizard in having no legs, and to be so far a snake. Indeed, the terror inspired by this peaceful reptile must stand it in good stead with any except human foes. But its whole anatomy is built upon the lizard, and not upon the snake, plan. We disregard, therefore, in a scheme of classification the likeness to a snake, remembering that in Nature, as in morals, appearances are apt to be deceptive. The owls, among birds, are believed by many to offer an instance of the same kind of deception. By all the older systematists, and by many of the more modern, they are placed with the hawks in one group. No doubt the owls bear a certain likeness to the hawks. They have formidable claws and a hooked and powerful beak; they kill their prey; and only differ superficially in that they love the darkness, while the hawks hunt by day. Now, in certain details of anatomy, particularly in the windpipe and the muscles, the owls are much more like that division of birds which includes the goatsuckers. The mention of this latter family brings us face to face with another difficulty. If the superficial likeness of the owls to the hawks is to be distrusted,

as merely due to a similar mode of life, and therefore to the development of certain structures which are in direct relation to that mode
of life, how about the superficial likeness of the owls to the goatsuckers, which is almost as well marked as to the hawks? In
Australia and other parts of the East there are two genera of goatsuckers which have received the names of Podargus and Batracho-
stomus. These birds are wonderfully like owls. They have the
same brown-and-grey and soft plumage; their flight is equally noise-
less—and, altogether, anyone who saw the living Cuvier's Podargus
recently on view at the Zoological Gardens might well be pardoned
for thinking it an owl. The fact is that we must be careful not to
be prejudiced in any direction. Superficial similarities may or may
not go with real likeness. Speaking generally, one should be disposed
to lay greatest stress upon characters which have no obvious relation
to mode of life as likely to be of the most use in indicating blood
relationship. It is easier, however, to lay down general principles
of this kind than to apply them to birds. As has been already
mentioned, birds are so uniform in anatomy that in such characters
as brain, lungs, and other internal organs which are not so directly
under the immediate influence of their surroundings, there is but
little difference. Such characters afford no help to the systematist.
We are obliged, therefore, to rely upon other and really less
important points.

In most books upon ornithology—in this one, for instance—the
scheme of classification is set forth in the shape of a list beginning
with one particular group and ending with another. This is merely
due to the physical properties of sheets of paper. A linear scheme
is really an impossibility; to represent classification properly we
want a solid diagram, showing how from a root-stock branches
arose and pushed their way in every direction. Another defect of
the linear scheme is that we must begin somewhere and end somewhere. In this book we begin with the Passeres and end with the
Parrots; others start with the Accipitres, in spite of the protest of
Michelet against placing the cowardly, flat-headed, stupid hawks at
the summit of bird creation. It doesn't matter where we begin or
where we end as long as we carefully bear in mind that a linear
classification is only a convenient way of briefly stating certain
facts, and that it does not pretend to be a copy of Nature. An
alternative method of expressing the facts of structure in space of
two dimensions is the Stammbaum, originally made in Germany;
but this inevitable tree of life is open to the serious objection of

undue dogmatism ; and besides, it must be inaccurate, as it is not in three dimensions. A given naturalist may have strong reasons for believing, let us say, that the Struthious birds represent the lowest bird stock, from which arose in a regular series of branches, indepen- dently, and alternately from one side or the other, the various groups into which we divide the class in the present book ; if so, then the Stammbaum is easily constructed. But the general consensus of opinion is that the inter-relationships of the different groups cannot be expressed with so much simplicity. It is clear that, in any case, the most modified offshoots must occupy the highest branches of the tree, and that we may in a linear scheme conveniently begin or end with them. But it is impossible to arbitrate as to which group is the most specialised. It is, on the whole, agreed that the Ostrich tribe have retained more primitive characters than other birds ; but is the elaborate voice-mechanism of the Nightingale, or the almost human intelligence of the Raven or Parrot, to rank first as evidence of high position, *i.e.* specialisation, remoteness from the original stock ? This is a matter about which everybody can legitimately have an opinion ; and we cannot at present formulate a creed—for those, that is to say, who are acquainted with the facts.

The scheme that I adopt here is the same as that which Mr. Hudson uses in the pages which follow ; it is the plan followed in the B.O.U. list, and approved by most ornithologists in this country as a convenient working outline. I have added to it the fossil groups, and those groups which do not occur in Great Britain. The main scheme is that of Dr. Gadow, used in his valuable account of the anatomy of birds in Bronn's 'Klassen und Ordnungen des Thierreichs.' There is no deep-seated and mysterious reason for my placing Parrots at the end of the Aves Carinatæ : it is simply sheer inability to place them anywhere in particular.

CLASS. AVES.

SUB-CLASS I. Archæornithes (contains genus Archæopteryx only).
SUB-CLASS II. Neornithes.
    Division i. Neornithes Ratitæ.
        Order i. Ratitæ (contains Struthio, Rhea, Dinornis, &c.).
        Order ii. Stereornithes (contains a few fossil genera, Gast-
             ornis, Dasornis, &c.).
    Division ii. Neornithes Odontolcæ.
        Order i. Hesperornithes (the extinct Hesperornis and
             Enaliornis).

Division iii. Neornithes Carinatæ.

Order i. Ichthyornithes (fossil Ichthyornis only).

Order ii. Passeres (thrushes, swallows, flycatchers, tits, &c.).

Order iii. Picariæ (rollers, cuckoos, hornbills, woodpeckers, swifts, colies, trogons, goatsuckers, kingfishers).

Order iv. Striges (owls).

Order v. Accipitres (hawks, eagles, American vultures, &c.).

Order vi. Steganopodes (cormorants, pelicans, solan geese, frigate bird).

Order vii. Herodiones (herons, storks, ibis, spoonbills).

Order viii. Odontoglossi (flamingoes).

Order ix. Anseres (screamers, ducks, geese).

Order x. Columbæ (doves).

Order xi. Pterocletes (sand-grouse).

Order xii. Gallinæ (curassows, megapodes, pheasants, grouse, Opisthocomus, &c.).

Order xiii. Tinamidæ (tinamous).

Order xiv. Fulicariæ (rails, coots).

Order xv. Alectorides (cranes, bustards, Cariama, &c.).

Order xvi. Limicolæ (plovers, snipe, knots, &c.).

Order xvii. Gaviæ (gulls, skuas).

Order xviii. Pygopodes (auks, divers, grebes).

Order xix. Sphenisciformes (penguins).

Order xx. Tubinares (petrels, albatross).

Order xxi. Psittaci (parrots).

It will be noticed that, out of these twenty-one groups into which we may divide the Neornithes Carinatæ of Gadow, only three are not represented in Great Britain, viz. the Sphenisciformes, Psittaci, and Tinamiformes. So that the student of bird anatomy in this country has plenty of chance of making himself acquainted with the main outlines of structure of the entire class of living birds. Out of the thirty-two minor divisions of these birds, no fewer than twenty-one are to be met with in these islands; and of those that are not, some are quite easy to get hold of—a parrot, for instance.

FIELDFARES.   MISSEL-THRUSH.   BLACKBIRD.

Missel-Thrush, or Stormcock.

Turdus viscivorus.

UPPER parts ash-brown; under parts white, faintly tinged with yellow, marked with numerous black spots; under wing-coverts white; three lateral tail feathers tipped with greyish white. Length, eleven inches.

There are six British thrushes. Of these the missel-thrush and blackbird are residents throughout the year; the song-thrush is also found with us at all seasons, and is a winter songster, but many birds migrate; the ring-ouzel is a summer visitor; the red-wing and fieldfare are winter visitors.

The missel or mistletoe thrush, or stormcock, is the largest, exceeding the fieldfare, which comes next in size, by at least an inch in length and two inches in spread of wings. This species possesses in a marked degree all the characters that everywhere distinguish the true thrushes, which are world-wide in their range. Theirs is a modest colouring:—olive-brown above, paler and spotted below; a loud and varied song, and harsh cry; a statuesque figure; rapid, startled movements on the ground, with motionless intervals. when the bird stands with head and beak much raised, in an attitude denoting intense attention; and, finally, a free, strong, undulating flight.

The missel-thrush inhabits almost the whole of the British Islands, and is most abundant in Ireland. Throughout England and Wales he is fairly common, less common in Scotland, and becoming rarer the farther north we go. He is found in all woods and plantations, but is most partial to wooded parks, orchards, and gardens, which afford him food and shelter throughout the year.

He is the hardiest of our vocalists, and is better known as a winter than a summer songster. His song may be heard in the autumn, but from midwinter until spring his music is most noteworthy. Its loudness and wild character give it a wonderful impressiveness at that season of the year. He is not of the winter singers that wait for a gleam of spring-like sunshine to inspirit them, but is loudest in wet and rough weather; and it is this habit and something in the wild and defiant character of the song, heard above the tumult of nature, which have won for him the proud name of storm-cock.

This thrush is an early breeder, and pairs about the beginning of February. The birds, after mating, are exceedingly pugnacious, and attack all others, large or small, that approach the chosen nesting-site. The nest is not often made in evergreens, to which blackbirds and song-thrushes are so partial; as a rule, a deciduous tree—oak, elm, or beech—is made choice of, and the nest may be at any height, from a few feet above the ground to the highest part of a tall tree; and as it is built so early in the year, when trees are leafless, it forms a most conspicuous object. Furthermore, the missel-thrush, a shy and wary bird at other times, becomes strangely trustful, and even careless, when nesting, and often builds in the neighbourhood of a house, or in an isolated tree at the roadside. When building and breeding the birds are silent, except when the nest is threatened with an attack, when they become clamorous and bold beyond most species in defence of their eggs or nestlings.

The nest is large and well made, outwardly of dry grass, moss, and other materials, woven together; it is plastered with mud inside, and thickly lined with fine dry grass. The four eggs vary in ground-colour from bluish white to pale reddish brown, and are spotted, blotched, and clouded, with various shades of purple, brown, and greyish under-markings. Two or three broods are reared in the season.

At the end of June the missel-thrushes begin to unite in small parties numbering a dozen to twenty birds, and to range over the open country, seeking their food in the pastures and turnip-fields, and on moors and commons. Where the birds are abundant much larger congregations are seen. In Ireland I have seen them in August in flocks of about a hundred birds. They do not keep close together, as is the manner of starlings and finches, but fly widely scattered, and alight at a distance apart, a flock of fifty to a hundred birds sometimes occupying half an acre or more ground. They then look very large and conspicuous, scattered over the green grass, standing erect and motionless, or hopping about in their wild, startled manner. These flocks diminish in number as the season progresses, and finally break up about midwinter.

In autumn the missel-thrushes devour the yew-berries, and the fruit of the rowan and service trees; later in the year they feed on the glutinous berries of the mistletoe, on haws and ivy-berries, and other wild fruits; but their food for the most part consists of earthworms, snails, grubs, and insects of all kinds.

Throstle, or Song-Thrush.

Turdus musicus.

FIG. 18.—SONG-THRUSH. ¼ natural size.

Upper parts olive-brown, throat white in the middle; sides of neck and under parts ochreous yellow spotted with dark brown; under wing-coverts pale orange-yellow. Length, nine inches.

The protest and recommendation implied by the use of the first name at the head of this article may be futile; but it is impossible not to feel and to express regret that so good and distinctive and old a name for this familiar bird should have been replaced by a name which is none of these things. Song-thrush is an unsuitable name, for the very good reason that we have several thrushes, all of them songsters. By most persons the bird is simply called 'thrush,' which is neither better nor worse than 'song-thrush.'

The throstle is one of the smaller members of the genus, being about a third less in size than the noble stormcock. In form, colouring, motions, language, and habits, he is a very thrush. It cannot be said that his music is the best—that, for instance, it is finer than that of the blackbird. The two songs differ in character; both are good of their kind, neither perfect. The throstle is, nevertheless, in the very first rank of British melodists, and it is often said of him that he comes next to the nightingale. The same thing has been said of other species, tastes differing in this as in other matters. It is worth remarking that most persons would agree in regarding the nightingale, song-thrush, blackbird, blackcap, and skylark, as our five finest songsters, and that these all differ so widely from each other in the character of their strains that no comparison between them is possible, and there is no rivalry.

The only species which may be called the rival of the song-thrush is the missel-thrush, as their music has a strong resemblance. That of the stormcock has a wonderful charm in the early days of the year, when it is a jubilant cry, a herald's song and prophecy, sounding amidst wintry gloom and tempest. Heard in calm and genial weather in spring, the throstle is by far the finer songster. His chief merit is his infinite variety. His loudest notes may be heard half a mile away on a still morning; his lowest sounds are scarcely audible at a distance of twenty yards. His purest sounds, which are very pure and bright, are contrasted with various squealing and squeaking noises that seem not to come from the same bird. Listening to him, you never know what to expect, for his notes are delivered in no settled order, as in some species. He has many notes and phrases, but has never made of them one completed melody. They are snatches and portions of a melody, and he sings in a scrappy way—a note or two, a phrase or two, then a pause, as if the singer paused to try and think of something to follow; but when it comes it has no connection with what has gone before. His treasures are many, but they exist jumbled together, and he

takes them as they come. As a rule, when he has produced a
beautiful note, he will repeat it twice or thrice; on this account
Browning has called him a 'wise bird,' because he can

recapture
The first fine careless rapture.

There is not in this song the faintest trace of plaintiveness, and
of that heart-touching quality of tenderness which gives so great a
charm to some of the warblers. It is pre-eminently cheerful; a
song of summer and love and happiness of so contagious a spirit
that to listen to it critically, as one would listen to the polished
phrases of the nightingale, would be impossible.

The throstle is a very persistent singer : in spring and summer
his loud carols may be heard from a tree-top at four o'clock or half-
past three in the morning; throughout the day he sings at intervals,
and again, more continuously, in the evening, when he keeps up an
intermittent flow of melody until dark. His evening music always
seems his best, but the effect is probably due to the comparative
silence and the witching aspect of nature at that hour, when the sky
is still luminous, and the earth beneath the dusky green foliage lies
in deepest shadow.

So far only the music of the throstle has been considered; but
in the case of this bird the music is nearly everything. When we
think of the throstle, we have the small sober-coloured figure that
skulks in the evergreens, and its life-habits, less in our minds than
the overmastering musical sounds with which he fills the green
places of the earth from early spring until the great silence of July
and August falls on nature.

The song-thrush is a common species in suitable localities
throughout the British Islands, being rarest in the north of Scotland.
He is found in this country all the year round, but it was discovered
many years ago, by Professor Newton, that a very limited number
of birds remain to winter with us. Probably they migrate by night,
as the fieldfare and redwing are known to do, and, being much less
gregarious than those birds, come and go without exciting attention.
The fact remains that, where they are abundant in summer, a time
comes in autumn when they mysteriously vanish. One or two
individuals may remain where twenty or thirty existed previously;
and if they only shifted their quarters, as the missel-thrushes do in
some parts of the country, they would be found in considerable
numbers during the winter in some districts. But the disappearance

E

is general. I am inclined to think that this thrush migration is not so general as Professor Newton believes, and that the birds that leave our shores are mainly those that breed in the northern parts of the country. During the exceptionally severe winter of 1894–5 the thrushes that remained with us suffered more than most species, and in the following spring I found that the song-thrush had become rare throughout the southern half of England.

Nesting begins in March, the site selected being the centre of a hedge, or a thick holly or other evergreen bush, or a mass of ivy

FIG. 19.—THROSTLE'S NEST.

against a wall or tree. The nest is built of dry grass, small twigs, and moss, and plastered inside with mud, or clay, or cow-dung, and lined with rotten wood. This is a strange material for a nest to be lined with, and is not used by any other bird; the fragments of rotten wood are wetted when used, and, being pressed smoothly down, form a cork-like lining, very hard when dry. Four or five eggs are laid, pale greenish blue in ground-colour, thickly marked with small deep brown spots, almost black. Two, and sometimes three, broods are reared in the season.

During the day, when not singing, the thrush is a silent bird; in the evening he becomes noisy, and chirps and chatters and screams excitedly before settling to roost.

Insects of all kinds, earthworms, and slugs and snails, are eaten by the song-thrush. The snail-shells are broken by being struck vigorously against a stone; and as the same stone is often used for the purpose, quantities of newly broken shells are sometimes found scattered round it. He is a great hunter after earthworms, and it would appear from his actions that the sense of hearing rather than that of sight is relied on to discover the worm. For the worm, however near the surface, is still under it, and usually a close bed of grass covers the ground; yet you will see a thrush hopping about a lawn stand motionless for two or three seconds, then hop rapidly to a spot half a yard away, and instantly plunge his beak into the earth and draw out a worm. The supposition is that he has *heard* it moving in the earth. He is also a fruit and berry eater, both wild and cultivated.

Redwing.

Turdus iliacus.

Upper parts olive-brown; a broad white streak above the eye under parts white, with numerous oblong, dusky spots; under wing-coverts and flanks orange-red. Length, eight and a half inches.

In size and general appearance the redwing resembles the song-thrush. Like the fieldfare, he is a winter visitor from northern Europe, arriving a little earlier on the east coast, and differing from his fellow-migrants in being less hardy. He is more of an insect-eater, and is incapable of thriving on berries and seeds; hence in very severe seasons he is the greater sufferer, and sometimes perishes in considerable numbers when, in the same localities, the fieldfare is not sensibly affected. Nor is he of so vagrant a habit as the larger thrush: year after year he returns to the same place to spend the winter months, feeding in the same meadows, and roosting in the same plantations, until the return of spring calls him to the north. He is partial to cultivated districts where there are woods and grass-lands, and passes the daylight hours in meadows and moist grounds near water, returning regularly in the evening to the roosting-trees.

At all seasons the redwing is gregarious, and in its summer haunts many birds are found nesting in close proximity. A good deal of interest attaches to the subject of its song, which Linnæus thought ' delightful,' and comparable to that of the nightingale—an opinion ridiculed by Professor Newton in his edition of Yarrell. Richard Jefferies, who found the redwing breeding and heard its summer song in England, describes its strain as ' sweet and loud—far louder than the old, familiar notes of the thrush. The note rang out clear and high, and somehow sounded strangely unfamiliar among English meadows and English oaks.' [1]

Fieldfare.

Turdus pilaris.

Head, nape, and lower part of the back dark ash-grey; upper part of the back and wing-coverts chestnut-brown; a white line above the eye; chin and throat yellow streaked with black; breast reddish brown spotted with black; belly, flanks, and lower tail-coverts white, the last two spotted with greyish brown; under wing-coverts white. Length, ten inches.

In size and colouring, more especially in the spotted under parts, the fieldfare comes near enough to the missel-thrush to be sometimes confounded with it. Thus, flocks of missel-thrushes seen in autumn are sometimes mistaken for fieldfares that have come at an exceptionally early date to warn the inhabitants of these islands that the winter will be a severe one. The fieldfare is slightly less in size than the missel-thrush, and has a more variegated plumage, and when seen close at hand is a handsome bird.

He is one of the latest winter visitors to arrive, seldom appearing before the end of October. The return migration takes place at the end of April, or later; flocks of fieldfares have been known to remain in this country to the end of May, and even to the first week in June. Like the redwing, he is gregarious all the year round; in his summer home in the Norwegian forests he exists in communities, and the nests are built near each other. The migration is usually performed by night, and the harsh cries of the travellers may be heard in the dark sky, on the east coasts of England and

---

[1] *Wild Life in a Southern County.*

Scotland, at the end of October, and in November. From the time of their arrival until they leave us they are seen in flocks of twenty or thirty to several hundreds of individuals. They do not, like the redwings, attach themselves to certain localities, but wander incessantly from place to place, ranging over the entire area of Great Britain and Ireland. Owing to this vagrancy, the fieldfare is an extremely familiar bird to the countryman, and invariably its first appearance, and harsh yet joyous clamour, as of jays screaming and magpies chattering in concert, call up a sudden image of winter —cold, brief days and a snow-whitened earth, and memories of that early period in life when the great seasonal changes impress the mind so deeply.

In open weather the fieldfares seek their food in meadows and pastures, also in the fields. Unlike the missel-thrushes, that move about in all directions over the ground, the fieldfares when feeding all move in the same direction. In like manner, when the flock repairs to a tree, the birds on their perches are all seen facing one way—a very pretty spectacle. When their feeding-grounds are frozen, or covered with snow, they go to the hedges and devour the hips and haws, and any other wild fruit that remains ungathered; if severe weather continues, they take their departure to more southern lands. Their flight is strong, easy, and slightly undulating, and before settling to feed the flock often wheels gracefully about over the field for some time.

The song of the fieldfare, described by Seebohm as a 'wild desultory warble,' uttered on the wing, is not known to us in this country—it is a song of summer and of love; but in genial weather, when the birds are faring well, they often burst out into a concert of agreeable sounds just after alighting in a tree.

In the evening when settling to roost they are extremely noisy like most thrushes, and their cries may be heard until dark.

Blackbird.

Turdus merula.

Black; bill and orbits of the eyes orange-yellow. *Female:* sooty brown. Length, ten inches.

Among the feathered inhabitants of these islands there is scarcely a more familiar figure than that of the blackbird. Not only is he

very generally diffused, and abundant in all suitable localities, but
he is attached to human habitations—a bird of the garden, lawn, and
shrubberies.   His music is much to us, his beautiful mellow voice
being unique in character in this country.   But, more than his voice,
his love of gardens and their produce, and whatever else serves to

Fig. 20.—Blackbird's Nest.

make him better known than most birds, is his blackness.   Excepting
the crows, he is the only British bird in the passerine order with a
wholly black plumage ; and his bright yellow bill increases the
effect of the blackness, and, like a golden crown, gives him a strange

beauty. Like his companion of the garden and shrubbery, the throstle, he is a skulker, and on the least alarm takes shelter under the thickest evergreen within reach. When disturbed from his hiding-place he rushes out impetuously with a great noise, making the place resound with his loud, clear, ringing and musical chuckle. But he is not so inveterate a skulker and in love with the shade as the other. You will sometimes find him on hillsides and open moors, or nesting in the scanty tufts of sea-campion on rocky islands where he has for only neighbour the rock-pipit. But above all situations he prefers the garden and well-planted ground, and in such places is most abundant. His food is the same as that of the throstle, and is taken in much the same way : he listens for the earthworms working near the surface of the ground, and hammers the snails against a stone to break the shells. In the fruit season he is very troublesome to the gardener, and greedily devours strawberries, cherries, currants, gooseberries and mulberries.

The song of the male begins early in spring, and is mostly heard during the early and late hours of the day. Its charm consists in the peculiar soft, rich, melodious quality of the sound, and the placid, leisurely manner in which it is delivered. But the manner varies greatly. 'He sings in a quiet, leisurely way, as a great master should,' says Richard Jefferies ; unfortunately, the great master too often ends his performance unworthily with an unmusical note, or he collapses ignominiously at the close. John Burroughs, the American writer on birds, thus describes it : ' It was the most leisurely strain I heard. Amid the loud, vivacious, work-a-day chorus it had an easeful *dolce far niente* effect. . . It constantly seemed to me as if the bird was a learner, and had not yet mastered his art. The tone is fine, but the execution is laboured ; the musician does not handle his instrument with deftness and confidence.' Perhaps it may be said that, of all the most famed bird-songs, that of the blackbird is the least perfect and the most delightful.

The blackbird places his nest in the centre of a hedge or in an evergreen ; it is formed of herbs, roots, and coarse grass, plastered inside with mud, and lined with fine dry grass. Four to six eggs are laid, light greenish blue in ground-colour, mottled with pale brown. Two or three, and sometimes as many as four, broods are reared in the season.

In the northern and more exposed parts of the country the blackbird has a partial migration, or shifts his quarters to more sheltered localities in the winter.

Ring-Ouzel.

Turdus torquatus.

Fig. 21.—Ring-Ouzel. ⅕ natural size.

Black, the feathers edged with greyish white; a large crescent-shaped, pure white spot on the throat. Length, eleven inches. *Female*: plumage greyer; the white mark narrower and less pure.

The ring-ouzel is sometimes called the 'mountain blackbird,' on account of his likeness to the common species. He is more a ground bird and less skulking in habit than the garden blackbird, but in appearance and motions strongly resembles him. On alighting he throws up and fans his tail in the same way, and is very clamorous when going to roost in the evening. His manner of feeding is much the same : hopping along the ground, frequently pausing to look up, and anon plunging his beak into the soil to draw out a grub or earthworm. He breaks the snail-shells in the same way, and is equally fond of fruits and berries, both wild and cultivated.

The ring-ouzel is a summer visitor to this country, arriving about the beginning of April, and spends the summer months and breeds in the higher, least-frequented parts of Dartmoor, in Devonshire, and the hilly part of Derbyshire, and many localities in the north of England. He is also found in various localities in Wales, Scotland, and Ireland. On their arrival the birds are seen for a short period in flocks, sometimes of considerable size, frequenting wet and marshy grounds. As soon as pairing takes place the flocks break up, and the birds distribute themselves over the mountains and high uplands. The song of the male is heard after the birds have paired and made choice of a breeding-site. It is a powerful song, delightful to listen to, partly for its own wild, glad character, but more on account of the savage beauty and solitariness of the nature amidst which it is usually heard. The nest is placed upon or close to the ground, beneath or in a tuft of heather; and occasionally is built in a low bush or tree. Outwardly it is made of coarse grass or twigs of heather, plastered inside with mud or clay, and lined with fine dry grass. The four or five eggs are bluish green, blotched with reddish brown.

Seebohm has the following spirited description of the ring-ouzel's action in the presence of danger to its nest : ' Approach their treasure, and, although you have no knowledge of its whereabouts, you speedily know that you are on sacred ground. . . . *Something* sweeps suddenly round your head, probably brushing your face. You look round, and there the ring-ouzel, perched close at hand, is eyeing you wrathfully, and ready to do battle, despite the odds, for the protection of her abode. Move, and the attack is resumed, this time with loud and dissonant cries that wake the solitudes of the barren moor around. Undauntedly the birds fly around you, pause for a moment on some mass of rock, or reel and tumble on the ground to decoy you away. As you approach still closer the anxiety of the female, if possible, increases ; her cries, with those of her mate, disturb the birds around ; the red grouse, startled, skims over the shoulder of the hill to find solitude ; the moor-pipit chirps anxiously by ; and the gay little stonechat flits uneasily from bush to bush. So long as you tarry near their treasure the birds will accompany you, and, by using every artifice, endeavour to allure or draw you away from its vicinity.'

Besides the six species described, there are three thrushes to be found in works on British birds : the black-throated thrush (*Turdus atrigularis*), a straggler from Central Siberia; White's thrush (*T. varius*), from North-east Siberia; and the rock-thrush (*Monticola saxatilis*), from South Europe, a member of a group that connects the true thrushes (Turdus) with the wheatears (Saxicola).

Wheatear.

Saxicola œnanthe.

Fig. 22.—WHEATEAR. ⅓ natural size.

Upper parts bluish grey; wings and wing-coverts, centre and extremity of the tail, feet, bill, and area comprising the nostrils, eyes, and ears, black; base and lower portion of the side of the tail pure white; chin, forehead, stripe over the eye, and under parts, white. In autumn, upper parts reddish brown and tail feathers tipped with white. *Female*: upper parts ash-brown tinged with yellow; stripe over the eye dingy. Length, six and a half inches.

To those who are attracted to solitary, desert places, who find in wildness a charm superior to all others, the wheatear, conspicuous in black and white and bluish grey plumage, is a familiar

figure—a pretty little wild friend; for he, too, prefers the uncultivated wastes, the vast downs, the mountain slopes, and the stony
barren uplands. He is one of the earliest, if not the first, of the
summer migrants to arrive on our shores. They appear early in
March, sometimes at the end of February, on the south and east
coasts, after crossing the Channel by night or during the early hours
of the morning. They come in ' rushes,' at intervals of two or three
days. In the morning they are seen in thousands; but after a few
hours' rest these travellers hurry on to their distant breeding-grounds,
and perhaps for a day or two scarcely a bird will be visible; then
another multitude appears, and so on, until the entire vast army has
distributed itself far and wide over the British area, from the Sussex
and Dorset coasts to the extreme North of Scotland and the Hebrides,
the Orkneys, and Shetlands. The return migration begins early in
August, and lasts until the middle of September. During this period
the downs on the Sussex coast form a great camping-ground of the
wheatears, and they are then taken in snares by the shepherds for
the markets. Most of the birds taken are young; they are excessively fat, and are esteemed a great delicacy. The wheatear harvest
has, however, now dwindled down to something very small compared
with former times; it astonishes us to read in Pennant that a
century and a quarter ago eighteen hundred dozens of these birds
were annually taken in the neighbourhood of Eastbourne alone.
The great decrease in the number of wheatears is no doubt due to
the reclamation of waste lands, where this bird finds the conditions
suited to it. To a variety of climates it is able to adapt itself: the
vast area it inhabits includes almost the whole continent of Europe,
from the hot south to the furthermost north; and westwards its
range extends to Iceland, Greenland, and Labrador. But cultivation
it cannot tolerate: when the plough comes the wheatear vanishes.
Fortunately, there must always be waste and desert places—the
scattered areas on mountain-sides, barren moors and downs, and
rocky coasts, that cannot be made productive. In such spots the
wheatear is an unfailing summer companion, and at once attracts
attention by his appearance and motions. He is fond of perching
on a rock, stone wall, or other elevation, but seldom alights on
bushes and trees. He runs rapidly and freely on the ground, and,
pausing at intervals and standing erect, moves his tail deliberately
up and down. He flies readily, his rump and tail flashing white as
he rises; and after going but a short distance, flying close to the
ground, he alights again, and jerks and fans his tail two or three

times. He feeds on grubs, small beetles, and other insects picked up from the ground, but also pursues and catches flying insects. He has a short, sharp call-note that sounds like two pieces of stone struck smartly together; hence the name of 'stone-clatter,' by which he is known in some localities. His short and simple song would attract little attention in groves and gardens; it is charming on account of the barren, silent situations it is heard in. It gives life to the solitude, and is a love-song, accompanied by pretty gestures and motions, and is frequently uttered as the bird hovers in the air.

The wheatear breeds in a cavity under a stone, or in a hole or crevice in a stone wall; also in cairns and in the cavities in peat-stacks, and occasionally in a disused rabbit-burrow or under a clod of earth. The nest is made of dry grass, loosely put together and slightly lined with some soft material—moss and rootlets, rabbits' fur, horsehair, or wool, or feathers. From four to seven eggs are laid, pale greenish blue in colour, in some cases faintly marked with purplish specks at the large end.

The wheatear, owing to its wide distribution in this country, is known by a variety of local names in different districts; of these may be mentioned *fallowchat, whitetail, stone-cracker, chack-bird,* and *clod-hopper.*

Two other species of the genus Saxicola have been included in the list of British birds. These are the black-throated wheatear (*Saxicola strapazina*), of which a single specimen has been obtained, and the desert wheatear (*Saxicola deserti*), of which two or three specimens have been shot.

Whinchat.

Pratincola rubetra.

Upper parts dusky brown edged with reddish yellow; broad white stripe over the eye; throat and sides of neck white; neck and breast bright yellowish red; a large white spot on the wings and base of the tail; tip of the tail and the two middle feathers dusky brown; belly and flanks yellowish white. *Female* : colours duller ; white spot on the wing smaller. Length, five inches and a quarter.

Of the three British species forming this group of two genera

(Saxicola and Pratincola)—the fallowchat, stonechat, and whinchat—the last-named is the least striking, whether in appearance or habits. His modest plumage has neither brightness nor strongly contrasted colours ; and although he is a frequenter of furze-grown commons, and named on this account furzechat, or whinchat, he is not, like the stonechat, restricted to them. He inhabits both wild and cultivated grounds, rough commons and waste lands, mountain-sides, and meadows and grass fields divided by hedgerows. He roosts, breeds, and obtains most of his food on the ground ; but he loves to perch on bushes and low trees, and in most open situations where these grow the whinchat may be met with. On his arrival in April he feeds very much on the fallows, but later, in May, forsakes them for the neighbouring grass fields, where he makes his nest. He is commonly seen perched on the summit of a bush, low tree, or hedgerow, and, like the stonechat, he makes frequent short excursions in pursuit of flying insects. When approached he grows restless on his perch, fans his tail at intervals, and frequently utters his low call or alarm note ; then flies away, to perch again at a short distance from the intruder, and flies and perches again, and finally doubles back and returns to the first spot. Besides the insects he catches flying, he feeds on small beetles, grubs, worms, &c., found about the roots of the grass. He is frequently seen fluttering close to the surface of the tall grass, picking small insects from the leaves, and is most active in seeking his food during the evening twilight.

The whinchat's low warbling song, which has some resemblance to that of the redstart, is mostly heard in the love season, and is uttered both from its perch on the summit of a bush or tree, and when hovering in the air.

The nest is placed on the ground, usually in a cavity under the grass in a field, not far from a hedgerow, or under a thick furze-bush on commons, or at the roots of the heather on moors. It is formed of dry grass and moss, and lined with horsehair and root-lets. Four to six eggs are laid, greenish blue in colour, faintly marked with a zone of brown spots at the larger end.

Stonechat.

Pratincola rubicola.

Head, throat, bill, and legs black; sides of neck near the wing, tertial wing-coverts, and rump white; breast bright chestnut-red, paling to white on the belly; feathers of the back, wings, and tail black with reddish brown edges. *Female*: head and upper parts dusky brown, the feathers edged with yellowish red; throat black with small whitish and reddish spots; less white in the wings and tail;

FIG. 23.—STONECHAT. ¼ natural size.

the red of the breast dull.   Length, five and a quarter inches.

In his colouring and appearance, and to some extent in habits, the small stonechat is unlike any other bird. His strongly contrasted tints—black and white, and brown and chestnut-red—make him as conspicuous to the eye as the goldfinch or yellowhammer, and thus produce much the same effect as brilliancy of colour. The effect is increased by the custom the bird has of always perching on the topmost spray of a furze-bush on the open commons which it inhabits. Perched thus conspicuously on the summit, he sits erect and motionless, a small feathered harlequin, or like a painted image of a bird. But his disposition is a restless one · in a few moments he drops to the ground to pick up some small insect he has spied, or else dashes into the air after a passing fly or gnat, and then returns to his stand, or flits to another bush some yards away, where he reappears on its top, sitting erect and motionless as before. He is always anxious in the presence of a human being, flying restlessly from bush to bush, incessantly uttering his low, complaining note, which has a sound like that produced by striking two pebbles together; hence his name of stonechat. But it is a somewhat misleading name. He is not, like the wheatear, an inhabitant of barren stony places. but is seen chiefly on commcns abounding in furze-bushes and thorns and brambles. He is seen in pairs, but is nowhere a numerous species, although found in most suitable localities throughout the three kingdoms. He is also to be met with throughout the year, but is much rarer in winter than in summer ; and probably a great many individuals leave the country in autumn, while others seek more sheltered situations to winter in, or have a partial migration.

The stonechat has a slight, but sweet and very pleasing, song, uttered both when perched and when hovering in the air. Towards the end of March the nest is made, and is placed on or close to the ground, under a thick furze-bush ; it is large, and carelessly made of dry grass, moss, heath and fibrous roots, lined with fine grass, horse-hair, feathers, and sometimes with wool. Five or six eggs are laid, pale green or greenish blue in colour, and speckled at the large end with dull reddish brown. When the nest is approached the birds display the keenest distress.

Redstart.

Ruticilla phœnicurus.

Forehead white ; head and upper part of back bluish grey; throat black ; breast, tail-coverts, and tail, except the two middle feathers, which are brown, bright bay. *Female* : upper parts grey deeply tinged with red ; throat and belly whitish ; breast, flanks, and under tail-coverts pale red. Length, five and a quarter inches.

Fig. 24.—Redstart. ½ natural size.

The redstart is found from April to the end of August throughout England and Wales, but is nowhere common; in Scotland and Ireland he is rare. He is, nevertheless, a better-known bird to people in the country districts than some of the migratory songsters which are more abundant. Not, however, on account of his song, which is inferior to most, but partly because he 'affects neighbour-hoods,' as Gilbert White says, and partly on account of his pure and prettily contrasted colours—the white forehead, slaty grey upper parts, and chestnut rump and tail. The bright-coloured tail, which he flirts often as he flits before you, quickly attracts the eye. ' Firetail ' is a common name for this bird. Redstart is Saxon for redtail. When seen perched upright and motionless he resembles the robin in figure, but does not seek his food so much on the ground, and in his restless disposition and quick, lively motions, he is like the warblers. A peculiarity of the redstart is his fondness for old walls; he is attracted by them to orchards and gardens, where he is most often seen, although always a shy bird in the presence of man.

Seebohm says : 'As the wheatear is the tenant of the cairns, the rocks, and the ruins of the wilds, in like manner the redstart may be designated a bird of the ruins and the rocks in the lower, warmer, and more cultivated districts. You will find it in orchards and gardens, about old walls, and in the more open woods and shrub-beries. Another favourite haunt of the redstart is old crumbling ruins, abbeys, and castles, on whose battlements and still massive walls, ivy-covered and moss-grown, it delights to sit and chant its short and monotonous song.'

The song consists of one short phrase, dropping to a low twitter at the end, which varies in different singers ; but the opening note is always a beautiful expressive sound.

The redstart feeds on small beetles, caterpillars, spiders, and grubs, which it picks up in walls, trees, and bushes ; and on gnats, flies, and butterflies, captured on the wing after the manner of the flycatcher.

The nest is almost always made in a hole, usually in an old stone wall, but occasionally in a hole in a tree, and sometimes in the cleft formed by two branches. It is loosely built with dry grass and moss, and lined with hair and feathers. The eggs are four to six in number ; sometimes as many as eight, or even ten, are laid. They resemble the hedge-sparrow's eggs, being of a uniform greenish blue colour.

The black redstart (*Ruticilla titys*) is a winter visitor in small numbers to the south-west of England, and has been known to breed on two or three occasions in this country. It is common throughout Central and Southern Europe, wintering in North Africa, and in its nesting and other habits and language resembles the redstart.

Between the redstarts (Ruticilla) and the redbreast (Erithacus), next to be described, the bluethroats (Cyanecula) are placed, of which two species have been recorded as casual visitors to this country—the white-spotted bluethroat (*C. Wolfi*), from Western Europe; and the red-spotted bluethroat (*C. Suecica*), a breeder in the arctic regions.

Redbreast.

Erithacus rubecula.

Fig. 25.—REDBREAST. ¼ natural size.

Upper parts olive-brown; forehead and breast red, the red edged with grey; belly white. *Female*: a trifle smaller than the male, and less bright in colour. Length, five inches and three-quarters.

Of man's feathered favourites—the species he has thought proper to distinguish by a kindly protective sentiment—the redbreast probably ranks first, both on account of the degree of the feeling and

F

its universality.   The trustfulness of the familiar robin, especially in seasons of snow and frost, in coming about and entering our houses in quest of crumbs, is the principal cause of such a sentiment ; but the highly attractive qualities of the bird have doubtless added strength to it.   The bright red of his breast, intensified by contrast with the dark olive of the upper parts, gives him a rare beauty and distinction among our small songsters, which are mostly sober-coloured.   Even more than beauty in colouring and form is a sweet voice ; and here, where good singers are not few, the robin is among the best.   Not only is he a fine singer, but in the almost voiceless autumn season, and in winter, when the other melodists that have not left our shores are silent, the robin still warbles his gushing, careless strain, varying his notes at every repetition, fresh and glad and brilliant as in the springtime.   His song, indeed, never seems so sweet and impressive as in the silent and dreary season.   For one thing, the absence of other bird-voices causes the robin's to be more attentively listened to and better appreciated than at other times, just as we appreciate the nightingale best when he ' sings darkling ' —when there are no other strains to distract the attention.   There is also the power of contrast—the bright, ringing lyric, a fountain of life and gladness, in the midst of a nature that suggests mournful analogies—autumnal decay and wintry death.   There cannot be a doubt that the robin gives us all more pleasure with his music than any other singing-bird ; we hear him all the year round and all our lives long, and his voice never palls on us.   But those who have always heard it, for whom this sound has many endearing associa-tions, might have some doubts about its intrinsic merits as a song— they might think that they esteem it chiefly because of the associa-tions it has for them.   In such a case one is glad to have an inde-pendent opinion—that, for instance, of an ' intelligent foreigner,' who has never heard this bird in his own country.   Such an opinion we may find in John Burroughs, the American writer on birds ; and it may well reassure those who love the robin's song, but fear to put their favourite bird in the same category with the nightingale, blackcap, and garden-warbler.   He writes : ' The English robin is a better songster than I expected to find him.   The poets and writers have not done him justice.   He is of the royal line of the nightin-gale, and inherits some of the qualities of that famous bird.   His favourite hour for singing is the gloaming, and I used to hear him the last of all.   His song is peculiar, jerky, and spasmodic, but abounds in the purest and most piercing tones to be heard—piercing from their smoothness, intensity, and fulness of articulation ; rapid and crowded at one moment, as if some barrier had suddenly given way, then as suddenly pausing, and scintillating at intervals bright, tapering shafts of sound. It stops and hesitates, and blurts out its notes like a stammerer; but when they do come, they are marvellously clear and pure. I have heard green hickory-branches thrown into a fierce blaze jet out the same fine, intense, musical sounds on the escape of the imprisoned vapours in the hard wood as characterise the robin's song.'

The robin is an early breeder, and makes its nest beneath a hedge, or in a bank, or in a close bush not far above the ground; it is formed of dry grass, leaves, and moss, and lined with feathers. Six or seven eggs are laid, reddish white in ground-colour, clouded or blotched, and freckled with pale red. When the nest is approached the old birds express their anxiety by a very curious sound—a prolonged note so acute that, like the shrill note of some insects and the bat's cry, it is inaudible to some persons. Two, and even three, broods are raised in the season.

At the end of summer the old birds disappear from their usual haunts to moult; and during this perhaps painful, and certainly dangerous, period, they remain secluded and unseen in the thickest foliage. When they reappear in new and brighter dress, restored to health and vigour, a fresh trial awaits them. The young they have hatched and fed and protected have now attained to maturity, and are in possession of their home. For it is the case that every pair of robins has a pretty well-defined area of ground which they regard as their own, jealously excluding from it other individuals of their own species. The young are forthwith driven out, often not without much fighting, which may last for many days, and in which the old bird is sometimes the loser. But in most cases the old robin reconquers his territory, and the young male, or males, if not killed, go otherwhere. And here we come upon an obscure point in the history of this familiar species; for what becomes of the young dispossessed birds is not yet known. It has been conjectured that they migrate, and that not many return from their wanderings beyond the sea. And it is not impossible to believe that the migratory instinct may exist in the young of a species, although obsolete at a later period of life.

Nightingale.

Daulias luscinia.

FIG. 26.—NIGHTINGALE.　⅓ natural size.

Upper plumage uniform brown tinged with chestnut; tail rufous; under parts greyish white; flanks pale ash. Length, six inches and a quarter.

The nightingale is the only songster that has been too much lauded, with the inevitable result that its melody, when first heard, causes disappointment, and even incredulity. More than once it has been my lot to call the attention of someone who had not previously heard it to its song, at the same time pointing out the bird; and after a few moments of listening, he or she has exclaimed, 'That the nightingale! Why, it is only a common-looking little bird, and its song, that so much fuss is made about, is after all no better than that of any other little bird.' And then it is perhaps added: 'I don't think the nightingale—if the bird you have shown me *is* the nightingale—sings so well as the thrush, or the blackbird, or the lark.' The song is, nevertheless, exceedingly beautiful; its phrasing is more perfect than that of any other British melodist; and the voice has a combined strength, purity, and brilliance probably without a parallel. On account of these qualities, and of the fact that the song is frequently heard in the night-time, when other voices are silent, the nightingale was anciently selected as the highest example of a perfect singer; and, on the principle that to him that hath shall be given, it was credited with all the best qualities of all the other singers. It was the maker of ravishing music, and a type, just as the pelican was a type of parental affection and self-sacrifice, and the turtle-dove of conjugal fidelity. Only, when he actually hears it for the first time, the hearer makes the sad discovery that the bird he has for long years been listening to in fancy—the nightingale heard by the poet with an aching heart, and the wish that he, too, could fade with it into the forest dim—was a nightingale of the brain, a mythical bird, like the footless bird of paradise and the swan with a dying melody. Beautiful, nay, perfect, the song may be, but he misses from it that something of human feeling which makes the imperfect songs so enchanting—the overflowing gladness of the lark; the spirit of wildness of the blackcap; the airy, delicate tenderness of the willow-wren; and the serene happiness of the blackbird.

The nightingale arrives in this country about the middle of April, returning to the same localities year after year, apparently in the same numbers. It is scarcely to be doubted that the young birds that survive the perils of migration come back to the spot where they were hatched, since the species does not extend its range nor establish new colonies. It is most common in the southern counties of England, above all in Surrey, but rare in the western and northern counties, and in Scotland and Ireland it is unknown.

The nightingale so nearly resembles the robin in size, form, and manner that he might be taken for that bird but for his clear, brown colour. Like the robin, he feeds on the ground, seeking grubs and insects under the dead leaves, hopping rapidly by fits and starts, standing erect and motionless at intervals as if to listen, and occasionally throwing up his tail and lowering his head and wings, just as the robin does. He inhabits woods, coppices, rough bramble-grown commons, and unkept hedges, and loves best of all a thicket growing by the side of running water.

Two or three days after arriving he begins to sing, and continues in song until the middle, or a little past the middle, of June, when the young are hatched. In fine weather he sings at intervals throughout the day, but his music is more continuous and has a more beautiful effect in the evening. For an hour or two after sunset it is perhaps most perfect. In the dark he is silent, but if the moon shines he will continue singing for hours. That is to say, *some* birds will continue singing ; as a rule, not half so many as may be heard during daylight.

The nest is nearly always placed on the ground beneath a hedge or close thicket ; it is rather large, and composed of dry grass and dead leaves loosely put together, the inside lined with fine dead grass, rootlets, and vegetable down. The eggs are four or five in number, and of a uniform olive-brown colour.

During incubation and after the young are hatched the parent birds display the most intense solicitude when the nest is approached, and flit from bough to bough close to the intruder's head, incessantly repeating two strangely different notes—one low, clear, and sorrowful, the other a harsh, grinding sound.

The return migration is in August and September.

Whitethroat.

Sylvia cinerea.

Fig. 27.—Whitethroat.   ⅓ natural size.

Head ash-grey tinged with brown ; rest of upper parts reddish brown ; wings dusky, the coverts edged with red ; lower parts white faintly tinged with rose colour ; tail dark brown, the outer feathers white on the tips and the outer web, the next only tipped with white. *Female* without the rosy tint on the breast. Length, five and a half inches.

The whitethroat, or greater whitethroat, as the name is some-times written, is one of the commonest and best known of the soft-billed songsters that spend the summer and breed in our country. It inhabits all parts of the British Islands, excepting the most barren. Even to those who pay little attention to the small birds that come in their way the whitethroat is tolerably familiar, less on account of its song, which is in no way remarkable, than for the excited notes and actions of the bird, sometimes highly eccentric, which challenge attention. The whitethroat is, moreover, readily distinguishable from its colour—the reddish brown hue of its upper plumage and the unmistakable white throat, which give it a con-spicuous individuality among the warblers. It inhabits the wood-side, the thickets, the rough common, but of all places prefers the thick hedge for a home. Shortly after the bird's arrival, about the middle or near the end of April, he quickly makes his presence known to any person who walks along a hedgeside. The intruder is received with a startled, grating note, a sound expressive of surprise and displeasure, and, repeating this sound from time to time, the bird flits on before him, concealed from sight by the dense tangle he moves amidst. Presently, if not too much alarmed, he mounts to a twig on the summit of the hedge to pour out his song—a torrent of notes, uttered apparently in great excitement, with crest raised, the throat puffed out, and many odd gestures and motions. Sometimes he springs from his perch as if lifted by sheer rapture into the air, and ascends, singing, in a spiral, then drops swiftly back to his perch again. It is a peculiar song on account of its vehement style and the antics of the singer, more so when he flies on before a person walking, now singing, now moving farther ahead in a succession of wild jerks, then suddenly ducking down into the hedge. It is also a pleasing song in itself, although for pure melody the whitethroat does not rank very high among the greatly gifted birds of its family, or sub-family. If we include the nightingale and robin, it should be placed about the sixth on the list, the other singers that come before it being the willow-wren, blackcap, and garden warbler.

The nest of the whitethroat is a round, flimsy structure, formed of slender stalks of grass and herbs, and lined with horsehair, and is placed two or three feet above the ground, in the brambles and briers of the hedge, or in a large furze-bush. The five eggs are of a greenish white, speckled with olive, and sometimes blotched and marked with grey and light brown. One brood only is reared.

Nettle-creeper is a common name for this bird, on account of its love of weeds, especially of nettles, no doubt because the small caterpillars it feeds on are most abundant on them. It is also fond of fruit, wild and cultivated, and visits the gardens near its haunts to feed on currants and raspberries.

Lesser Whitethroat.

Sylvia curruca.

Head, neck, and back smoke-grey; ear coverts almost black; wings brown edged with grey; tail dusky, outer feather as in the last species, the two next tipped with white; lower parts nearly pure white; feet lead colour. Length, five and a quarter inches.

The difference in size between this warbler and the one last described is very slight; still, there is a difference; and the descriptive epithet of *lesser* would also be a suitable one if applied in another sense. He is a less important bird. To begin with, he is much rarer, being only of local distribution in England and Scotland, and unknown in Ireland; in colouring he is more obscure; his trivial song has nothing in it to attract attention; he is shyer in habits, passes much of the time among the higher foliage of the trees he frequents, and is, consequently, not often seen.

He arrives in this country about or shortly after the middle of April, and is found in thickets and copses, and hedges in the neighbourhood of trees. Like most of the warblers, he is exceedingly restless, and moves incessantly among the leaves, picking up the aphides and minute caterpillars, and from time to time darts into the air to capture some small passing insect. Like the common whitethroat, he is also fond of ripe fruit, especially currants and raspberries. He is often on the wing, passing directly from place to place with an undulating flight and rapidly-beating wings. When singing he swells his throat out, and delivers his strain with considerable vigour; but his song is of the shortest, and is composed of one or two notes, hurriedly repeated two or three times without variation, and with scarcely any musical quality in it. No sooner is it finished than the bird is off again on his flitting rambles among the leaves and twigs; it is less like a song than an exclamation of pleasure—a cheerful call that bursts out from time to time.

The lesser whitethroat nests in orchards, coppices, thick hedgerows, bramble and furze bushes on commons, and among tangled vegetation overhanging streams, but in all cases the nest is placed in the midst of a dense mass of foliage. This is a somewhat loosely made and shallow structure, composed of dry grass-stems and small twigs, bound together with cobwebs and cocoons, and lined with fine rootlets and horsehair. Four or five eggs are laid, in ground-colour white or dull buff, blotched and speckled with greenish brown, with underlying markings of purplish grey.

Blackcap.

Sylvia atricapilla.

FIG. 28.—BLACKCAP. ½ natural size.

Head above the eyes jet - black, in the *female* chocolate-brown; upper parts, wings, and tail ash-grey slightly tinged with olive; throat and breast ash-grey; belly and under wing-coverts white. Length, five and a half inches.

This brilliant song-ster arrives in this country about the middle of April, in some years consider-ably earlier. It is found throughout England and Wales, and extends its range to Scotland and Ireland, only in lesser numbers. Though widely distributed it is rare, except in some districts in the southern and western counties of England. A person familiar with the ornithological literature of this country, but having little personal knowledge of the birds, who should go out to make acquaintance with the blackcap, would be surprised at its rarity. After much seeking, he would probably come to the conclusion that, speaking of warblers only, there are at least half a hundred willow-wrens, and perhaps twenty whitethroats, to one blackcap. Another curious point about the blackcap is that it appears to be almost unknown to the country people. It is a rare thing to find a rustic, man or boy, who knows it by that or any other name, though he may be quite familiar with the redstart and whitethroat. On these last two points I find that my experience coincides with that of John Burroughs, the American writer on bird life, in the accounts of his observations on British song-birds. There is a third point on which I also agree with him; this, however, is not a question of fact, but of opinion or of individual taste, and refers to the merit of the blackcap as a singer. His is a song which has always been very highly esteemed, and it has often been described as scarcely inferior to that of the nightingale. Gilbert White of Selborne described it as ' a full, deep, sweet, loud, wild pipe ; yet that strain is of short continuance, and his motions are desultory; but when that bird sits calmly and engages in song in earnest, he pours forth very sweet, but inward, melody, and expresses great variety of soft and gentle modulations, superior, perhaps, to those of any of our warblers, the nightingale excepted.' After reading such a description it is a disappointment to hear the song. Nevertheless, it is very beautiful, and given out with immense energy, as the bird sits on a spray with throat puffed out, and moves its head, sometimes its whole body, vigorously from side to side. The song is a clear warble composed of about a dozen notes, rapidly enunciated, loud, free, of that sweet, pure quality characteristic of the melody of our best warblers. The strain is short, and repeated from time to time, the intervals often being filled by lower notes, sweet and varied—the 'inward melody' which White describes. Burroughs's description of the song is as follows: ' While sitting here I saw, and for the first time heard, the blackcapped warbler. I recognised the note at once by its brightness and strength, and a faint suggestion in it of the nightingale's ; but it was disappointing: I had expected in it a nearer approach to its great rival. . . . It is a ringing, animated strain, but as a whole seemed to me crude, not smoothly and finely modulated. I could name several of our own birds that surpass it in pure music. Like its congeners, the garden warbler and the whitethroat, it sings with great emphasis and strength, but its song is silvern, not golden.' This account of the blackcap's song is interesting as coming from a foreigner who has paid great attention to the bird music of his own country, and it is on the whole a very good description; but I should not say that the blackcap's strain is crude, however wild and irregular it may be ; nor that there is in it even a faint suggestion of the nightingale's.

In its active, restless habits this warbler resembles the other members of its group ; but it exceeds them all in shyness. When approached it becomes silent, and conceals itself in the interior of the thicket. It frequents woods and orchards; also hedges and commons where large masses of furze and bramble are found, especially in the vicinity of trees. The nest is made of dry grass, lined with hair or fibrous roots, and is placed in the forked branches of a thick bush, three or four feet above the ground. The eggs, of which five or six are laid, are of a light reddish colour. mottled and blotched with darker red and reddish brown. They vary greatly, both in the depth of colour of the mottlings and in the pale ground-tints.

The blackcap lives on insects, which it often captures on the wing, and on fruits, and is fond of raspberries and currants. Its autumn migration is in September.

Garden Warbler.

Sylvia hortensis.

Upper plumage greyish brown tinged with olive; below the ear a patch of ash-grey ; throat dull white ; breast and flanks grey tinged with rust colour; rest of under parts dull white. Length, five and a quarter inches.

This warbler was first described as a British species by Willughby, more than two centuries ago, under the name of 'prettichaps ' ; and Professor Newton, in a note to Yarrell's account of it, says: 'This name (prettichaps) seems never to have been in general use in England, or it would be readily adopted here.' The old name of prettichaps, it may be mentioned, does not appear to be quite obsolete yet: I have heard it in Berkshire, where it was applied indiscriminately to the garden warbler and blackcap.

The garden warbler is not common anywhere. In Ireland it is scarcely known; in Scotland, Wales, and a large part of England it is very rare. It is most frequently to be met with in the southern counties, especially in Hampshire. Very curiously, Gilbert White did not know this warbler, which may now be heard singing any day in spring in the neighbourhood of Selborne village.

The garden warbler is often said to rank next to the blackcap as a melodist. The songs of these two species have a great resemblance; it is, indeed, rare to find two songsters, however closely allied, so much alike in their language. The garden warbler's song is like an imitation of the blackcap's, but is not so powerful and brilliant: some of its notes possess the same bright, pure, musical quality, but they are hurriedly delivered, shorter, more broken up, as it were. On the other hand, to compensate for its inferior character, there is more of it; the bird, sitting concealed among the clustering leaves, will sing by the hour, his rapid, warbled strain sometimes lasting for several minutes without a break.

The garden warbler is a late bird, seldom arriving in this country before the end of April. It builds a rather slight nest, in a bush near the ground, of dry grass and moss, lined with hair and fibrous roots. The eggs are five in number, and are dull white, sometimes greenish white, blotched and speckled with dull brown and grey.

The food of this warbler consists of small insects; and it is also fond of fruit and berries.

Six species of the genus Sylvia are included in books on British birds: the four already described, the orphean warbler (*Sylvia orphea*), an accidental visitor from Central and Southern Europe, and the barred warbler (*Sylvia nisoria*), from Central, South, and East Europe.

Furze-Wren, or Dartford Warbler.

Melizophilus undatus.

Upper parts greyish black; wing-coverts and feathers blackish brown; outer tail feathers broadly, and the rest narrowly, tipped with light brownish grey; under parts chestnut-brown; belly white. Tail long; wings very short. Length, five inches.

The furze-wren, never a common species in this country, is now become so scarce, and is, moreover, so elusive, that it is hard to find, and harder still to observe narrowly. Its somewhat singular appearance among the warblers—its small size, short, rounded wings, great length of tail, and very dark colour—its peculiar song, and excessively lively and restless habits, and the fact that it was

FIG. 29.—DARTFORD WARBLER. ⅓ natural size.

first discovered in this country (1773), where, though so small and delicate a creature, it exists on open, exposed commons throughout the year, have all contributed to make it a fascinating subject to British ornithologists. In England it inhabits Surrey and the counties bordering on the Channel; but it has also been found in suitable localities in various other parts of the country, and ranges as far north as the borders of Yorkshire. I have sought for it in many places, but found it only in Dorset. Forty or fifty years ago it was most abundant in the southern parts of Surrey; it was there observed by the late Edward Newman, who gave the following lively and amusing account of its appearance and habits in his 'Letters of Rusticus on the Natural History of Godalming' (1849): 'We have a bird common here which, I fancy, is almost unknown in other districts, for I have scarcely ever seen it in collections. . . . I mean the furze-wren, or, as authors are pleased to call it, the Dartford warbler. We hear that the epithet of Dartford is derived from the little Kentish town of that name, and that it was given to the furze-wren because he was first noticed in that neighbourhood. . . . If you have ever watched a common wren (a kitty-wren we call her), you must have observed that she cocked her tail bolt upright, strained her little beak at right angles, and her throat in the same fashion, to make the most of her fizgig of a song, and kept on jumping and jerking and frisking about, for all the world as though she was worked by steam; well, that's more the character of the Dartford warbler, or, as we call her, the furze-wren. When the leaves are off the trees and the chill winter winds have driven the birds to the olive-gardens of Spain, or across the Straits, the furze-wren is in the height of his enjoyment. I have seen them by dozens skipping about the furze, lighting for a moment on the very point of the sprigs, and instantly diving out of sight again, singing out their angry, impatient ditty, for ever the same. Perched on the back of a good tall nag, and riding quietly along the outside, while the foxhounds have been drawing the furze-fields, I have often seen these birds come to the top of the furze. . . . They prefer those places where the furze is very thick, and difficult to get in. . . . And although it is so numerous in winter, and so active and noisy when disturbed by dogs and guns, still, in the breeding season it is a shy, skulking bird, hiding itself in thick places, much in the manner of the grasshopper lark, and seldom allowing one to hear the sound of its voice.'

Spring is, however, the season of the furze-wren's greatest activity : its lively gestures, antics, and dancing motions on the topmost sprays of the bushes are then almost incessant, as it pursues the small moths and other winged insects on which it feeds; and its curious and impetuous little song is then delivered with the greatest vigour. It has also a harsh, scolding note, uttered several times in rapid succession, and a loud musical call-note.

The nest is placed among the dense masses of the lower, dead portion of a thick furze-bush. It is a flimsy structure, composed of dead furze-leaves, small twigs, and grass-stems, lined with finer stems, and sometimes with horsehair. Four or five eggs are laid, white in ground-colour, sometimes tinged with buff or with greenish, thickly spotted and freckled with pale brown over paler brown and grey markings. Two broods are reared in the season.

Golden-crested Wren, or Goldcrest.

Regulus cristatus.

Upper parts olive tinged with yellow ; cheeks ash-colour; wing greyish brown, with two transverse white bands ; crest bright yellow

in front, orange behind, bounded by two black lines ; under parts
yellowish grey. *Female*: colours not so bright; crest lemon-colour.
Length, three and a half inches.

The golden-crested wren has the distinction of being the smallest
British bird; it is also one of the most widely distributed, being
found throughout the United Kingdom. Furthermore, it is a resident throughout the year, is nowhere scarce, and in many places
is very abundant. Yet it is well known only to those who are
close observers of bird life. The goldcrest is not a familiar figure,
owing to its smallness and restlessness, which exceed that of all
the other members of this restless family of birds, and make it difficult for the observer to see it well. Again, it is nearly always concealed from sight by the foliage, and in winter it keeps mostly among
the evergreens, and at all times haunts by preference pine, fir, and
yew trees. In the pale light of a winter day, more especially in
cloudy weather, it is hard to see the greenish, restless little creature
in his deep green bush or tree. Standing under, or close to, a wide-
spreading old yew, half a dozen goldcrests flitting incessantly about
among the foliage in the gloomy interior of the tree look less like
what they are than the small flitting shadows of birds.

In March, and even as early as the latter part of February, the
male is frequently heard uttering his song ; but he is not of the
songsters that perch to sing, and pour out their music deliberately
and with all their might. The goldcrest's song comes in as a sort
of trivial distraction or relief—a slight interlude between the more
important acts of passing from one twig or spray to another. and
snatching up some infinitesimal insect so quickly and deftly that to
see the action one must watch the bird very closely indeed. And
the music, of which the musician makes so little, is of very little
account to the listener. It is the smallest of small songs—two notes,
almost identical in tone, repeated rapidly, without variation, two or
three times, ending with a slight quaver, scarcely audible, on the
last note. The sound is sharp and fine, as of young mice squealing,
but not quite so sharp, and more musical ; it is a sound that does
not travel : to hear it well one must stand not farther than a dozen
or fifteen yards from the singer.

Yarrell has the following passage on the song of the goldcrest:
' Pennant says he has observed this bird suspended in the air for a
considerable time over a bush in flower, while it sang very melodi-
ously ; but this peculiarity does not appear to have been noticed by

other naturalists.' I have observed the male, in the love season, hovering just above the bush, in the topmost foliage of which its mate was perched, and partially hidden from view. It is when engaged in this pretty, aërial performance, or love-dance, that the golden-crested wren is at his best. The restless, minute, sober-coloured creature, so difficult to see properly at other times, then becomes a conspicuous and exceedingly beautiful object; it hovers on rapidly-vibrating wings, the body in almost a vertical position, but the head bent sharply down, the eyes being fixed on the bird beneath, while the wide-open crest shines in the sun like a crown or shield of fiery yellow. When thus hovering it does not sing, but emits a series of sharp, excited, chirping sounds.

The goldcrest builds a pendent nest, made fast to the small twigs under a branch of yew or fir, and uses a variety of materials—fine dry grass, leaves, moss, and webs—closely woven together, lining the cavity with feathers. It is a very ingenious and pretty structure. The eggs laid are from six to ten, of a pale yellowish white, spotted and blotched, chiefly at the large end, with reddish brown.

In the autumn, in the months of October and November, a great migratory movement takes place among the goldcrests in the north of Europe ; and in some seasons incredible numbers of these small travellers arrive, often in an exhausted condition, in Northumberland and on the east coast of Scotland. After resting close to the sea for a day or two, they resume their journey, and distribute themselves over the country.

The firecrest (*Regulus ignicapillus*), which closely resembles the species just described, is an accidental visitor from the continent of Europe.

Chiffchaff.

Phylloscopus rufus.

Upper plumage olive-green tinged with yellow; above the eye a faint yellowish white streak ; under parts yellowish white; feathers of the leg greyish white. Length, four inches and three-quarters.

The chiffchaff, although his song is so simple—the simplest song of all—and after a time is apt to become wearisome from incessant repetition, is, nevertheless, one of the most welcome visitors of the early spring ; for this small bird, in spite of its smallness and frailty, is the first of the migratory warblers to make its appearance on our coasts. Shortly after the middle of March, and even earlier in some years, the well-remembered, familiar sound, full of promise of the beautiful budding season, begins to be heard here and there in the more sheltered and sunny spots in woods and copses, and by the first week in April it is one of the most familiar sounds in the country. It is not, however, so general as the strain of the willow-wren, this species being more local in its distribution.

It is this early appearance of the chiffchaff, coming 'before the swallow dares,' that endears it to the lover of Nature and of bird life. Mr. Warde Fowler, in his 'Year with the Birds,' has well expressed the feeling which so many have for this small warbler. ' No one,' he says, ' who hails the approach of spring as the real beginning of a new life for men and plants and animals, can fail to be grateful to this little brown bird for putting on it the stamp and sanction of his clear, resonant voice. We grow tired of his two notes—he never gets beyond two—for he sings almost the whole summer through ; . . . but not even the first twitter of the swallow, or the earliest song of the nightingale, has the same hopeful story to tell me as this delicate traveller who dares the east wind and the frost.'

The two notes, which vary as slightly in tone as two taps of a hammer on an anvil delivered with equal force on the same spot, are emitted with great vigour and spirit, as if the little creature's whole heart was in the performance, and repeated several times without a pause. This is the whole song, and, when not engaged in uttering it, the singer is incessantly moving about in pursuit of small insects and their larvæ, now searching for them in the small twigs and buds, after the manner of the titmice, and at times capturing them on the wing. Meanwhile the song is repeated at frequent intervals from morning until dark. It is not suspended, as in the case of most of the warblers, after the young have been hatched, but continues throughout the summer and autumn, when it degenerates somewhat in character, the sound losing the little musical quality it originally possessed.

The nest is made in the ground, a hedgebank being the situation preferred, and is round and domed, with an opening at the side. Dry grass, leaves, and moss are the materials used in its construction, the cavity being plentifully lined with feathers. The eggs are six, pure white, spotted and speckled with brown and brownish purple.

Willow-Wren.

Phylloscopus trochilus.

Upper plumage bright olive-green; a narrow streak of yellow over the eye; under parts yellowish white, palest in the middle; feathers of the legs yellow.   Length, nearly five inches.

The willow-wren, or willow-warbler, is one of the earliest of our summer songsters to arrive, usually following the chiffchaff—which it resembles in size and general appearance—by a few days. During the last week of March, if the weather be not too cold, its delicate strain may be heard in sheltered situations in the southern parts of England, and by the second week in April it is one of the most frequently heard songs throughout the length and breadth of the land. Not only is this species very much more generally diffused than its two nearest relations—the chiffchaff and wood-wren—but it is met with in a much greater variety of situations—on commons, in hedgerows, gardens, woods, and plantations.   Yet, in spite of its abundance and wide distribution, it is nowhere a familiar bird to the country people ; the small, delicate voice does not compel attention and is well-nigh lost in the summer concert that has so many loud, jubilant strains in it.

The willow-wren is a pretty little bird, although without any bright colour in its plumage, which at a short distance looks of a soft greenish yellow tint.   He is best seen when the trees are opening their buds, before the thickening foliage hides his tiny, restless, flitting form from sight.   He is the least shy of the warblers, his trustfulness being in strong contrast to the suspicious manner and love of concealment of the blackcap and whitethroat.   He will unconcernedly continue his hunt for minute insects, and utter his melody at intervals, within a few feet of a person, sitting or standing, quietly observing him.   The song, although a small one, both as to duration and power, has a singular charm : not merely the charm of association experienced in a voice long absent and heard once more—a voice of the spring, that comes before the loud call of the cuckoo and the familiar, joyous twitter of the swallow; it is in itself a beautiful sound, one of the sweetest bird-songs heard in our country.   'A song which is unique among British birds,' says Mr. Warde Fowler, whose description of it is, perhaps, the most perfect which we have. 'Beginning with a high and tolerably full note, he drops it both in force and pitch in a cadence short and sweet, as though he were getting exhausted with the effort. . . . This cadence is often perfect; by which I mean that it descends gradually, not, of course, on the notes of our musical scale, . . . but through fractions of one, or perhaps two, of our tones, and without returning upward at the end; but still more often, and especially, as I fancy, after they have been here a few weeks, they take to finishing with a note nearly as high in pitch as that with which they began.'

After this it is interesting to read Mr. J. Burroughs's impressions of the willow-wren's song. He writes: 'The most melodious strain I heard, and the only one that exhibited to the full the best qualities of the American songsters, proceeded from a bird quite unknown to fame—in the British Islands, at least. I refer to the willow-warbler. . . . White says it has a "sweet, plaintive note," which is but half the truth. It has a long, tender, delicious warble, not wanting in strength and volume, but eminently pure and sweet —the song of the chaffinch refined and idealised. . . . The song is, perhaps, in the minor key, feminine and not masculine, but it touches the heart.

'That strain again; it had a dying fall.

'The song of the willow-warbler has a dying fall; no other bird-song is so touching in this respect. It mounts up round and full, then runs down the scale, and expires upon the air in a gentle murmur.'

The willow-wren breeds early, making a circular domed nest on the ground, among the long grass and weeds, under a hedge or beneath a bramble bush on a bank, and occasionally at a distance from sheltering bushes in the grass of a field. It is made of dry grass, and lined with rootlets and horsehair, and, lastly, with feathers. The eggs are six or seven in number, pure white, the yolk showing through the frail shell, and giving it a faint yellow tinge; they are blotched and spotted with reddish brown. When the nest is approached the parent birds display the greatest anxiety, hopping and flitting about close to the intruder, and uttering low, plaintive notes.

The willow-wren stays longer with us than any migratory warbler except the chiffchaff, and its song is, without exception, the most persistent. From the time of its arrival in March, or early in April, it sings without ceasing until July; then for a few weeks its song is heard only in the early morning, and it ceases at the end of August, during the moult, but is renewed a little later, and is then continued until the bird's departure at the end of September.

Wood-Wren.

Phylloscopus sibilatrix.

Upper plumage olive-green tinged with sulphur-yellow ; a broad streak of sulphur-yellow over the eye ; sides of head, throat, and insertion of the wings and throat bright yellow ; rest of under plumage pure white. Length, nearly six inches.

This warbler arrives in England at the end of April, being later by many days than its two nearest relations, the chiffchaff and willow-wren. As its name implies, it is a bird of the woods, with a preference for such as are composed wholly or in part of oak and beech trees. It is not easily discerned, on account of its restless disposition; also because it chiefly frequents the uppermost parts of the trees it inhabits. Its instinct appears to be to live and hunt for the small insects it preys on among the green leaves at the greatest possible height from the earth ; this may account for its love of the beech, which is the tallest of our forest trees. But if difficult to see as it flits lightly from place to place among the higher foliage, it is easy to hear, and its frequently uttered song sounds very loud in the woodland silence, and is strangely unlike that of any other songster. It may be said to possess two distinct songs : of these, the most frequently uttered and unmistakable begins with notes clear, sweet, and distinct, but following more and more rapidly until they run together in a resonant trill, and finally end in a long, tremulous note, somewhat thin and reedy in sound. At longer intervals it utters its other song, or call, a loud, clear note, slightly modulated, and somewhat plaintive, repeated without variation three or four times.

The wood-wren, although so great a lover of the tall tree-tops, breeds on the ground, like the two species described before it, and, like them, builds an oval-shaped domed nest. It is placed among the herbage, and is composed of moss, dry leaves, and grasses, lined with fine grass and horsehair. Feathers are never used in the nest-lining, and in this the wood-wren differs from the two preceding species. Six eggs are laid, transparent white, spotted and speckled with dark brown, purple and grey.

The wood-wren differs from most of the warblers in being exclusively an insect-eater.

A fourth member of this genus, the yellow-browed warbler (*Phylloscopus superciliosus*), which breeds in Northern Siberia, has been met with as a rare straggler in this country.

Two more warblers, belonging to different genera, must be mentioned here as stragglers to England: the icterine warbler (*Hypolaïs icterina*) and the rufous warbler (*Aëdon galectodes*).

Reed-Warbler.

Acrocephalus streperus.

Upper plumage uniform reddish brown, without spots; a white streak or spot between the eye and bill; throat white; under plumage very pale buff. Length, five and a half inches.

The reed-warbler closely resembles the sedge-warbler, next to be described, in size, colouring, and general appearance, also in language and habits; but is a much less common species, more local in its distribution, and is, consequently, not nearly so well known. He arrives in this country about the middle of April, and inhabits dense reed-beds in dykes, marshes, and the borders of rivers, where he skulks, for the most part out of sight; but his loquacity betrays his presence, for he is a persistent singer, especially in the early part of the day, and again in the evening. His song resembles that of the sedge-warbler in its curious mingling of musical and harsh notes, its hurried and somewhat angry scolding character, but is less powerful, the harsh notes less harsh and vigorous—a sweeter but not so interesting a performance. Like the nearly allied species, he bursts into singing when excited by fear or solicitude for the safety of his nest. He is an exceedingly restless little creature, incessantly hopping from stem to stem, now mounting to the surface of the reeds, and almost instantly dropping into concealment again. Even where the birds are many, it is only by patient waiting and watching that an occasional glimpse of one can be got. His food consists of small insects, caught on the wing and on the leaves and stems of the reeds and aquatic herbage. The nest is a deep, beautiful structure, suspended on two or three, or more, slender reed-stems, or on the twigs of a willow, osier, or other plant growing near the water. It is made of long dry grass-leaves woven together, with finer grass-leaves and horsehair for a lining. The eggs are four or five in number, greenish white in colour, clouded, blotched, and freckled with dark olive and ash-grey.

Sedge-Warbler.

Acrocephalus phragmitis.

FIG. 30.—SEDGE-WARBLER. ⅓ natural size.

Upper plumage greyish brown ; above the eye a broad, distinct, yellowish white streak ; under plumage pale buff; throat white. Length, four inches and three-quarters.

The sedge-warbler, usually called sedge-bird, and in some localities river-chat, is a common species in most waterside places where there are reed-beds and willows; it also frequents rough hedges and bramble and furze bushes in the neighbourhood of a watercourse.   Sometimes, but not often, it is found breeding at a considerable distance from a stream. It comes to us in April, and is a most active and lively little creature. Although not shy of man, it is less easy to observe than any other species in this group, except, perhaps, the grasshopper warbler, on account of its excessive restlessness, the rapidity of its movements, and its habit of keeping near the surface in the close reeds and bushes it lives in. The grasshopper warbler, and, indeed, most small birds that inhabit bushes, love to come to the surface to sing ; the sedge-warbler sings much as he hurries about in search of his food, which consists of small caterpillars and slugs, and aquatic insects. Occasionally the restless little yellowish brown figure appears for a moment or two near the top of a bush, and then vanishes again.

The song is curious, and delivered in a curious manner, with hurry and vehemence ; and this, as well as the character of the sounds emitted, gives the idea that the bird is excited to anger—that he is scolding at, rather than singing to, the listener. The opening note, hurriedly repeated several times, and recurring at short intervals as long as the song lasts (its keynote and refrain), resembles the chiding note of the whitethroat when its nest is approached, but is louder and more strident. It is the loudest sound the sedge-warbler emits, and when the song is heard at a distance of fifty or sixty yards it seems all composed of chiding notes. But on a nearer approach—and the bird will allow the listener to get quite close to it—the performance is found to be a very varied one. Listening to it, one finds it hard not to believe that this warbler possesses the faculty it has often been credited with, of mocking other species. But if he indeed has such a talent, he reproduces not so much the songs of other birds as the notes and chirps and small cries of anxiety and alarm the various sounds emitted by singing-birds in the presence of danger to their young or incubated eggs. Thus, in the medley of hurried and strongly contrasted sounds that come in a continuous stream from the sedge-warbler one seems to recognise the low girding of the nightingale, and the different notes of solicitude of the sparrow, reed-bunting, and chaffinch, of the wren and the willow-wren, the meadow-pipit and pied wagtail. But whether these various sounds are really borrowed or not one can never feel sure.

The sedge-warbler is a very persistent singer. Some birds are too chary of their strains ; but of this waterside music any person may have as much as he likes in May and June. Singing is apparently as little tiring to this bird as rushing through the air is to the swift. At the season of his greatest vigour he appears to pour out his rapid notes almost automatically ; and when silent, a stone or stick flung into his haunts will provoke a fresh outburst of melody. He also sings a great deal at night in the love season.

The sedge-warbler makes its nest among the tangled vegetation at the waterside ; as a rule it is placed near the ground, and is composed outwardly of moss, leaves, and aquatic grasses, and lined with fine grass and hair. The eggs are five, of a dirty white or pale brownish ground-colour, with yellowish brown spots, sometimes with hairlike marks among the spots.

Besides the two described, three more species of this group of warblers have been numbered as British birds, having been found as stragglers in this country. These are the marsh-warbler (*Acrocephalus palustris*), the great reed-warbler (*Acrocephalus turdoïdes*), and the aquatic warbler (*Acrocephalus aquaticus*).

Grasshopper Warbler.

Locustella nævia.

Upper parts light greenish brown; the middle of each feather, being darker, gives a mottled appearance; under parts very pale brown, spotted with darker brown on neck and breast; feet light brown. Length, five and a half inches. *Female* without the brown spots on the breast.

This warbler arrives in our country about the middle of April, sometimes a week, or even a fortnight, earlier. In the melodious family to which it belongs it is distinguished by the singularity of its voice, which has no musical, or songlike, or even birdlike quality in it, but is like the sound produced by some stridulating insects. It is to be found in suitable situations throughout England and Wales, and in many parts of Scotland and Ireland. It frequents both dry and marshy ground where dense masses of vegetation afford it the close cover which would seem necessary to its frail existence; thus it is found in reed-beds growing in the water, and in hedges and thorny thickets, and among the furze-bushes on open commons. Although thus widely distributed in the British Islands, it is, like the nightingale, very local, and reappears faithfully each spring at the same spot. How strong the attachment to place, or home, is in this species will be seen in the following fact: Having found a small colony of about half a dozen grasshopper warblers inhabiting a circumscribed spot in the middle of an extensive common, I went back to the place in three consecutive summers, and each time found the birds in the same bushes. Yet the dozen or twenty furze and bramble bushes which they inhabited were in no way, that one could see, better suited to their requirements than hundreds of other bushes of the same description scattered over the surrounding land. Nor were any other individuals of the species to be found in the neighbourhood, except one pair, which were always to be met with in some brambles about a quarter of a mile from the spot inhabited by the other birds. Such a fact appears to show that, not only do the old birds return year after year to the same breeding-place, but that the young also come back to the spot where they were hatched ; also, it appears to show that in this frail and far-travelling species the annual increase is only sufficient to make good the losses from all natural causes.

Immediately after their arrival in April the males begin their curious vocal performance, at first with a feeble and broken strain ; but in a little while the voice gains in strength and shrillness, and the utterance becomes more sustained, lasting sometimes without a break for thirty or forty seconds, and even longer. This is renewed again and again at short intervals throughout the day, and continued far into the night. Indeed, the song may be heard all night long in fine summer weather. The sound is recognised by few of those who hear it as coming from a bird. It is usually attributed to an insect, and if the hearer grows curious, and tries to find the exact spot from which it issues, he finds this a somewhat difficult task. The sound seems now on this side, now on that, now far away, and anon close at hand ; it is here, there, and everywhere. A good plan is to put the open hands behind the ear, then to turn slowly round until the exact spot is discovered. When the bush from which it proceeds has been found, the listener should advance cautiously to within a few yards of it, and sit down and wait until the hidden bird, recovering from his alarm, comes up to the summit and resumes his singing. It is then most interesting to observe him. The bird sits motionless, turning its head from side to side, and so long as the strain continues the yellow mouth is wide open, like the gaping mouth of a fledgeling waiting to receive food, the slender body trembling with the sound, as if an electric current were passing through it. The sound produced has been compared by different writers to the song of a grasshopper, only more sustained ; to the cicada ; to the whirring of a wool-spinner's reel, and to that of a well-oiled fisherman's reel made to run at a very rapid rate ; and, finally, to the sharp, vibrating sound of the rattlesnake, and to an electric bell ; but it is not so sharp as these last two.

The grasshopper warbler builds on the ground, and so well concealed is the nest that it is only possible to find it by watching the birds when carrying nesting materials into the bush. The nest is formed of dry grass and moss, and lined with fine fibres. Five to seven eggs are laid, white or pale pink, spotted with reddish brown over the entire egg ; and sometimes fine hairlike lines are mixed with the spots.

A small warbler, closely resembling the grasshopper warbler in its language and habits, and once an indigenous British species, is *Locustella luscinioïdes*, locally known as the reelbird, red night-reeler, and red craking night-wren, and in books as Savi's warbler, after its discoverer. It bred regularly in the Norfolk Broads and the fen districts in Lincolnshire down to about 1849, when it became extinct.

Hedge-Sparrow.

Accentor modularis.

FIG. 31.—HEDGE-SPARROW. ⅓ natural size.

Crown ash-colour with brown streaks; side of neck, throat, and breast bluish grey; back and wings reddish brown streaked with dark brown; breast and belly buffy white. Length, five and a half inches.

Most people know that a sparrow is a hard-billed bird of the finch family, and that the subject of this notice is not a sparrow, except in name. It is, in fact, a soft-billed bird belonging to that large and musical family which includes the nightingale, the red-breast, and the warblers. 'How absurd, then, to go on calling it a sparrow!' certain ornithologists have said from time to time, and have re-named it the hedge-accentor. But, as Professor Newton has said in his addition to Yarrell's account of the bird, a name which has been part and parcel of our language for centuries, and which Shakespeare used, 'is hardly to be dropped, even at the bidding of the wisest, so long as the English tongue lasts.' Now, as the

English tongue promises to last a long time, it seems safest to retain the old and, in one sense, incorrect name. Dunnock is another common name for this species; it is also called shufflewing, from the habit the bird has, when perched, of frequently shaking its wings.

Among our small birds, the hedge-sparrow is regarded with some slight degree of that kindly feeling, or favouritism, which is extended to the robin redbreast, the swallow, and the martin. It is one of the few delicate little birds that brave the rigours of an English winter, and occasionally enliven that dead season with their melody. With the wren and missel-thrush, it is a prophet, in February, of the return of brighter sunshine and lengthening days; and in hard weather it comes much about the house, for the sake of the small morsels of food to be picked up; and, while retaining its sprightliness at such times, it learns to be trustful. It is possible that the feeling or sentiment which no person, not even the most matter-of-fact scientific ornithologist, is quite proof against, is the cause of this species having been a little overpraised in many books about birds. The hedge-sparrow is often spoken of as a very charming little creature, while its song has been described as pleasing, as sweet, and as delightful. All birds are in a sense attractive, and even charming in appearance, but in different degrees, and the plain-coloured dunnock strikes one as being the least attractive among our birds. In the same way, the song may be said to be pleasant because it is a natural sound, and is heard in the open air when the sun shines, when leaves and blossoms are out, and it expresses the gladness which is common to all sentient things. But it has none of the rare qualities which are requisite to make a pleasant sound anything more than a merely pleasant sound.

The hedge-sparrow is a common bird throughout the British Islands—so common as to be familiar to most people, in spite of its shyness and love of concealment. It is pre-eminently a hedge-bird, and in that respect has been well named; even in the most populous districts, and in the suburbs of large towns, where a hedge remains, there the smoke-grey and brown little bird will have its home and make its nest, although it may seldom be able to rear its young. It is a very early breeder, a first brood being often reared in March. As a rule, the nest is placed in the centre of a hedge or thorny bush, three or four feet from the ground; it is made of dry grass and fine roots, and lined with hair; the eggs are five or six in number, bright greenish blue in colour, without spots. Two or three broods are reared in the season.

The alpine accentor (*Accentor collaris*), a larger species than our hedge-sparrow, which it resembles in colour, is known as a straggler to England from the mountainous districts of Central and Southern Europe.

Dipper.

Cinclus aquaticus.

FIG. 32.—DIPPER. ⅕ natural size.

Upper plumage brownish black tinged with grey; throat and breast pure white; belly chestnut-brown; bill black; feet horn-colour. *Female* : colours dingy. Length, six inches and a half.

The dipper, or water-ouzel, differs considerably in appearance, and still more in habits, from all other British birds ; as is the case with such species as the wryneck, cuckoo, kingfisher, bearded tit, tree-creeper, starling, and nuthatch, there is no other like him. In figure he is wren-like, stout and compact in body, with short, rounded wings and short, square tail, which, as with the wren, is often carried upright and jerked. He is a little less than the song-thrush in size, and is conspicuously coloured, the greater part of the plumage being black, or blackish brown ; and, in strong contrast, the throat and upper part of the breast shining white—a big black wren with a silvery white bib.

Some species always live and move within such narrow limits, or, in other words, are so dependent on certain conditions, that we invariably think of them in association with their surroundings :— the snipe with the boggy soil ; the rock-pipit with the rock-bound seashore ; the tree-creeper with the tree he climbs upon ; the lark with the cultivated fields; and the swift with the void blue sky, through which he is perpetually rushing. In like manner we invariably think of the dipper in connection with the swift, brawling mountain-torrent he inhabits. He is never, or very seldom, found removed from it, and is probably more restricted to certain conditions, and consequently more bound to his home, than any one of the species just named. The stream he attaches himself to must have quiet and comparatively deep pools, and the water must be clear to enable him to detect the larvæ of water-beetles, dragon-flies, and other aquatic insects he preys on, all of which have a protective colouring. He does not range up and down a stream, like the kingfisher, to visit the various feeding-places; he limits himself to a portion of it, in many cases not more than a hundred yards in length, and explores the bottoms of the same pools from day to day, until they must be as familiar to him—all their inequalities, their stony ridges and half-buried boulders, and sandy or pebbled places, and all the holes and secret corners where sediment collects—as the rooms we live in are to us, and about which we are able to move freely in the dimmest light. In ascending a mountain stream such as these birds love, abounding in deep, quiet pools, with noisy cascades and shallow rapids, its bottom strewn with great fallen boulders partly submerged, the rocky banks overgrown with sheltering bushes and vines, when you disturb a dipper he flies up stream a short distance, perhaps twenty yards, and alights on a boulder, or in the shadow of an overhanging rock, and there waits, silent and motion-less, until, disturbed again, he takes a second short flight up stream, and so on to the limit of his range, whereupon, rising up and doubl-ing back, he flies to the spot he started from. And as often as you disturb him he will act in the same way, going just so far, and no farther. If you leave him behind and go on, you will find another pair of dippers, whose portion of the stream begins just where that of the first pair ends. They, too, will act in the same way, and fly on until the end of their range is reached, and will not venture beyond where a third pair are in possession. Where they are not disturbed a mountain stream may be found parcelled out in this way among a dozen or twenty couples. Probably the dipper, like the robin, jealously resents the intrusion of another bird of his kind into his chosen ground. Concerning this habit of the dipper, and its strange way of feeding under the water, something still remains to be known. It is, indeed, strange that this little perching song-bird should have the habit of diving for its food like a grebe or a guille-mot, and other species that have structures specially adapted to such a way of life. For there is absolutely nothing in the dipper's structure to lead anyone unacquainted with its habits to believe that it ever approaches the water, unless to drink and bathe, and perhaps to pick up an insect floating on the surface. That it is able to sink into and move freely about beneath the water close to the bottom of a stream, in spite of gravity, seems very astonishing, and would be incredible if the fact were not so familiar. Some ornithologists believe that it is related to the wren, others to the thrush;—that is a question capable of solution; but how by a short-cut it became a diver must remain a mystery.

Formerly it was believed that the dipper was able to walk freely about on the bottom of the stream, but that was an error. It is difficult to watch the bird moving about under water; but a few good observers have succeeded in doing so, and from their accounts it would appear that the dipper propels itself by powerful wing-beats, moving by a series of rushes or jerks, keeping close to the bottom of the stream. It appears to swallow its food under water, but comes up at intervals to breathe, then sinks again beneath the surface.

On land the dipper is somewhat inactive, and will stand on a boulder or under an overhanging rock without moving for a long time. One would imagine that their eyes, fitted so well to see in the dim light beneath the surface, must be very sensitive to the glare above.

The dipper's song is short but brilliant, and very much like that of the wren in character; it is heard most frequently in the love season, and occasionally in autumn and in winter, when the sun shines, even during very cold weather.

The nest is made among the rocks, usually in a crevice, and is very large for the size of the bird, being sometimes a foot across, and is globular in form, with a small opening near the top. It is composed principally of moss, loosely felted, the inside lined with dry grass, fine rootlets, and dead leaves. Four to six eggs are laid, pure white, and unspotted.

The dipper is most common in mountainous districts in Scotland, Ireland, and Wales, and is found in suitable localities in England.

The black-billed dipper (*Cinclus melanogaster*), the Scandinavian and North Russian form of *Cinclus aquaticus*, has been met with on two or three occasions as a straggler to the east coast of England.

PLATE IV. BEARDED TITMOUSE. $\frac{3}{4}$ NAT. SIZE.

Bearded Titmouse.

Panurus biamicus.

Head bluish grey; between the bill and eye a tuft of pendent black feathers, prolonged into a pointed moustache; throat and neck greyish white; breast and belly white tinged with yellow and pink; upper parts light orange-brown; wings variegated with black, white and red : tail very long, orange-brown, the outer feathers variegated with black and white. *Female* : the moustache the same colour as the cheek; the grey on the head absent. Length, six inches and a half.

This bird, although by name a tit, and placed next to the titmice by many naturalists in their systems, differs widely from those birds in some points. The question of its true position among passerine birds has, indeed, been a subject of controversy for a long time past, and is not yet settled. Some writers would have it that it comes nearest to the shrikes; others, that it is most closely related to the buntings, and still others place it next to the waxwing. Leaving aside anatomical subjects, it may be said that the bearded tit is unlike all these different birds and the titmice in habits, language, colouring, and in its curious feather-ornaments—the erectile, pointed, black feathers that grow between the beak and eyes, and form the curious long moustache which gives the bird its name.

The bearded tit, although at all times an extremely local species, on account of its being exclusively an inhabitant of reed-beds, was once fairly common in many parts of England; but owing to the draining of marshes and to the persecution of collectors, it has now become one of the rarest of British birds. At present it is confined to the district of the Broads in Norfolk, where it is, unhappily, becoming increasingly rare, and is threatened with extinction at no distant date.

It is a very pretty bird in its buff and fawn coloured dress; very elegant in form, its singular black moustache and long, graduated tail enhancing the beauty of its appearance; and exceedingly graceful in its motions. It lives in the beds of reeds growing in the water; and the slim, graceful, clinging bird, and the tall, slender stems, with their pale, pointed leaves and feathery flowers, seem adapted each to the other. In seeking its food it clings to the reeds, much as the blue tit does to the pendent twigs of the birch. Its food consists of small insects and their larvæ, small molluscs, and the seeds of the reeds. In autumn and winter it is gregarious, three or four, or more, families uniting in a flock, and roaming from reed-bed to reed-bed and from broad to broad. When disturbed, or alarmed at the appearance of a hawk, they drop down into concealment among the reeds, but in a short time rise to the surface again, climbing parrot-like up the slender stems. There are few birds without a brilliant colouring that have so attractive an appearance as the bearded tit, especially when seen flying just above the top of the reeds, or when perched on a slender stem near its top, and swayed to and fro by the wind. Their alarm-note is harsh, but they have a variety of calling and singing notes, which are somewhat metallic in sound and very musical. A writer in Loudon's ' Magazine of Natural History ' describes the bearded tits in flight as ' uttering in full chorus their sweetly musical notes ; it may be compared to the music of very small cymbals, is clear and ringing, though soft, and corresponds well with the delicacy and beauty of the form and colour of the bird.'

The nest is made at the end of March or early in April, and is placed on the ground, under a bush, or among the grass and herbage near the water. It is composed of leaves of reeds, bents, and grass-blades, and lined with the fine fibres of the reed-tops. The eggs are four to six in number, and sometimes eight ; they are white, with a few minute specks, blotches, and lines of dark reddish brown.

Long-tailed Titmouse.

Acredula rosea.

Head, neck, throat, breast, and a portion of the outer tail-feathers white ; back, wings, and six middle feathers of the tail black ; a black streak above the eye ; sides of the back and scapulars tinged with rosy red ; under parts reddish white. Tail very long ; beak very short. Length, five inches and three-quarters.

The long-tailed tit is the least of the titmice, and is only saved from being described as the smallest British bird on account of its loose plumage and long tail, which make it look a trifle more bulky than the golden-crested wren. In many of its habits, and to some extent in its appearance, it resembles the typical tits, the five species of the genus Parus which remain to be described, and is often seen associating with them in winter. In its colouring, language, and nesting habits it differs from them. It is a somewhat singular-looking little bird, with grey and rose-coloured plumage, short wings, a very long tail, and a short, conical beak, which gives the round head something of a parrot-like appearance.

This species is found throughout Great Britain and Ireland, but is less common in Scotland than in England.

Fig. 33.—Long-tailed Tit. ¼ natural size.

It inhabits woods and plantations, and, like the other tits, is social, active, and restless in its habits. After the breeding season the old and young birds remain united, and spend the autumn and winter months in perpetually wandering through the woods; but their travels do not take them far from home. They are seen in a scattered party, each member of which appears wholly occupied with his own search for minute insects and their eggs and larvæ, but is ready at a given signal to abandon his food-getting and join the others in their hurried flight to the next tree. And as they pass from tree to tree their short wings and long tails give them, as Knapp said, the appearance of a flight of arrows. Leaving the woods, they roam over the surrounding country, making their way by short stages from tree to tree and from bush to bush, along lanes and hedges, and visiting the clumps of trees in parks and pasture-lands. They also come about houses, not for the crumbs that fall from the table, but to continue in gardens and shrubberies their endless search for minute insects. Very restless and anxious little hearts are theirs, one would imagine, from their incessant hurried flittings from place to place, and the small, querulous sounds in which they converse together.

H

At night they roost huddled together in a cluster composed, in some cases, of half a dozen or eight birds in a row, with three or four others perched on their backs, and one or two more resting on these.

Early in spring these curious little companies break up, and the song or love-call of the male bird, so unlike that of the other tits, may be heard—a prolonged trill, low and aërial, and very delicate in sound. The nest is placed on a tree or bush, and is long in building, and a marvel of bird architecture. It is domed, oval in shape, with a small aperture near the top, and is composed of moss, lichens, and hair closely felted, and the interior thickly lined with feathers. Macgillivray says that the feathers taken from one nest numbered 2,379. Six to eleven eggs are laid, sometimes a larger number. They are pure white or pearly grey in ground-colour, thinly spotted with light red and a few faint purple marks.

The continental form of the long-tailed tit, *Acredula caudata*, differs from *A. rosea* in wanting the dark stripe on the head; specimens without the stripe are sometimes met with in this country, but whether or no they are visitors from the Continent is not known.

Great Titmouse.

Parus major.

Head, throat, and a band passing down the centre of the breast black; back olive-green; cheeks and a spot on the nape white; breast and belly yellow. Length, six inches.

The great tit, or oxeye, is a resident species throughout the British Islands, and inhabits woods and plantations, and is also seen in orchards, gardens, and shrubberies. He is nowhere abundant, yet very well known, being one of those species it would be difficult for even the least observant person to overlook. He has a comparatively gay plumage, and the various colours are disposed and contrasted in a striking way. The intense glossy black of the head, throat, and broad band which divides the bright greenish yellow of the under parts lengthways, make him a conspicuous object.

His voice, for so small a bird, is a powerful and far-reaching one; and his frequently uttered spring call, or song, composed of two notes repeated two or three times in succession, strikes so sharply on the sense that it compels attention, like ringing blows

on an anvil or on the rivets of iron rails and girders, or the sound
of sharpening a saw. Saw-sharpener is one of its local names.

FIG. 34.—GREAT TIT. ⅓ natural size.

Another thing—the oxeye is the largest of the tits, consequently
the principal member of a group of small birds exhibiting very
strongly marked characters. They differ from most small birds, to
some extent, in form, colouring, and general appearance, and, in a
greater degree, in language and habits. They are extremely active
and restless, and spend most of their time in trees, from the bark
of the trunk and large branches to the smallest terminal twigs and
leaves. In winter, when the elms and other deciduous trees have
shed their foliage, and their fine upper boughs appear like a sombre
fretwork against the pale sky, the tits are seen at their best; they
are then gathered into small flocks or family parties, and may be
observed, as they scatter about the tree, clinging to the twigs in
every conceivable position, and looking like a company of small
sober-coloured paroquets of this cold northern world. They subsist principally on small insects and their eggs, larvæ, and chrysalids, but are almost omnivorous in their diet, feeding on buds, seed,
and fruits, and on animal food when it can be had. A meaty bone
or a piece of bacon, cooked or raw, or a lump of suet, will quickly
attract them, as is well known. The oxeye, pretty little bird as it
is, will eat carrion like any crow, and even kill and devour other
small birds as big as himself. His rapacious habits have, however,

not been very well established. In a captive condition he will occasionally attack a small bird in the same cage, killing it by vigorous blows on the head, and picking out its brains; but in a state of nature the great tit would probably be able to kill only a young or sick bird. For so small a bird he is, undoubtedly, very resolute and strong; the rapid blows of his short, strong bill on the bark sound like those of a nuthatch. Like that bird, he splits open the hard shells of seeds to get at the kernels.

The great tit is less social and gregarious than the other species of this group; still, he does unite in small parties, and joins the bands of mixed titmice and other small birds that form so familiar and interesting a feature of woods and copses in autumn and winter.

The nest is placed in a variety of situations, but a covered site is usually preferred to an open one, and nests may be found in holes and cavities in decayed timber, holes in walls, and in old nests of magpies, crows, and rooks. In a well-covered site the nest is loosely built; if in an open one, such as a crow's nest, the structure is much more elaborate, dry grass, moss, hair, and wool, being closely woven together, and the inside thickly lined with feathers.

The eggs vary from five to eleven in number; usually they are seven or eight. They are pure white or faintly tinged with yellow, blotched and spotted with reddish brown. Two broods are reared in the season. The parent birds are very bold in defence of their eggs and young, and vigorously attack any bird that approaches the nest, without regard to its size. The sitting-bird sometimes refuses to leave her eggs, and when taken in the hand will bite and hiss like the wryneck.

In autumn and winter the number of great tits is considerably increased by a migration from the Continent.

Coal-Titmouse.

Parus ater; Parus britannicus.

Crown, throat, and front of the neck black; cheeks and nape pure white; upper parts grey; wings bluish grey, with two white bands; under parts white tinged with grey. Length, four and a quarter inches.

The coal-tit of our country (*P. britannicus*) differs slightly from the continental form (*P. ater*), the British bird having the slate-grey of the upper parts suffused with brown or olive, while in the continental form the brown tinge is confined to the rump. The European coal-tit visits our islands on migration, and doubtless interbreeds with our bird, as intermediate varieties are found.

The coal-tit, or coalmouse, like the oxeye and the blue tit, is generally diffused throughout the British Islands, and is not uncommon, although nowhere abundant. In Scotland it is more local in its distribution, being found chiefly in districts abounding in pine and fir woods. It is believed to be increasing in numbers and extending its range in this country. In its social habits, its flight, and its manner of seeking its food—during which it clings to the smaller boughs and twigs in a variety of positions—it closely resembles the other members of its genus. It also resembles them in its language, although a shriller note may be detected in its voice, both in its call-note and song. It differs from other tits in its greater activity, in preferring conifers to other trees, in going more often to the ground to feed, and in being a greater wanderer out of the breeding season.

The nest, as a rule, is placed near the ground, in a hole in a rotten tree-stump, or in a wall, or any other suitable place. It is composed of moss, hair, and feathers, felted together, and lined with more feathers. Six to eight eggs are laid, like those of the great tit in colour. Like the oxeye, it is omnivorous, but in summer it feeds principally on insects.

After the breeding season the old and young birds keep together, and several families may unite and form a flock. One of the most interesting winter sights in a wood composed of pine and fir growing together with beech and other deciduous trees is afforded by a wandering flock of coal-tits. As they move from tree to tree they attract other species of similar habits—the oxeye and blue and marsh tits, and goldcrests, and siskins, and perhaps a couple of tree-creepers. Occasionally a party of long-tailed tits will join, and keep with the flock for some time; but the long-tails are the most restless and vagrant of all, and eventually hurry on by themselves, leaving the more patient plodders behind. It is wonderful and very beautiful to see so many species thus drawn into companionship by a common social instinct, and by a similar manner of seeking their food; a mental likeness serves to keep them together for hours at a time, or for a whole day, in spite of so great a diversity in form and colour and language.

Marsh-Titmouse.

Parus palustris.

Forehead, crown, head, and nape black; upper parts grey
wings dark grey, lighter at the edges; cheeks, throat, and breast
dull white. Length, four inches and a half.

It is curious that, of the seven species of birds inhabiting this
country called titmice in the vernacular, six have been named from
some character that strikes the eye : greater size in one, a peculiar
feather-ornament in two, and in the remaining species a distinctive
shape or colour; and the names in all cases are suitable—bearded,
long-tailed, great, blue, coal, and crested. In the one case where
this rule has been neglected the name is unsuitable and misleading
The marsh-tit may be more partial to low or wet ground than the
blue tit, and oxeye, and coal-tit, but the bird is found everywhere—in
woods, groves, hedgerows, orchards, and gardens—and in autumn
and winter is seen associating with the other species in their wandering bands. But it would have been difficult to name this species
from its colouring, which is more uniform and sober than in any of
the others. He is the plainest of them all, but in his lively, social
habits, and in his various pretty motions and attitudes, he is one of
the family; and so strong in him is the family likeness, that some
find it not easy to distinguish marsh-tit from coal-tit, except when
seen closely. In its language, also, it is unmistakably a titmouse;
but it is not so vociferous as the oxeye and blue tit, and its tinkering
voice is not so sharp and loud.

The nest is placed in a rotten stump or trunk of a tree, an old
pollarded willow being a favourite site; and sometimes the bird
excavates a hole for itself in the decayed wood. The nest is made
of moss and hair, felted together, and lined with willow down. The
eggs are five or six in number, and are similar to those of the great
tit in colouring.

The marsh-tit is common in England, rarer in Scotland, and
does not extend to Ireland.

Blue Titmouse.

Parus cæruleus.

Crown blue encircled with white; cheeks white bordered with dark blue; back olive-green; wings and tail bluish; greater coverts and secondaries tipped with white; breast and belly yellow, traversed by a dark blue line. Length, four and a half inches.

The blue tit is a commoner species than the oxeye, and is even more widely diffused in this country, its range extending from the Channel Islands to the northernmost parts of Scotland, and it has been found as a straggler in the Orkneys and the Shetlands. All the qualities that distinguish the tits and make them such engaging birds are found in a marked degree in the present species—sociability; extreme vivacity, especially in the cold season; and the power to assume an endless variety of graceful positions when clinging to the slender branches and twigs, upright or pendulous, of the leafless trees in winter. And as the blue tit is more abundant, and more familiar with man than the others, besides having a gayer colouring, he is the favourite member of his genus. He promises, indeed, to become in time our first feathered favourite; for though he is without melody, and does not come to us with a glad message, like the swallow, and has no ancient sentiment and nursery literature, like the robin, to help him to the front, he possesses one unfailing attraction—he is an amusing creature. Perhaps our progenitors were less susceptible in that way than we are, and took no notice of the tomtit and his vagaries. In winter he may be easily won with a little food; and when he joins the mixed company of sparrows, dunnocks, blackbirds, and starlings that come to the door for crumbs and scraps, he is by contrast among them a 'winged jewel'—a small wanderer from the tropics. In works of ornithology you will find the blue tit described as a little acrobat and harlequin, droll and grotesque and fantastic in his ways; and if this Puck among our feathered fairies can win expressions such as these from the gravest scientific writers, it is not strange that ordinary folk should find him so fascinating.

The language of the blue tit resembles that of the oxeye. Its voice is not so powerful, but the various sounds, the call and love notes, or song, composed of one note repeated several times without variation, have similar sharp, incisive, and somewhat metallic qualities.

In spring the wandering little companies break up, and about the end of April breeding begins. The nest is placed in a hole in a tree or wall, or wherever a suitable cavity is found. It is loosely formed of dry grass or moss, lined with wool, hair, and a quantity of feathers. Five to eight eggs are usually laid, in some cases as many as twelve and fourteen; in colour they are like those of the great tit, and, as in the case of that species, the incubating bird sits closely on her eggs and hisses like a snake when interfered with.

The blue tit is omnivorous in its diet. In summer it feeds principally on caterpillars, aphides, and insects of all kinds, sometimes catching them on the wing. At other seasons it eats fruit and seeds of various kinds, buds, flesh, and, in fact, almost anything it can get.

Crested Titmouse.

Parus cristatus.

Fig. 35.—Crested Tit. ⅓ natural size.

Feathers of the crown elongated, and forming when erected a pointed crest, black, edged with white; cheeks and sides of the neck white; throat, collar, and a streak across the temples black; all the other parts reddish brown; lower parts white, faintly tinged with red. Length, four inches and three-quarters.

The crested tit is one of the rarest and most local of British birds, being restricted to a few extensive pine-forests in the north of Scotland;

indeed, there are few who know it from personal observation in this country. Although modest in colour, it is a pretty little bird, and its high, pointed crest gives it a somewhat distinguished appearance. In its language and habits it resembles the other members of the genus, and associates in the same way with birds of different species. Like the coal-tit, it makes its nest in a hole in a rotten tree-stump, and it will also breed in a crow's or magpie's old nest, or a squirrel's drey. The nest is made of dry grass, moss, wool, hair, fur, and feathers, thinly felted together ; and five or six eggs are laid, white in ground-colour, spotted and speckled with brownish red.

Nuthatch.

Sitta cæsia.

Upper parts bluish grey; a black streak across the eye ; cheeks and throat white; breast and belly buff; flank and lower tail-coverts chestnut-red ; outer tail feathers black, with a white spot near the end tipped with grey, the two central ones grey ; beak bluish black, the lower mandible white at the base;

FIG. 36.—NUTHATCH. ¼ natural size.

feet light brown. Length, five inches and a half.

The nuthatch, although a small bird, not brightly coloured, and scarcely deserving the name of songster, exercises a singular attraction ; and if it were possible to canvass all those who love birds, and have not fewer than half a dozen favourites, it is probable that in a great majority of cases the nuthatch would be found among them. When I see him sitting quite still for a few moments on a branch of a tree in his most characteristic nuthatch attitude, on or under the branch, perched horizontally or vertically, with head or tail uppermost, but always with the body placed beetle-wise against the bark, head raised, and the straight, sharp bill pointing like an arm lifted to denote attention—at such times he looks less like a living than a sculptured bird, a bird cut out of a beautifully variegated marble—blue-grey, buff, and chestnut—and placed against the tree to deceive the eye. The figure is so smooth and compact, the tints so soft and stone-like ; and when he is still, he is so wonderfully still, and his attitude so statuesque ! But he is never long still, and when he resumes his lively, eccentric, up-and-down and sideway motions he is interesting in another way. One is not soon tired of watching his perpetual mouse-like, independent-of-the-earth's-gravity perambulations over the surface of the trunk and branches. He is like a small woodpecker who has broken loose from the woodpecker's somewhat narrow laws of progression, preferring to be a law unto himself.

Without a touch of brilliant colour, the nuthatch is a beautiful bird on account of the pleasing softness and harmonious disposition of his tints ; and, in like manner, without being a songster in the strict sense of the word, his voice is so clear and far-reaching, and of so pleasant a quality, that it often gives more life and spirit to the woods and orchards and avenues he frequents than that of many true melodists. This is more especially the case in the month of March, before the migratory songsters have arrived, and when he is most loquacious. A high-pitched, clear, ringing note, repeated without variation several times, is his most often-heard call or song. He will sometimes sit motionless on his perch, repeating this call at short intervals, for half an hour at a time. Another bird at a distance will be doing the same, and the two appear to be answering one another. He also has another call, not so loud and piercing, but more melodious : a double note, repeated two or three times, with something liquid and gurgling in the sound, suggesting the musical sound of lapsing water. These various notes and calls are heard incessantly until the young are hatched, when the birds all at once become silent.

A hole in the trunk or branch of a large tree is used as a nesting-place, the entrance, if too large, being walled up with clay, only a small opening to admit the bird being left. At the extremity of the hole a bed of dry leaves is made. The eggs are five to seven in number, white, and spotted with brownish red, sometimes with purple. When the sitting-bird is interfered with she defends her treasures with great courage, hissing like the wryneck, and vigorously striking at the aggressor with her sharp bill.

The food of the nuthatch during a greater portion of the year consists of small insects and their larvæ, found in the crevices of the bark ; hence the bird is most often seen frequenting old rough-barked trees, the oak being a special favourite, more especially if it happens to be well covered with lichen. At times, when seeking its prey, its rapid and vigorous blows on the bark or portion of rotten wood can be heard at a considerable distance, and are frequently mistaken for those of the woodpecker. In autumn the nuthatch feeds largely on nuts and fruit-stones, and to get at the kernel he carries the nut to a tree, and wedges it firmly in a crevice or in the angle made by a forked branch, then hammers at the end with his sharp beak until the shell is split open and the kernel disclosed. Its love of nuts makes it easy to attract the bird to a tree or wall close to the house by fixing nuts in the crevices. If supplied regularly with this kind of food it soon grows trustful, and may even be taught to come to call, and even to catch morsels of food thrown to it in the air. Canon Atkinson, in his lively and interesting ' Sketches in Natural History,' has described the amusing manners of a pair of nuthatches which he thus made tame by feeding. Since his book was published, about twenty-five years ago, many persons have adopted the same plan with success.

Wren.

Troglodytes parvulus.

Upper parts reddish brown with transverse dusky bars; quills barred alternately with black and reddish brown; tail dusky, barred with black ; over the eye a pale narrow streak; under parts pale reddish brown ; flanks and thighs marked with dark streaks. Length, three inches and a half.

The little nut-brown wren—nut-like, too, in his smallness and round, compact figure—with cocked-up tail and jerky motions and gesticulations, and flight as of a fairy partridge with rapidly-beating, short wings, that produce a whirring noise if you are close enough to hear it, is a familiar creature to almost every person throughout the three kingdoms, and is even more generally diffused than the house-sparrow. Something of the feeling which we have for the swallow, the house-martin, and the robin redbreast, falls to the share of the small wren. He is one of the few general favourites, although, perhaps, not so great a favourite as the others just named. The

reason of this is, doubtless, because he is less domestic, never so familiar with man or tolerant of close observation. The wren is never tame nor unsuspicious; he is less dependent on us than other small birds that attach themselves to human habitations, never a 'pensioner' in the same degree as the blue tit, dunnock, blackbird, and sparrow. The minute spiders, chrysalids, earwigs, and wood-lice

FIG. 37.—WREN. ¼ natural size.

with other creeping things to be found in obscure holes and corners in wood-piles, ivy-covered walls, and outhouses, are more to his taste than the 'sweepings of the threshold.' His small size, modest colouring, and secrecy; his activity, and habit of seeking his food in holes and dark places which are not explored by other insectivorous species, enable him to exist in a great variety of conditions—gardens, orchards, deep woods, open commons, hedgerows, rocky shores, swamps, mountains, and moors; there are, indeed, few places where the small, busy wren is not to be met with. This ability of the wren to find everywhere in nature a neglected corner to occupy would appear to give it a great advantage over other small birds; moreover, it is very prolific, and excepting, perhaps, two species of tits, is more successful than any other small bird in rearing large broods of young. Nevertheless, the wrens do not seem to increase. At the end of summer they are very abundant, and you will, perhaps, be able to count a dozen birds where only one pair appeared in spring; but when spring comes again you will generally find that the population has fallen back to its old numbers. The larger increase in summer indicates a greater mortality during the rest of the year than is suffered by other species. The wren is said to eat fruit occasionally, and even seeds; but it is almost exclusively insectivorous, and probably perishes in large numbers during periods of frost, when larks, pipits, and titmice become seed-eaters. Yet the wren is a hardy little bird, a resident all the year round in the coldest parts of our country, and one of the few songsters which may be heard in all seasons. Even during a frost, if the sun shines, the wren will sing as gaily as in summer. His song is his greatest charm. It is unlike that of any other British melodist—a loud, bright lyric, the fine, clear, high-pitched notes and trills issuing in a continuous rapid stream from beginning to end. Although rapid, and ending somewhat abruptly, it is a beautiful and finished performance, in which every note is distinctly enunciated and has its value. When near it sounds very loud : one is surprised to hear so loud a song from so small a creature. But it does not carry far : the notes of the song-thrush, blackbird, and nightingale can be heard at nearly three times the distance.

The wren begins his nest-building at the end of April, and in selecting a site exercises a greater freedom than most small birds. The nests may be found in trees, bushes, masses of ivy or other dense vegetation, hedgerows, holes in banks and walls, crevices in rocks, in furze-bushes, and close to the ground among the bramble-bushes. There is also a great variety in the materials used in building different nests. As a rule, one kind of material is used for the outer part of the structure, which is domed, and very large for the bird. It may be moss or dead leaves, or moss and leaves woven together, or dry grass leaves and stems, or dead fern-fronds. The nest is not only well concealed, but in most cases the outside is made to assimilate in colour to the vegetation surrounding it. The opening is near the top of the nest ; inside, the cavity is lined with moss, hair, and feathers. Four or five eggs are laid, often a larger number, and it is not unusual to find as many as eight or nine eggs in a nest. Not long ago, in a wood in Berkshire, I saw eight young wrens sitting in a row on a branch near the ground, and watched them being fed by the old birds. The eggs are pure white, thinly spotted with pinkish red. Two broods are reared in the season. Imperfect or false nests are often found near the nest containing the eggs, and are called 'cocks' nests,' the belief being that they are made by the male bird.

Pied Wagtail.

Motacilla lugubris.

Fig. 38.—Pied Wagtail. ¼ natural size.

Summer plumage variegated with white and black; back and scapulars, chin, throat, and neck black; a small portion of the side of the neck white. Winter plumage: back and scapulars ash-grey; chin and throat white, with a black, but not entirely isolated, gorget. Length, seven and a half inches.

The pied wagtail is probably not more abundant in this country than the yellow wagtail, but is far better known, being a more generally diffused species, often seen in the neighbourhood of houses where the yellow wagtail never comes. And if there be a pied wagtail anywhere within range of sight, it is sure to be seen and recognised, for in its black-and-white plumage it is the most conspicuous small bird in this country, not excepting the kingfisher, snow-bunting and blackbird. When tripping about a smooth lawn he looks double his real size, and reminds one of a magpie in a field or an oyster-catcher on a wide stretch of level sand.

The pied wagtail is found in this country all the year round, but many birds (probably the large majority) migrate annually. Knox, in his ' Ornithological Rambles in Sussex,' says that they arrive on the Sussex coast about the middle of March, the old males first, the females and the males of the previous year a few days later. They are sometimes seen in large numbers near the coast, resting after their voyage before proceeding inland. The return migration takes place at the end of August or early in September.

Meadows and pasture-lands in the neighbourhood of a running stream are favourite resorts of the wagtail, and it is fond of attending cattle for the sake of the numbers of insects driven from their shelter in the grass by the grazing animals.

The pied wagtail is not so lively, quick, and graceful as the yellow and the grey species; but if you watch him for any length of time he, too, gives you the idea of a creature that never continues in the same mind for a minute at a time, but acts according to the impulse of the moment, and is as unstable as a ball of thistle-down. He runs, then stands, and shakes his tail; for two or three moments he searches for food; then chases an insect, and is still again, waiting for a new impulse to move him:—suddenly he flies away, not straight, as if with an object in view, but with a curving, dipping, erratic flight, governed seemingly by no will; and just as suddenly alighting again, when he is once more seen standing still and shaking his tail. The call-note, a sharp chirp of two syllables, is emitted once or twice during flight. The song is a loud, hurried warble, uttered on the wing as the bird hovers at a moderate height from the ground. But the pied wagtail has another way of singing, especially in early spring: this is a warble so low that at the distance of fifteen yards it is just audible, and is sometimes uttered continuously for two or three minutes at a stretch.

The nest is made, as a rule, in a hollow or cavity in the ground, or in a crevice or hole in a bank or rock, or under a stone, or at the roots of a furze-bush. It is built of fine dry grass, moss, and various other materials, and lined with hair and feathers. The eggs are four or five, pale bluish in tint, and spotted with greyish brown.

Grey Wagtail.

Motacilla melanope.

Summer plumage : head and back bluish grey; a pale streak over the eye; throat black; under parts bright yellow. Winter plumage : chin and throat whitish, passing into yellow. Length, seven inches and a half.

The grey wagtail is the prettiest and the least common of the three species of Motacilla inhabiting the British Islands. Like

FIG. 39.—GREY WAGTAIL. ⅓ natural size.

the dipper, it frequents mountain streams, but is not restricted to them. In England it is a somewhat rare species, but is more common in Scotland and Ireland. It remains with us throughout the year, but although a permanent resident in most parts of the country, it is certain that it disappears in autumn from many of its breeding-haunts in Scotland and the north of England, and that a large number of these northern birds winter in the southern and western counties.

The grey wagtail is frequently spoken of as a bird of brilliant plumage. It is not exactly that, but the various colours are so soft and delicate, they harmonise so admirably, and show in the velvet-black of the gorget and pure canary-yellow of the breast so fine a contrast, that the effect is most beautiful, and pleases, perhaps, more than the colouring of any other British bird. And this is not all. The charm which the grey wagtail has for those who know it intimately consists in the union of delicate colouring with a delicate form and exquisitely graceful motion. Ornithologists have called it a ' fairy-like bird,' and the terms in which they have sometimes recorded their impressions of it might lead one to imagine that they are speaking, not of a bird, but of some elusive nymph of the mountain rivulets, of whom they had caught a glimpse in their rambles. To its other charms may be added that of melody. Its spring song is sweet and lively, a little like that of the swallow in character, and is uttered as the bird hovers in the air. The alarm-note is like that of the pied wagtail, a sharp double note, emitted as the bird passes away in undulating flight.

The grey wagtail is more exclusively a bird of the waterside than either of the other two species, seldom being met with away from the margins of its beloved mountain streams; in its flight, motions on the ground, and manner of taking its insect prey, it closely resembles the pied and yellow wagtails, the only difference being that it is even more volatile, and that it is the most graceful of these three feathered Graces.

The nest is made on the ground, concealed by grass and herbage, or under a bush, and often under the shelter of an overhanging rock. It is formed of fibrous roots, dry grass, and moss, and lined with hair, wool, and feathers. The eggs are five or six in number, French white or grey in ground-colour, mottled and spotted with pale brown and olive.

Yellow Wagtail.

Motacilla rayii.

Top of head, lore, nape, back, and scapulars greenish olive; a bright yellow streak over the eye; lower parts sulphur-yellow Length, six inches.

The yellow wagtail is a summer visitor, arriving at the end of March or early in April in this country, and is found very nearly in all parts of England, and is also common in the southern counties of Scotland; farther north it is rare, and in Ireland it is only known to breed in one locality. On its arrival it frequents open downs and sheepwalks, pastures, commons, and arable lands, more especially fields where spring sowing is in progress. On this account it has been named in some districts the barley-bird and oat-seed-bird, and in Scotland seed-bird and seed-lady—the last a suitable appellation for so sweet and dainty a creature. Seebohm says of it : ' Its active, sylph-like movements, and its delicate form and lovely plumage, make it a general favourite.' In its motions on the ground, its tail shaking and fanning gestures, and in its fitful curving and dipping flight, accompanied with a sharp double call-note, it closely resembles the species already described. From the pied wagtail it differs in never coming about houses or breeding in their vicinity; and from the grey wagtail in not being restricted to the waterside. In the fields it follows the plough, and in the pastures it is often seen with the cattle, chasing the small twilight moths and other insects driven from the grass.

As the season advances it forsakes the cultivated lands and open downs, and is more restricted to borders of streams, and to meadows and pastures not far from water. The nest is placed on the ground under the grass and herbage, and is formed of dry bents and fibrous roots, and lined with hair. Four to six eggs are laid, mottled with pale brown and olive on a French-white ground.

Besides the three species described we have the white wagtail (*Motacilla alba*) as a rare visitor to the south of England and Ireland, and the blue-headed yellow wagtail (*Motacilla flava*), an accidental straggler to the southern, south-western, and eastern counties of England. These two species breed throughout Europe, the first being the continental form of our pied wagtail, which it closely resembles; and the second, of the yellow wagtail.

Meadow-Pipit.

Anthus pratensis.

Hind claw longer than the toe, slightly curved. Upper parts ash tinged with olive, the centre of each feather dark brown; under parts dull buffy white, with numerous elongated spots of dull brown. Length, five inches and three-quarters.

To the uninformed the pipits are lesser larks; they are lark-like in figure, in their sober, mottled colouring, in habits, language, and, to some extent, in the action which accompanies their song. But, in spite of these outward resemblances, modern authorities have removed them from the position they once occupied next to the larks in classification, to place them by the side of the wagtails, which are now supposed to be their nearest relations. And when wagtails and pipits are seen running and flying about together, it strikes us that there is among them a certain family resemblance; but we see, too, that the wagtails have diverged greatly, and are much more graceful in figure, have longer tails, and a gayer plumage; they are also more aërial in habit, and warble a more varied strain. From the fact that the numerous species of pipits are so much alike, not only in appearance, but also in habits, language, and flight, and that they are so widely distributed on the globe, being found both on continents and oceanic islands, it may be inferred that the modest earth-loving pipit represents the original form from which the wagtails have sprung.

Of our three species, the meadow-pipit is by far the most numerous, being found in all open situations, moist or dry, meadow and waste-land, moor and mountain-side, and close by the sea, where one can listen to meadow-pipit and rock-pipit singing together, or alternately, like birds of one species, and compare the two songs, that are so much alike. This species is, moreover, to be met with in all parts of our country, from the warm Hampshire and Dorset coasts to the western islands of Scotland; but while in the main a resident all the year round in the southern parts of the country, in the bleak and barren districts of the farther north he is migratory, and moves southward in winter in considerable flocks.

The meadow-pipit seeks his food on the ground, and moves nimbly about in search of minute beetles, caterpillars, and seeds, pausing at intervals to stand motionless for a few seconds, with head raised and tail slowly moving up and down. When approached he displays a curious mixture of timidity and tameness, and eyes the intruder with suspicion, but flies with reluctance. The flight is a succession of jerky movements, the bird rising and falling in a somewhat wild, erratic manner.

In the love season the male pipit occasionally takes his stand on a weed or low bush; but on moors, hills, and stony waste lands he prefers a stone or mound of earth for a perch. From such an elevation he is able to keep watch on the movements of his mate, and, when the singing spirit takes him, to launch himself easily on the air. To sing he soars up to a height of forty feet or more, then glides gracefully down, with tail spread and wings half-closed and motionless, presenting the figure of a barbed arrow-head. In his descent he emits a series of notes with little or no variation in them, slightly metallic in sound, and very pleasing. These notes are occasionally repeated as the bird sits motionless on the ground.

In describing bird-melody it is sometimes borne in on us that all that has, or can be, said about the song of any species is not only inadequate, but in a sense even false, inasmuch as a single song of an individual is described as compared with that of some other, usually nearly related, species. Thus, the meadow-pipit's song is said to be less rich and varied, and in every way inferior to that of the tree-pipit. This is true enough, so far as it goes, but it does not take into account the different scenes in the midst of which the two distinct sounds are heard. The song of a single meadow-pipit, heard close at hand, is a slight performance—an attenuated and not very dulcet sound. The effect is wholly different and most delightful when a dozen or twenty birds are within hearing, singing at intervals at a distance, on a perfectly calm day on the moors or downs. As the little widely-scattered, unseen melodists rise and fall, the sounds they emit are refined to something bell-like and delicate: the effect is unique and indescribably charming and fairy-like.

The nest is a neat structure, usually placed in a small cavity in the ground, under a bunch of grass or heather, and is made of dry bents, and lined with fine grass, fibrous roots, and hair. Four to six eggs are laid; these vary greatly in colour and markings, but the most common form is white, thickly mottled over with greyish brown. When the nest is approached the parent birds display great solicitude, flying from place to place, and incessantly uttering a sharp but plaintive chirp of alarm.

Tree-Pipit.

Anthus trivialis.

FIG 40.—TREE-PIPIT. ¼ natural size.

Upper parts ash tinged with olive, the centre of each feather dark brown; a double band across the wing, formed by the yellowish white tips of the lesser and middle wing-coverts; the outer pair of tail feathers white; throat and region of the eye dull white; breast buff, with elongated spots of dark brown; belly and lower tail-coverts dull white. Length, six inches.

Of the three species of Anthus inhabiting the

British Islands, and which are appropriately named of the tree, rock, and meadow, according to their respective habits, the tree-pipit alone is migratory, appearing in this country about the third week in April, to remain until the end of September, and sometimes longer. In size, colour, and general appearance it so closely resembles the meadow-pipit that the two species are hardly distinguishable, except by examination in the hand. They also resemble each other in their feeding habits, running about in the grass in a mouse-like manner in search of the small insects and seeds on which they subsist, and, when flushed, starting up suddenly, with a sharp chirp of alarm, and going away with a wild, jerky flight. The tree-pipit is distributed widely over the country, and is found at most wood sides, and where trees grow singly or in isolated groups about the pasture-lands. Where the conditions are favourable he is a common bird, but never abundant. In spring and summer the tree-pipit is solitary, and it is possible that the males, as with the redbreast and nightingale, are not tolerant of other singers of their own species near them, as they are always found occupying trees far apart—seldom, in fact, within hearing distance of one another. On the arrival of the birds in April each male chooses a home, a feeding-ground, with a tree or trees to sing on, and this spot he will occupy until the end of the breeding season, after which the birds resort to the fallows and stubbles, and sometimes before departure they are seen gathered in small flocks.

It has been said of the tree-pipit's song that it is like that of the canary, and that it ' is perhaps more attractive from the manner in which it is given than from its actual quality.' Both statements are true in a measure : that is to say, they will be found true in many instances, but not always. For there are few birds in which the song varies so much in different individuals. The reiterated, clear thin notes and trills that so closely resemble those of the caged canary are heard in some songs, and not in others. As a rule, the bird perches on a favourite tree, very often using the same branch, and at intervals, rising into the air, ascends with rapidly-beating wings, and when it attains to the highest point—usually as high again as the tree, but sometimes considerably higher—the song begins with a succession of notes resembling the throat-notes of the skylark, but very much softer. With the song the descent begins, the open wings fixed motionless, and so raised as to give the bird a parachute-like appearance, falling slowly in a beautiful curve or spiral ; on the perch the song continues, but with notes of a different quality—clear, sweet and expressive—repeated many times. Having ended its song, it remains perched for a few moments silent, or else uttering notes as at the beginning, until once more it quits its perch, either to repeat the flight and song, or to drop to the ground, from which it shortly ascends to sing again. The manner in which the song is given is thus always beautiful, and in some individuals there is a wonderful sweetness in the quality of the voice.

The nest is built near the male bird's favourite tree, and is placed in a hollow in the ground, and so well concealed by the grass and herbage that it is almost impossible to find it, unless by flushing the incubating bird from it. It is formed of fine dry grass and fibrous roots, and lined with horsehair. Four to six eggs are laid, of a dull white ground-colour, spotted with dull brown, grey, and purple, sometimes with blotches and hair-like marks among the spots. The eggs of this species vary a great deal.

Rock-Pipit.

Anthus obscurus.

FIG. 41.—ROCK-PIPIT. ⅓ natural size.

Hind claw equal to the toe in length, much curved. Upper parts greenish brown, the centre of each feather darker brown ; a whitish streak over the eye ; under parts dull white, spotted and streaked with dark brown. Length, six and a quarter inches.

The rock-pipit is the only songster that inhabits the seashore, and this is the one distinction of this small dull-coloured bird. It is true that the starling sometimes nests, like the jackdaw, in cliffs, and that sparrows, wagtails, and a few other species, are occasionally to be seen on the sands and among the rocks; but they are only casual visitors in such places—they are inland birds, that live and breed in meadows, hedgerows, woods, and commons. The rock-pipit is of the seashore exclusively, and everywhere inhabits the coasts of Great Britain and Ireland where there are rocks and cliffs, and all the rocky islands and islets in the neighbouring seas; his nest is not found nor his song heard out of sound of the ocean. In summer he keeps very close to the sea, and his food then consists principally of minute crustaceans and marine insects and worms; in the autumn and winter months he unites in small flocks, and visits the salt-marshes and low grounds near the shore, and he then feeds mostly on small seeds. His song, if heard at a distance from the sea, would not be distinguished from that of the meadow-pipit; the action which accompanies the song is also the same in both species. Occasionally he delivers his notes while sitting on a rock; but as a rule he soars up to a moderate height, either silent or else repeating the first note of the song at regular intervals, then descends with a slow, sliding flight to the earth, and descending emits his best notes, short and simple, but with a melodious tinkling sound which is very pleasant to listen to, especially when several individuals are heard at once. When intruded on in his rocky haunts, or anxious for the safety of his young, his alarm-note, sharp yet plaintive, closely resembles that of the meadow-pipit. The nest, built in May, is carefully concealed among the rocks, beneath a tuft of grass, or in a well-sheltered hole or crevice in the rock, and is composed of small scraps of seaweed, dry grass, and moss, and lined with fine dry grass or hair. Four or five eggs are laid, white or pale bluish in ground-colour, thickly mottled with dull greyish brown or reddish brown spots.

Besides those described, three other species of Anthus have been included among British birds. These are the tawny pipit (*Anthus campestris*), Richard's pipit (*Anthus richardi*), and the water-pipit (*Anthus spipoletta*). The first two are occasional visitors to the south of England; of the water-pipit, a very few specimens have been obtained in different parts of the country.

Two beautiful British birds, unfortunately not indigenous nor regular in their visits to our country, may be mentioned in this place. They represent two families: Oriolidæ, which follows Motacillidæ (wagtails and pipits); and Ampelidæ, which comes after

Laniidæ (shrikes). One is the golden oriole (*Oriolus galbulus*), a rare straggler to England on migration from Central and Southern Europe. It has been known to breed in the southern counties, and, if protected, would probably become an annual visitant. The other species is the waxwing (*Ampelis garrulus*), an irregular visitor in winter, sometimes in considerable numbers, from the arctic circle.

Red-backed Shrike.

Lanius collurio.

FIG. 42.—RED-BACKED SHRIKE. ¼ natural size.

Frontal band, lores, and ear-coverts black; crown and nape grey; mantle chestnut-brown; quills dark brown edged with rufous; tail-coverts grey; tail-feathers white at their bases, the other portion and the whole of the two central ones black; under parts rose-buff; bill and feet black. Length, seven inches.

The shrike is distinguished among perching birds by its sharply hooked, toothed, rapacious beak, and its hawk-like habit of preying on small birds, mice, shrews, frogs, and lizards. The extraordinary custom it has of impaling its victims on thorns has won for it the unpleasant name of butcher-bird, by which it is best known to country-people. Some naturalists have expressed the opinion that the shrike does not often attack small birds ; and this would seem a reasonable view to take when we consider that the bird is no bigger than a skylark. But it is impossible to follow with the eye all the wanderings and the actions of all kinds that go to make the day of any wild bird ; we really see only a very small part of the killing that goes on. The little feathered butcher is small in size, but his spirit is bold, and his taste for flesh not to be doubted. In a question of this kind I believe our slight intermittent observation is less to be depended on than the reputation—if such a word may be used in this connection—which the shrike bears among his feathered fellow-creatures. He is by them reputed dangerous, a bird of prey to be avoided, or at least regarded with extreme suspicion. We are accustomed to say that we do not know a man until we come to live with him ; and the small birds live with the shrike, and there-fore know him best.

The red-backed shrike is a summer visitor, arriving in this country early in April, and is not an uncommon species in England and Wales, being most numerous in the southern counties ; but its range does not extend to Ireland, and in North Britain it is only known as a straggler. It inhabits the open borders of woods, rough commons, and high hedges, and has the habit of sitting con-spicuously perched, often for an hour at a stretch, on the summit of an isolated bush or low tree, or on a fence or any other elevated stand, where it has a pretty appearance. From its perch it watches for its prey, but is by no means a motionless and depressed-looking watcher, like the flycatcher : its movements on its stand, as it turns its head from side to side and jerks and fans its tail, frequently uttering its low, percussive, chat-like chirp or call-note, give the impression of a creature keenly alive to everything passing around it. The shrike is, in fact, attentively watching air, earth, and the surrounding herbage and bushes for a victim, which he captures by a sudden dart, taking it by surprise. Besides small vertebrates, he preys on various large insects—beetles, grasshoppers, wasps, bees, &c.—seizing them in the air as they fly past, or dropping upon them on the ground. He often devours the insects captured on the spot, then returns to his stand ; but he also has a favourite thorn-bush or tree to which he is accustomed to convey many of the creatures he takes, to impale them on thorns or fix them on forked twigs. He has the habit of plucking birds before devouring them ; and it is doubtless easier for him to pluck a small bird and pull anything he catches to pieces when fixed on a thorn, for, being without crooked claws, he is incapable of grasping his victim and holding it steady while operating on it. This is one of those instincts which simulate reason very closely. The number of remains of victims sometimes found suspended to a butcher-bird's tree shows that he is occasionally very destructive to small birds. In a case recorded in the ' Zoologist' (1875, p. 4723), bodies of the great tit, blue tit, long-tailed tit, robin, hedge-sparrow, and young of blackbirds and thrushes, were found.   The indigestible portions swallowed—bones, fur, and wing-cases of large beetles—are cast up in pellets.

In the pairing season the shrike utters at times a chirruping song, not unlike the attempted singing of a sparrow in sound. The nest is large, and placed in a thick bush or hedge, and is composed outwardly of stalks, and inside of fibrous roots and moss, lined with fine bents and a little horsehair.   Four to six eggs are laid ; these vary a good deal, the ground being pale green, pale buff, cream or pale salmon-colour, spotted and blotched, principally at the large end, with reddish brown and purplish grey.

After leaving the nest the young keep company with their parents until their departure in September and October.

There are four more species of Lanius in the list of British birds, all stragglers—the great grey shrike (*Lanius excubitor*), a breeder in Central Europe ; Pallas's great grey shrike (*Lanius major*), from North Scandinavia and Siberia ; the lesser grey shrike (*Lanius minor*), from Central and Southern Europe ; the woodchat (*Lanius pomeranus*), also from Central and Southern Europe.

Spotted Flycatcher.

Muscicapa grisola.

Upper parts ash-brown ; feathers of the head marked with central dark line ; under parts white, the sides marked with longitudinal brown streaks ; flanks tinged with red. Length, five and a half inches.

The spotted flycatcher is one of our commonest summer migrants, and at the same time one of the least remarked. He is a late comer, arriving about the middle of May ; but he does not come after the leaves are out, to conceal himself among them, after the manner of the wood-wren and of other small insect-eaters. From the day of his arrival he is exposed to sight in the places he frequents — parks, skirts of woods, orchards, gardens, and the borders of fields and meadows. The area inhabited by each bird, or pair, is very circumscribed, and contains a few favourite perching-places, which are regularly occupied at different hours of the day. The perching-place is on a projecting branch, or, better still, a dead branch of a bush or tree, a wire fence, or a paling or gatepost. He comes near houses, and he may have a stand within twenty or thirty yards of the door, from which those who come and go may have him

Fig. 43.—Spotted Flycatcher.
¼ natural size.

full in sight for several hours each day. But little or no notice is taken of him. And it is not strange, for of all our birds he is the least attractive, in his pale, obscure plumage, as he sits silent and motionless, listless and depressed in appearance, showing neither alarm nor curiosity when regarded. Seen thus he is like a silent grey ghost of a little dead bird returned to haunt the sunlight. Despite this listless appearance he is keenly alive to outward things. As the motionless heron watches the water, with the creatures that move like vague shadows in it, the flycatcher watches the air and the living things, minute and swift-winged, that inhabit it. At intervals he quits his perch and makes a dash at some passing insect, which he captures, his mandibles closing on it with an audible snap; then returns to his stand and his watching once more.

His call-note is a feeble chirp, two or three times repeated; and he is said to have a song, which few have heard, composed of a few rambling notes in a low tone.

The flycatcher begins to build soon after its arrival, and a favourite site for the nest is in the ivy growing against a wall;

nests are also made in holes in walls and in the trunks of trees, on horizontal branches, and in a variety of situations. The nest is composed of dry grass and moss, mixed with a few feathers, and lined with rootlets and horsehair. Five or six eggs are laid; they are bluish white or pale green in ground-colour, clouded, blotched and spotted with reddish brown.

Flycatchers return to the same nesting-place year after year. One brood only is reared, and the birds leave us by the third week in September.

Pied Flycatcher.

Muscicapa atricapilla.

Upper parts and tail black; wings black, with the central coverts white; scapulars edged with white; under parts white. *Female*: greyish brown instead of black; the white dingy; the three lateral tail-feathers edged with white. Length, five inches.

The pied flycatcher is comparatively a rare bird, and is unknown to a great majority of the inhabitants of this country, being restricted to a few localities in the north of England and the south of Scotland, and to some parts of North Wales, and the English counties bordering on Wales. In its nesting and feeding habits, and its partiality for orchards and gardens, it is like the spotted flycatcher; but it arrives earlier than that species, usually during the last week in April or the first week in May. Its black-and-white plumage gives it a very different and a much more attractive appearance. The only other point in which the two species differ greatly is in the number and colour of the eggs. Those of the pied flycatcher number from five to eight, and are very beautiful, being of a uniform delicate pale blue, and unspotted.

A third species, the red-breasted flycatcher (*Muscicapa parva*), has been included in the list of stragglers from Central and Eastern Europe to this country.

Swallow.

Hirundo rustica.

Forehead and throat chestnut-brown; upper parts, sides of neck, and a bar across the breast black, with violet reflections; lower parts dull reddish white. Tail long and forked. *Female*:

less red on the forehead and less black on the breast; under parts white; outer tail-feathers shorter. Length, seven and a half inches.

The swallow, as we usually see him, gliding and doubling in the air with a freedom surpassing that of other birds, has considerable

Fig. 44.—Swallow. ¼ natural size.

beauty, being richly coloured and of an elegant figure, with sharply forked tail and long, pointed wings. But this is not the reason of the charm he has for us, since there are other more beautiful birds that inspire no such feeling. He is loved above most species on account of his domestic habits and familiarity with man. There would be few swallows in a dispeopled and savage England, with all its buildings crumbled to earth, for he would then be compelled to return to the original habits of the wild swallow, and build his mud cradle in rocky cliffs and caverns. As things are he is not dependent on cliffs, for he has taken kindly to human habitations, and increases with the increase of house-building, until he has become one of the commonest and most generally diffused species. And being a house-bird, and accustomed to the human form, when our summer migrants return to us with the return of the sun, and the others seek their customary homes in woods and groves by the sides of streams and marshes, and on downs and waste lands, the swallow alone comes direct to us to deliver the glad message, so that even the sick and aged and infirm, who can no longer leave their beds or rooms, are able to hear it. What wonder that we cherish a greater affection for, and are more intimate with, the swallow than with our other feathered fellow-creatures !

The swallow is very evenly distributed over the whole of Great Britain and Ireland, but the date of his arrival varies considerably in different districts. In the south of England he makes his appearance early in April, and arrives in the northern counties about the middle of that month, but in the north of Scotland not until the first week in May. He is most abundant about villages and large country-houses and farms ; but wherever human habitations exist, however modest in size they may be, he is to be met with. Swallows are eminently gregarious, and even during the breeding season all the birds inhabiting one neighbourhood are accustomed to feed and practise their aërial exercises in company. At this season their gatherings are, however, intermittent, and in part accidental. Where flying insects are abundant the swallows quicky gather. At one time of the day they may be seen coursing up and down the lanes and roads and village streets, gliding close to the ground with great speed ; in rough weather they will assemble in scores or hundreds on the sheltered side of a wood, or lane, or a row of elms ; but on a warm, damp day, they frequent the meadows and low grounds near the water, where insects are most abundant.

The swallow has a variety of sharp little chirps and twittering notes, and a loud, startled, double alarm-note, uttered at the appearance of a hawk speeding through the air, or at sight of a prowling cat. The appearance of a hawk excites as much anger as fear, and he generally goes in pursuit of it ; but the note is understood by other small birds, and has the effect of sending them quickly into hiding. The song, uttered sometimes on the wing, but more frequently when perched, is very charming, and seems more free and spontaneous than that of any bird possessing a set song, the notes leaping out with a heartfelt joyousness which is quite irresistible. The sound differs in quality from that of other birds ; it is, perhaps, more *human* : a swallow-like note may be heard in some of the most beautiful contralto voices. The dozen or more notes composing the song end with a little jarring trill, so low as to be hardly audible.

A favourite site for the swallow's nest is the top of a joist supporting the rafters of a barn or other outhouse to which there is free access. It is a saucer-shaped rim of mud or clay, placed on the wood. The inside is lined with dry grass and feathers. It is quite open at the top, but usually close to the roof. The eggs are four to six in number, and vary much in shape and disposition of markings. They are pure white, spotted with rich coffee-brown, light reddish brown, and purplish grey. During incubation the sitting-bird is fed at intervals by her mate.

Two broods are reared in the season, and the young are fed for some days after quitting the nest. The early broods are believed to leave this country in advance of the adults and the young of the later broods. The final and principal migration takes place at the end of September or early in October, the birds congregating some days before departure in large flocks, sometimes numbering many thousands.

Martin.

Chelidon urbica.

FIG. 45.—MARTIN. ⅛ natural size.

Head, nape, and upper part of the back black, with violet reflections; lower parts of the back and under parts pure white. Feet and toes covered with downy feathers; tail forked. Length, five and a half inches.

The martin, or house-martin, is as common and widely diffused in the British Islands as the swallow, and as it lives with man in the same way, making use of houses to build its nest on, it shares the affection with which that bird is generally regarded. Most people, in fact, regard them as one and the same species; for both are of one type, and are domestic in habit, and associate together, and unless looked at with attention they are not seen distinctly, and consequently not distinguished. The martin differs from the swallow in its slightly smaller size; in having its feet feathered and the rump and entire under parts pure white; and in its less sharply forked tail and shorter wings. On the wing it is not so perfectly free as the swallow: it cannot double so quickly, nor fly with such speed and grace.

The martin cannot be called a songster. His most common expression is a somewhat harsh note, often uttered as he sports with his fellows in the air; in the pairing and nesting time he occasionally attempts to sing, usually when clinging to a wall and to the rim of his nest, and emits a slight warbling sound, somewhat guttural, and so low that it can only be heard at a distance of a few yards.

He arrives in this country a little after the swallow, and immediately sets about making a new nest or repairing an old one. This is formed outwardly of mud or clay, and is placed under the eaves of a house, against the wall. He is able to build against a smooth brick or stucco wall, but prefers stone, which has a rougher surface. It is usual to find several nests near together, and the reason is, probably, that the surface of the wall is suitable to build on, and not, as is often stated, because the martins prefer to nest close to each other. The outer shell of the nest, like that of the swallow, is formed of mud or clay, mixed with hairs and fibres to strengthen it, and is placed against the wall at the side and the projecting eaves above, and forms a half or a portion of a hemisphere, a small opening being left at the top for entrance. The lining is composed of feathers and a little dry grass. Four or five pure white, unspotted eggs are laid. Two broods, and often three, are reared in the season.

For some days after the young are able to fly the whole family roost at night in the nest. The young of the first brood, as in the case of the swallow, are the first to migrate. The old birds and the young of the later broods take their departure about the middle of October.

Sand-Martin.

Cotile riparia.

Upper parts, cheeks, and a broad bar on the breast mouse-colour; throat, fore part of the neck, belly, and under tail-coverts white. Legs and feet naked, with the exception of a few small

feathers near the insertion of the hind toe ; tail forked, rather short.
Length, five inches.

The sand-martin, although common enough in some localities,
and found throughout the British Islands, including the Outer
Hebrides and the Orkneys, is not a very well-known bird ; for,
however populous the country may be, and though other hirundines
become increasingly domestic and breed under eaves, in porches,
barns, and chimneys, he always preserves his original wild character.
He is a swallow that is a stranger to man, and breeds in holes and
crevices in precipitous cliffs on the sea-coast.   But he prefers to
excavate a breeding-hole in a perpendicular bank of clay not too
stiff for his weak mining implements.   Earth-cliffs on the banks of
rivers and lakes and on the sea, are resorted to for this purpose, and
he also takes advantage of the steep sides of railway-cuttings and
sand and gravel pits.   A suitable bank or cliff will often attract a
large number of sand-martins, and the surface will appear riddled
with their holes.   It has always caused surprise in those who have
observed this bird that it should be able with its small, weak bill to
form such deep tunnels in the hard earth   The hole once made is,
however, often used by the same birds for several years.   They do
not work by digging into the earth with their bills as a man digs
with a knife or other implement.   They perch against the surface
and pick out small particles, and by means of this slow, laborious
process accomplish their great work.   The hole slants upwards, and
is from three to four feet in length and two or three inches in
diameter.   At its extremity the gallery is widened to form a
chamber about six inches in diameter, where the bed is made of
dry grass, with a few feathers for lining.   Male and female take
turns in boring, working only in the morning, the rest of the daylight hours being spent in feeding and play.   It sometimes happens
that in boring their hole a sunken boulder or vein of impenetrable
earth is met with; the hole is then abandoned and a new one begun
in another place.   By the end of May the eggs are laid.   These are
four to six in number, and are pure white.

When hovering before their holes, and passing to and fro with
wavering flight along the face of the bank, the sand-martins have a
curious moth-like appearance.   While flying about in company
they constantly utter a low monotonous note ; and this sound is
prolonged to a scream when the birds are excited by the presence

K

of some enemy. The male has, besides, a twittering song, uttered on the wing while hovering before the nesting-hole.

Two broods are reared, and as soon as breeding is over the birds forsake the bank and scatter about the country, and may then be seen associating with house-martins and swallows.

The sand-martin is the earliest of the swallows to arrive in this country, and the first to depart; it is rare to meet with them after the middle of September.

Tree-Creeper.

Certhia familiaris.

Fig. 46.—Tree-Creeper.　⅓ natural size.

Upper parts mottled with yellowish brown, dark brown, and white; a pale streak over the eye; throat and breast buff-white, becoming dusky on the belly; wings brown, tipped with white, and barred with white, brown, and dull yellow; tail-feathers reddish brown, stiff, and pointed. Length, five inches.

The little creeper appears to move more in a groove than almost any other passerine bird, and is the most monotonous in its life; yet it never fails to interest, doubtless because in its appearance and actions it differs so much from other species. A small bird—one of the very smallest—with striped and mottled brown upper, and silvery white under, plumage; long and slim in figure, with a slender curved bill and stiff, pointed tail-feathers, it spends its life on the boles and branches of trees, exploring the rough bark with microscopic sight for the minute insects and their eggs and larvæ it subsists on, moving invariably upwards in a spiral from the roots to the branches by a series of rapid jerks; its appearance as it travels over the surface, against which it presses so closely, is that of a mammal rather than a bird—a small mottled brown mouse with an elongated body. It is more of a parasite on the trees that furnish it with food than any other bird of similar habits. Nuthatches and woodpeckers are not so dependent on their trade; their habits and diet vary to some extent with the seasons and the conditions they exist in. The creeper is a creeper on trees all the year round, and extracts all his sustenance from the bark. His procedure is always the same: no sooner has he got to the higher and smoother part of the bole up which he has travelled than he detaches himself from it, and drops slantingly through the air to the roots of another tree, to begin as before. The action is always accompanied with a little querulous note, which falls like an exclamation, and seems to express disgust at the miserable harvest he has gathered, or else satisfaction that yet another tree in the long weary tale of trees has been examined and left behind. The fanciful idea is formed that the creeper has not found happiness in his way of life: it is so laborious a way; he must live so close to the dull-hued and always shaded bark, and examine it so narrowly! The contrast of such a method with that of other small birds—warblers and wagtails, and swallows and finches—is very great. Feeding-time with them is song-time and play time; their blithe voices and lively antics and motions show how happy they are in their lives. The creeper is a rather silent bird, but he utters in the pairing season a shrill, high-pitched call-note, and the same sound is emitted when the nest is in danger. The song, which is occasionally heard in spring, is composed of three or four shrill notes resembling the call-notes in sound.

The nest is a neat and pretty structure, and is often placed against the trunk of a tree, behind a piece of bark that has become partly detached. A hole in the trunk, or in a large branch, or in a cavity where a portion of the wood has rotted away, is often selected as a site. When the nest is made behind a piece of loose bark, the cavity is filled up with a quantity of fine twigs. Inside, the nest is formed of roots, moss, and sometimes feathers, and lined with fine strips of inside bark. Six to nine eggs are laid, pure white, with red spots. Two broods are reared in a season.

Goldfinch.

Carduelis elegans.

Back of the head, nape, and feathers round the base of the bill black; forehead and throat blood-red; cheeks, fore part of the neck, and under parts white; back and scapulars dark brown; wings variegated with black, white and yellow; tail black, tipped with white. Length, five inches.

We are rich in finches. No fewer than eighteen members of that family, including the snow-bunting, may be truly described as British. Among our passerine birds they excel in beauty of plumage, and by most persons the goldfinch, in his pretty coat of many colours—crimson, black, and white, and brown, and brilliant yellow —is regarded as the most beautiful of all. Certainly he is the most elegant in shape, the most graceful and engaging in his motions. It is charming to watch a small flock of these finches in the late summer, busy feeding on the roadside, or on some patch of waste land where the seeds, they best love are abundant, when they are seen clinging in various attitudes to the stalks, deftly picking off the thistle seed, and scattering the silvery down on the air. They are then pretty birds prettily occupied; and as they pass with easy, undulating flight from weed to weed, with musical call-notes and lively twitterings, bird following bird, they appear as gay and volatile as they are pretty.

They are found in suitable localities throughout England, and also inhabit Scotland and Ireland, but their distribution in the last two countries is much more local. During late summer and autumn they lead a gipsy life, incessantly wandering about the open country in search of their favourite seeds. They are also seen in winter, but few remain with us throughout the year, the majority passing over the Channel, to winter in a warmer climate. On their return in spring they come to the neighbourhood of houses, and build by preference in an apple or cherry tree in an orchard. The nest is well made, and composed of a great variety of materials—fine twigs, roots, grass, leaves, moss, and wool—and lined with hairs, feathers, and vegetable down. The four or five eggs are white, thinly spotted with reddish brown and pale purple.

As a vocalist the goldfinch does not rank high; but his lively,

PLATE V.   GOLDFINCH. $\frac{2}{3}$ NAT. SIZE.

twittering song, uttered both on the perch and when passing through the air, and his musical call-notes, have a very pleasing effect, especially when the birds are seen in the open country in bright, sunny weather. Unhappily, it is not now very easy to see them, except in a few favoured localities, owing to their increasing rarity. For the goldfinch is a favourite cage-bird, and so long as bird-catching is permitted to flourish without restriction, this charming species will continue to decrease, as it has been decreasing for the last fifty years and upwards.

Siskin.

Chrysometris spinus.

Crown black; a broad yellow streak behind the eye; the plumage variegated with grey, dusky, and various shades of green; wings dusky, with a transverse greenish yellow bar, and a black one above, and a second black bar across the middle of the tertiaries; tail dusky, the base and edge of the inner web greenish yellow. *Female*: colours less bright, and no black on the head. Length, four and a half inches.

The siskin, or aberdevine, as it is also called, is known to us as a winter visitant, but it is better known as a cage than a free bird. In the British Islands it breeds in various places in Scotland, in pine and fir woods; it has also been found breeding in various localities in England and Wales. In Ireland it is not so common as in England. The siskin is a pretty, active, musical little bird, somewhat tit-like in its manner of seeking its food, its sociability, and the various positions it assumes in its search for small insects and seeds in the higher branches of a tree, or when clinging to the terminal twigs. As a caged bird his song is a small musical twittering; but in a wild state, in the pairing season, the male has a more charming performance, for he then soars about the tree, and, with fluttering wings and outspread tail, floats down singing to his perch.

The nest is built in a pine or fir tree at a considerable height from the ground, and so hidden as to make it very hard to find. There is a legend in some districts on the continent of Europe that the siskin places a small stone among its eggs, which renders the nest invisible. This legend reminds me of a belief of the peasants of southern South America, that the rail-like, spotted tinamou—a bird that easily eludes one's sight among the grey and yellow herbage—has the faculty of making itself invisible. The primitive mind is much given to explanations of this kind.

The nest, placed as a rule in the fork of a horizontal branch, is composed of rootlets and moss, on a foundation of bents and twigs of heather, and is lined with fine dry grass and a little vegetable down, sometimes with a few feathers. Five or six eggs are laid, pale bluish green in ground-colour, and spotted with dark reddish brown and pinkish grey under-markings.

In autumn siskins unite in small flocks and migrate southward; and during winter they are found widely distributed over the country, but are most numerous in the northern counties of England. At this season they may be seen associating on trees and bushes with goldcrests, redpolls, and titmice of different species.

Closely allied to the siskin and goldfinch, and in its colouring intermediate between them, but differing in having the crown, nape, and chin black, is the serin (*Serinus hortulanus*). It breeds in North and Central Europe, and is only known in this country as a rare straggler.

Greenfinch.

Ligurinus chloris.

Yellowish green variegated with yellow and ash-grey. Length, six inches.

It has been a subject of mild wonder to me that the greenfinch is not more a favourite than I find him; for he is almost more with us than any other finch, and, in most cases, to know a bird well is to like it. Few of our eighteen finches can be seen and heard close to our houses. The brambling, siskin, redpoll, crossbill, and twite are scattered about the country in the cold and songless season; in summer we see little or nothing of them. The linnet is fairly abundant, but must be looked for on waste lands and commons; while the goldfinch, bullfinch, hawfinch, and tree-sparrow are either so shy or so rare that, to most persons, they might be non-existent. Three of our five buntings are common enough; but these, too, are birds of the open, that come little about houses, and are without

the qualities that go to make a favourite. Of finches of the homestead that possess beauty and melody there are only two—the chaffinch and the greenfinch; and it is the fact that most people have
a great esteem for the first, and pay but very slight attention to
the second. The greenfinch is not formed on the graceful lines of
the goldfinch and some other members of the family; he is made
more after the pattern of the hawfinch, and is somewhat heavy in
appearance. Regarding his colouring only, he is a prettier bird
than his neighbour, the chaffinch, his plumage showing two colours
that contrast beautifully—olive-green and brilliant yellow. It is
not often that we can see him in the proper light and position.
He is strangely fond of concealing himself in the green foliage,
which makes him in his green dress invisible. Seen in the shade
or against a bright light, his colour appears dull and indeterminate; but against a background of green leaves, with the sunlight
on him, he is certainly beautiful.

The greenfinches are very sociable in disposition, and all the
summer long, even when they are engaged in breeding, they may
be seen in parties of three, or four, or half a dozen; two or three
nests are often found on the same branch, or in close proximity.
The passions of jealousy and anger, so common among birds in the
pairing season, seem not to exist in this species. As a songster he
cannot compare with the linnet, the chaffinch, and the goldfinch,
but he probably produces more pleasant sound than any other finch,
unless we include the chirruping of the sparrow. He is attached to
gardens and shrubberies, to groves and hedges, and hedgerow trees,
especially elms, and among the clustering leaves in which he loves to
hide he is constantly uttering his various notes, the commonest of
which is a low and long-drawn trill. Occasionally he gives out
another long, single note, with a very different sound, a kind of soft-
toned, inflected scream, used sometimes as a call-note and sometimes to express alarm; and this he will often repeat again and
again at short intervals. When uttering his trill, which is his
favourite expression, among the leaves, bird answering bird with
trills that vary in tone, he gives out from time to time another
sound, a series of warbled notes, soft and melodious in character.
Occasionally, in the pairing season, the male bird flies up out of
the cloud of foliage and emits these warbling notes as he circles
round, and descends into the midst of the leaves again. The charm
of this perpetual summer music of the greenfinches is its airy, subdued character, as of wind-touched leaves that flutter musically.

The nest is placed among the close branches of a bush or low tree, and is somewhat loosely put together, straw, roots, and moss, mixed with wool, being used, with a lining of fibres, horsehair, and feathers. The eggs are four to six in number, and are white, faintly spotted and speckled with purplish red at the large end. The young are fed on seeds of various weeds and small caterpillars; and two, and sometimes three, broods are reared in the season. At the end of summer the greenfinches repair to the fields, and are seen in flocks of two or three score to a hundred or more individuals, and are also found associating with sparrows, chaffinches, and other species.

The greenfinch is a common bird throughout the British Islands.

Hawfinch.

Coccothraustes vulgaris.

FIG. 47.—HAWFINCH. ⅓ natural size.

Lore, throat, and plumage at the base of the bill black; crown and cheeks reddish brown; nape ash-grey; back dark reddish brown; wings black; great coverts white; under parts light purplish red. Length, seven inches.

The hawfinch has a somewhat curious history in this country. It was always believed to be an accidental autumn and winter visitor until, a little over half a century ago, the naturalist Doubleday, of Epping, discovered that it was a resident all the year round, and not a very rare species in that locality. Later it was found breeding in other places, and it is now known to inhabit all the Home Counties and various other parts of England. At present the belief is general that the bird is increasing in numbers and extending its range. This would seem the most natural explanation of the fact that the bird is often seen now in places where it was not seen formerly ; but it must be taken into consideration that nobody looked to find the hawfinch when it was not known to be a British species, and that now many sharp eyes watch for it. As it is, we are seldom rewarded by a sight of it, even in localities where it is known to exist, in spite of its conspicuous colouring and the somewhat singular appearance given to it by its large head and massive, conical beak. Its excessive wariness prevents it from being seen even when it is not rare. No other small bird is so shy with us, so vigilant, and quick to make its escape at the slightest appearance of danger. When not feeding it passes the time in woods, plantations, and copses, at a spot where the trees grow thickest and the foliage is most dense. Its love of concealing itself in the deepest shade is like that of a nocturnal species. When away from its obscure place of refuge it is extremely alert, perching in the tops of trees to survey the surrounding scene, and from which to drop silently into any garden or orchard which may be safely visited. Naturally, it has been assumed that this shy and watchful habit has been brought about by persecution, gardeners and fruit-growers being deadly enemies to hawfinches on account of their depredations ; but in the forests of North Africa, Mr. Charles Dixon found the bird just as vigilant and quick to take alarm as in England.

Hawfinches are rather silent birds : when flying from tree to tree in small flocks they utter a call-note with a clicking sound, and in spring the male sometimes emits a few low notes by way of song.

The nest is placed in a tree, or bush, or hedge, a thorn being the tree most frequently chosen for a site. The nest is rather large and well made, outwardly of twigs, dead stalks, and lichen, inside of dry grass, and lined with rootlets and a little hair. The eggs are four to six in number, pale olive or bluish green in ground-colour, spotted with black, and irregularly streaked with dark olive. In

some eggs the ground-colour is buff. The young are fed on caterpillars, and only one brood is reared. After leaving the nest the
young birds live with the parents, and sometimes several families
unite into a flock; as many as a hundred birds, or more, may be
seen together.

In autumn and winter the hawfinches feed on seeds of various
kinds—hornbeam, beech, yew, and hawthorn. The kernels only of
the haws are eaten; and, in like manner, cherries and other fruits are
robbed for the sake of the kernel, the hard stones being split open
with the powerful beak.

House-Sparrow.

Passer domesticus.

Lores black; a narrow white streak over each eye; crown, nape,
and lower back ash-grey; region of the ear-coverts chestnut; back
chestnut-brown streaked with black; wings brown, with white bar
on the middle coverts; tail dull brown; throat and breast black;
cheeks and sides of neck white; belly dull white. Length, six
inches. *Female*: without the black on the throat, and upper parts
striated dusky brown.

More, far more, has been written about the sparrow than about
any other bird, but as it is not advisable here to enter into the controversy on the subject of the injury he inflicts, or is believed by many
to inflict, on the farmer and gardener, a very brief account of its
habits will suffice. They are almost better known to most persons
than the habits of the domestic fowl, owing to the universality of
this little bird, to its excessive abundance in towns as well as in
rural districts, and to its attachment to human habitations. For
his excessive predominance there are several causes. He is exceedingly hardy, and more adaptive than other species; his adaptive-
ness makes it possible for him to exist and thrive in great smoky
towns like London. He is sagacious beyond most species, and although living so constantly with or near to man, he never loses his
suspicious habit, and of all birds is the most difficult to be trapped.
He is very prolific: as soon as the weather becomes mild, at the
end of February or in March, he begins to breed, and brood after
brood is reared until September, or even till November if the weather
proves favourable. He also possesses an advantage in his habit of

breeding in holes in houses, where his eggs and young are much safer than in trees and hedges. There is a curious diversity in his nesting habits : he generally prefers a hole in a wall, or some safe, convenient cavity, and will make vigorous war on and eject other species, like the house-martin, from their nests and nesting-holes ; but when such receptacles are not sufficiently numerous, or it appears safe to do so, he builds in trees, making a large, conspicuous, oval, domed nest of straw, mixed with strings, rags, and other materials, and thickly lined inside with feathers. Five to six eggs are laid, of a pale bluish white ground-colour, spotted, blotched, or suffused with grey and dusky brown. The young are fed on caterpillars ; and the adults also are partly insectivorous during the summer months, but in the autumn and winter grain, seeds, and buds are chiefly eaten.

Tree-Sparrow.

Passer montanus.

Crown and back of head chestnut-brown ; lore, ear-coverts, and throat black ; neck almost surrounded by a white collar ; upper parts as in the last ; wing with two transverse white bars. Length, five and a half inches.

By a careless observer the tree-sparrow would, in most cases, be taken for the house-sparrow, and not looked directly at. When we know that there is a tree-sparrow, and meet with it, we notice the chief points in which it differs from the common species—the chestnut-coloured head, with black and white patches at the side, and the double bar on the wing.

The tree-sparrow is locally distributed throughout England and Scotland, but is nowhere abundant ; in Wales and Ireland it is rare. With us it is a shy bird, being found, as a rule, at a distance from houses, in fields, on the borders of woods, in thickets growing beside streams, and in fir plantations. In some districts on the Continent it is far less shy of man, and lives in villages and towns, where it associates with the common sparrow, and is said to be just as tame. In many parts of Asia it is still more domestic. Edward Blyth wrote of it : ' In the great rice-exporting station of Akyab we have seen this species so familiarly hopping about in the public streets that it would only just move out of the way of the passers-by ; and we have also known it breeding so numerously in dwelling-houses as to be quite a nuisance from its shrill, incessant chirping.' This bird is the common house-sparrow of China and Japan, the Philippines, Burma, and more or less over the whole Malayan region.

In its habits it is more active and lively than its more domestic relation, and is more at home on trees, and may be seen moving about among the lesser branches and twigs with much freedom, sometimes seeking its food there, after the manner of the siskin and redpoll; but it feeds principally on the ground. It can scarcely be called a song-bird, its most song-like sounds being composed of a few chirruping notes uttered in the pairing season. Its voice, both in its attempted singing and in its ordinary chirp and call-notes, is much shriller than that of the common sparrow.

Like that species, it breeds both in holes and on trees. A hole in the rotten wood of a pollard willow by the waterside is a favourite site, and it also nests in holes under the eaves or thatch of a barn or other outhouse, and in holes in ruins, old walls, and rocks. The nest is made of dry grass, loosely put together, and lined with some soft material—wool, or feathers, or hair. Four to six eggs are laid, bluish white in ground-colour, the whole egg thickly mottled with brown of different shades. Two, and even three, broods are reared in the season.

In winter the tree-sparrows gather in small flocks, and are often found associating with the common sparrow, chaffinch, brambling, and other species. At this season they subsist principally on seeds of weeds and grass, but in summer they are partly insectivorous.

Chaffinch.

Fringilla cœlebs.

Forehead black; crown and nape greyish blue; back and scapulars chestnut tinged with green; rump green; breast chestnut-red, fading into white on the belly; wings black, with two white bands; coverts of the secondaries tipped with yellow; tail black, the two middle feathers ash-grey, the two outer, on each side, black, with a broad, oblique white band. *Female*: head, back, and scapulars ash-brown tinged with olive; lower parts greyish white; the transverse bands less distinct. Length, six inches.

The chaffinch is one of the most popular song-birds in Britain; it is very much with us, being universal in its distribution in this country, and a bird that attaches itself to the neighbourhood of houses, an inhabitant of gardens and orchards, and a resident throughout the year. He is a pretty bird, and, if not a brilliant songster, is at all events a very vigorous one; his lively, ringing lyric, being short and composed of notes invariably repeated in the same order, is capable of being remembered longer and more vividly reproduced in the mind than any other song. Sitting by the fireside in January, you can mentally hear the song of the chaffinch; but the brain is incapable of registering the more copious and varied bird-music in the same perfect way—the music, for instance, of the skylark and thrush and garden-warbler. It is not strange that, when Browning wished to be back in England in April, he thought of the spring song of the chaffinch, before that of any other species.

> O to be in England
> Now that April's there;
> And whoever wakes in England
> Sees, some morning, unaware,
> That the lowest boughs of the brushwood sheaf
> Round the elm-tree bole are in tiny leaf,
> While the chaffinch sings on the orchard bough
> In England now!

The chaffinch makes the most of his song. He appears, indeed, very much in earnest in whatever he does, his character in this respect offering a strong contrast to that of the goldfinch, siskin, and various other melodists. They sing at all times, anywhere and anyhow. With the chaffinch, singing is a business just as important as any other—feeding, fighting, pairing, and building. He flies to a tree, and deliberately takes his stand, often on the most commanding twig, and there delivers his few notes with the utmost energy, and so rapidly that they almost run into each other, ending with a fine flourish. At regular intervals of a few seconds the performance is repeated, the bird standing erect and motionless all the time; until, having given the fullest and most complete expression to his feelings, he flies away, to engage elsewhere in some task of another kind.

It is a loud song and a joyous sound—'gay as a chaffinch' is a proverbial saying of the French; but there is also a note of defiance in the song, as in the crow of a cock. Chaffinches sing, as cocks crow, against each other, and the music often ends in a combat. It is not, as some imagine, that there is a spirit of emulation in birds with regard to their singing—that they are rival musicians, like the shepherds in the old pastorals, that contended in song for mastery : it is simply that the cock chaffinch, like the robin and some other species, is a bird of a jealous and pugnacious disposition, and can brook no other male chaffinch near him. Another's singing tells him that another male is present, and his jealousy is at once excited. If the sound is at a distance, he will content himself by answering song with song; if near, he will quickly seek out the singer, and drive him from his chosen ground. It is this jealous temper of the chaffinch that gives it value to the bird-fanciers of a base kind.

The chaffinch is first heard before the end of February. He pairs early in March, and in April begins to build. The nest is placed in a shrub or tree, in a cleft, or on a horizontal branch. An apple, pear, or cherry tree in an orchard is a favourite site; but any tree, from an evergreen in a garden to the largest oak or elm, may be selected, and the nest may be at any height from the ground from half a dozen to fifty feet. It is a very beautiful structure, formed outwardly of lichen, moss, and dry grass, compactly woven together, and mixed with cobwebs; the cup-shaped inside is lined with hair, vegetable down, and feathers. In most cases the outer portion of the nest is composed of materials that give it a close resemblance to the tree it is built on. Thus, on an oak or apple tree overgrown with grey lichen, or on a silver birch, the framework is chiefly composed of lichen; but in deep green bushes evergreen moss is used. The nest is built by the female, but the male assists in collecting and bringing materials. A fortnight, or longer, is taken to complete this elaborate nest; but from the beginning, and even before the nest is begun, the birds exhibit the greatest excitement and distress if the chosen tree is approached, flying round and flitting from branch to branch, incessantly uttering their well-known alarm-notes, usually spelt *pink-pink* or *spink-spink*, a clear, penetrating sound, slightly metallic in character; also another sound, a lower and somewhat harsh note of anxiety.

The eggs are four or five in number, of a pale bluish green, spotted and blotched with dull purplish brown. The young are fed on caterpillars and small insects. The adults, too, subsist chiefly on insects in summer, seeking for them on the ground, and sometimes capturing them in the air, like the flycatcher.

In autumn the chaffinches congregate in flocks, and at this season the separation of the sexes, about which so much has been said since the days of Linnæus, takes place. Something remains to be known on this subject. It is beyond dispute that large flocks composed entirely of birds of one sex are often met with in autumn and winter, both in this country and on the Continent. The question about which ornithologists differ is as to whether or not a separation of the sexes takes place among chaffinches of British race. Seebohm says : ' It is probable that this peculiar habit is confined to the birds that come to our shores in autumn ' ; and we have it on good authority that no separation of males from females takes place in the south and west of England. In the month of September, at one place in Scotland, I observed the male chaffinches gathered in small parties of three or four to a dozen individuals ; these were the birds belonging to the district ; but the females had vanished. Selby observed the same thing many years ago in Scotland and the north of England. One can only suppose that the migratory impulse is a little stronger or earlier in the female of this species, and that the divergence between the sexes, in this respect, becomes greater as we go towards the northern limit of its range.

Brambling.

Fringilla montifringilla.

Head, cheeks, nape, and upper part of back black, the feathers (in winter) tipped with light brown or ash-grey ; neck and scapulars pale orange-brown ; wings black variegated with orange-brown and white ; rump and lower parts white ; the flanks reddish, with a few dark spots. *Female* : crown reddish brown, the feathers tipped with grey ; a black streak over the eye ; cheeks and neck ash-grey ; all the rest as in the male, but less bright. Length, six and a quarter inches.

The brambling, or mountain-finch, comes nearest in relationship to the chaffinch, but differs very much in its glossy black, white, and bright buff colouring, and is a much prettier bird. We do not see it in its bright nuptial plumage in this country ; for it is an arctic species, breeding in very high latitudes, in birch woods near the limit of forest growth. Its nest and eggs resemble those of the chaffinch, the nest being a compact and beautifully shaped fabric that assimilates in colour to the white and grey bark of the silver birch. The bramblings arrive in this country during September and October, and are found in winter throughout Great Britain and Ireland. They are, however, very irregular in their movements, and do not, like the redwings, return year after year to the same localities; but, as a rule, where a flock appears in autumn, there it will remain until the end of winter. Beech-woods form a great attraction to them, beech-mast being their favourite food, and where it is abundant they will sometimes congregate in immense numbers. As a songster the brambling ranks low among the finches, but the lively chirping and twittering concert of a large flock on a tree-top, and in the evening, before the birds settle to roost, has a very pleasing effect.

Linnet.

Linota cannabina.

Forehead and centre of the crown crimson; the rest of the head, nape, and sides of the neck, mottled brownish grey; mantle chestnut-brown; wing-feathers blackish, with outer edges white, forming a conspicuous bar; upper tail-coverts dark brown with whitish margins; tail-feathers black, narrowly edged with white on the outer and broadly on the inner webs; chin and throat dull white, striped with greyish brown; breast crimson; belly dull white; flanks fawn-brown. Length, five inches and three-quarters. In winter the crimson feathers are concealed by wide greyish margins. *Female*: duller in colour and without any crimson.

Next to the goldfinch, the linnet is the most sought after in this country as a cage-bird, and the demand for linnets is no doubt causing a great diminution in their numbers. But they are still fairly abundant, and to be met with in most waste and uncultivated places, especially where furze-bushes abound.

The linnet is one of the most social of the finches, being found gathered in small flocks and parties of three, or four, or half a dozen, even in the middle of the breeding season. When perched or flying they incessantly call to each other in sharp little chirps and twittering notes. They are more aërial in habit than most finches, and take to flight very readily, and fly high, with great velocity; and when at a great elevation they are often seen to check their rapid course very suddenly, and dart away in some other direction, or else to drop plumb down like falling hailstones to the earth. Being so free of the air, they are great rovers, and, except when engaged in breeding, are constantly travelling about in the open country at all times of the year.

In the colour of its plumage the linnet is one of the most variable of birds : it is common to meet with bird-catchers and bird-fanciers who hear with surprise, and even with incredulity, that all these birds of different tints are of one species. The cock linnet never, or very rarely, puts on his most beautiful colours in captivity, and even in a state of nature the individuals composing a flock are seen to differ greatly. Among a dozen birds, perhaps only one will exhibit the perfect male plumage—the blood-red forehead, grey head, rich chestnut-brown upper parts, and lovely carmine breast. There is one variety, known as the lemon linnet, in which the breast is lemon-yellow instead of carmine-red ; and there are other varieties. In song, too, the linnet greatly varies. When the singer is a good one, and listened to at a distance not exceeding twenty or thirty yards, the strain is sprightly, varied, and very agreeable ; but the sweetest part is a phrase of two or three notes which usually comes as a prelude to the song ; the sound has a quality that reminds one of the swallow's voice, but it is purer, and suggests a very delicate wind instrument. During the love season the male sometimes sings on the wing ; rising to a height of several yards, it drops slowly and gracefully down, uttering a series of beautiful notes and trills.

A furze-bush is the site most often selected for the nest ; this is formed of fine dry grass and fibres, and lined with wool and vegetable down, sometimes with hair. Four to six eggs are laid, chalky white, and faintly tinged with blue in ground-colour, and spotted with light reddish brown and purplish red.

After the breeding season the linnets unite in large flocks, and at this time there is a southward movement, and large numbers undoubtedly leave this country to winter elsewhere. But even in the cold season they are common enough, and their fitful winter-evening concerts, when they congregate on a tree-top before settling down for the night, are as pleasant to listen to as the love-song of the male heard in spring among the blossoming furze and broom.

Lesser Redpoll.

Linota rufescens.

Forehead, lore, and throat black ; crown deep crimson ; upper parts reddish brown with dusky streaks ; wings and tail dusky.

edged with pale reddish brown ; breast glossy rose-red, passing into light chestnut-brown on the sides ; belly and lower tail-coverts dull white. *Female*: less bright. Length, five and a quarter inches.

FIG. 48.—LESSER REDPOLL. ⅓ natural size.

The redpoll, or redpole, as it is often written, is a pretty and interesting little bird of the northern parts of Great Britain. It has been described by Seebohm as an immature linnet in appearance, but resembling a siskin in its habits. It is usually called the lesser redpoll, because it is slightly less in size than the continental redpoll, which sometimes visits this country in winter. This last subspecies is the mealy redpoll (*Linota linaria*). A third form of this wide-ranging little bird, the Greenland redpoll (*Linota hornemanni*), has been included in the list of British birds on account of a single specimen having been obtained in this country.

In its lively disposition, its flight, and to some extent in its language, the redpoll resembles the linnet; but its feeding habits vary according to the season of the year and the conditions it finds itself in. In summer it keeps much to the higher branches of the trees, where it moves deftly about like a siskin or a crested tit in its search after minute insects and their larvæ; but in winter it feeds principally on seeds which it finds on the ground. It is fond of the seeds of the birch-tree. The appearance of a flock of redpolls feeding among the birches is thus described by Warde Fowler : ' It is one of the prettiest sights that our whole calendar of bird life affords to watch these tiny linnets at work in the delicate birch-boughs. They fear no human being, and can be approached within a very few yards. They almost outdo the titmice in the amazing variety of their postures. They prefer in a general way to be upside down, and decidedly object to the commonplace attitudes of more solidly built birds.'

The song of the redpoll is described by Seebohm as a short, monotonous trill, clear, shrill, and not unmusical; and he adds that ' it might be said to resemble the rattling of loose cog-wheels.' It breeds in suitable localities, chiefly in birch-woods in Scotland, and in England north of Norfolk and Leicester. It also breeds occasionally in more southern localities. The nest is made of dry grass and moss on a foundation of slender twigs, and is well lined with vegetable down, or with wool and feathers. It is a very neat, cup-shaped nest, and contains four to six eggs, greenish blue in ground-colour, with spots and specks of purplish brown.

After the breeding season the redpolls begin to scatter about the country in small flocks ; as autumn approaches these flocks increase in size, and a southward movement begins, large numbers crossing the Channel. Many, however, remain to winter at home, and these may be met with in woods and plantations, leading a vagrant life in small flocks, and often associating on the trees with titmice, goldcrests, and siskins.

Twite.

Linota flavirostris.

Upper parts dark brown, the feathers edged with light brown ; rump (of the male) tinged with red ; throat tawny brown ; breast and belly dull white, streaked on the flanks with dark brown ; beak yellow ; feet dark brown. Length, five and a quarter inches.

The twite, or mountain-linnet, is a bird of the mountain and moorland, and of the north, being most abundant in the Hebrides ; but it also breeds in hilly districts throughout Scotland, and in suitable localities in the northern and midland counties. In the south it is a winter visitor, and is then found associating with the linnet, which it very closely resembles in flight, habits, and appearance ; when near it may be distinguished by its shriller voice, and by its longer tail, which makes it look slimmer. In its song, too, the twite resembles the linnet, and, like that bird, occasionally sings on the wing; but its music is wanting in the finer sounds— just as its plumage is without the lovely carmine tint—of the other species.

The nest is placed in a bunch of heather, or beneath it, on the ground, and sometimes in a furze-bush. It is made of dry grass, moss, and wool, lined with hair and fur. The eggs are five or six in number, and are like the linnet's in colour.

In autumn the twites unite in large flocks, and visit the stubbles and ploughed lands.

Bullfinch.

Pyrrhula europæa

Fig. 49.—Bullfinch. ⅓ natural size.

Crown, throat, region round the beak, wings, and tail lustrous purple-black; upper part of the back bluish ash; ear-coverts, sides of the neck, breast, and belly red; lower tail-coverts dull white; a broad buff and grey band across the wing. Length, six and a quarter inches.

The bullfinch stands out among British finches with a strange distinctness. He is gaily coloured, and the arrangement of colours is a striking one—glossy black, blue-grey, and pure white above, and a fine red beneath. This is described in the books as 'brick-red'; and there is no doubt that, among the thousand and more shades of the less vivid red seen in bricks taken fresh from the kiln, the exact tint of the bullfinch might be matched. In the same way you could match the most delicate floral red—that which we see in the spikes of the red horse-chestnut, and the almond blossom, and the briar rose. The earthy, uniform red of weathered bricks is not the colour of our bird. The beauty of such a tint as that of the bullfinch can be best appreciated where, indeed, it is most commonly seen, amidst the verdure of clustering leaves ; for greens and reds, pleasing in themselves, ever make the most agreeable contrasts among colours.

In its figure, too, this bird is very singular among the finches : his curiously arched beak gives him the look of a diminutive hawk in a gay plumage.

The bullfinch is greatly persecuted by gardeners on account of the mischief he is supposed to do, for he has the habit of feeding on the flower-buds of fruit-trees in winter and spring. On the other hand, he is greatly esteemed as a cage-bird, and the bird-catchers are ever on the watch for it. But the effect in both cases is pretty much the same, since the hatred that slays and the love that makes captive are equally disastrous to the species. There is no doubt that it is diminishing in this country, and that it is now a rare bird in most districts. Fortunately, it has a wide distribution in Great Britain : in Ireland, where it is said to be rare, I have found it not uncommon, and tamer than in England. It may be increasing there which would not be strange in a country where even the magpie is permitted to exist, and birds generally are regarded with kindlier feelings than in this country.

The bullfinch does not often go to the ground to feed ; he gets most of his food on trees and bushes—insects, buds, fruit, and seeds of various kinds. He inhabits woods, plantations, and thickets, and is often seen in thick hedges and in the tangled vegetation growing by the side of streams. Where he is not persecuted he is a tame and rather sedentary bird, and will allow a person to approach within a dozen yards before leaving his perch. His call and alarm note is a low, piping, musical sound, very pleasant to hear. The male sings in the spring, and so, it is said, does the female ; but his strain is short, and so feeble that it can be heard only at a distance of a few yards.

The nest is built during the last half of April in a holly or yew, or other dense, dark bush or tree, or in a thick hedge. It is unlike the nest of any other finch, being outwardly a platform-shaped structure made of interwoven twigs, with a cup-shaped nest in the centre, formed of fine rootlets, the rim of the cup projecting above the platform it is built on. The eggs are four to six, greenish blue in ground-colour, spotted and sometimes streaked with dark purplish brown, and blotched with pinkish brown.

Bullfinches pair for life, and at all seasons of the year male and female are seen together; if any young are reared, they usually remain in company with the parent birds during the autumn and winter months.

Nearly allied to the common bullfinch are two beautiful birds which have a place in our list of species. One of these is the rosy bullfinch (*Carpodacus erythrinus*), of which two or three stragglers have been found in England; it breeds in Finland, and is found throughout the Russian Empire. The other is the pine grossbeak *Pinicola* (*enucleator*), also a rare straggler to Britain from the north of Europe.

Crossbill.

Loxia curvirostra.

Fig. 50.—Crossbill. ¼ natural size.

Wing and tail feathers brown; all other parts green, yellow, orange, and tile-red, according to age and sex. Red is the colour of the adult male in a state of nature, and yellow in captivity. Length, six inches and a half.

The crossbills differ from all other birds in the extraordinary form of the parrot-like bill. In other birds, whatever the shape of the bill may be, straight or curved, or broad and flat, or conical, or hooked, the two mandibles correspond, and fit when closed like box and lid. In this bird both mandibles have prolonged curved points, and cross each other, much as the two forefingers of our hands cross when the fingers are loosely linked together. A full description of this form of beak and its use as a seed-extractor, together with an admirably written history of the common crossbill, is contained in the second volume of Yarrell's great work (fourth edition).

The crossbill is also remarkable on account of the changes of colour it undergoes and of the brightness of its colours. These are birds of the sombre pine-woods, inhabiting high latitudes; but in their various greens and reds and yellows they are like tanagers and other tropical families, and form an exception to the rule that birds of brilliant plumage are restricted to regions of brilliant sunlight.

No fewer than four species of this genus (Loxia) figure in the list of British birds; three of these may be dismissed in a few words :—

Parrot crossbill (*Loxia pittyopsittacus*) breeds in the pine-forests of Scandinavia and northern Russia, and is known in England as a rare straggler. It is scarcely distinct, specifically, from the common crossbill.

White-winged crossbill (*Loxia leucoptera*), a North American species, once obtained in England.

Two-barred crossbill (*Loxia bifasciata*) a Siberian species; a rare straggler to England and Ireland.

The fourth species (the common crossbill) has a better title to figure as a British species, and its winter visits to this country are much more frequent, although irregular; and it also breeds with us in some localities in Scotland, probably every year, and has also bred intermittingly in many districts in England, even so far south as Bournemouth. The reason of its irregularity in visiting our shores is that the crossbill is one of those species that do not go farther from home than they are compelled by severe cold and scarcity of food. Driven from home they become 'gipsy migrants,' and may be very abundant with us one year, and not one appear the following season, or for several seasons. At all times of the year the crossbill is gregarious in its habits. Throughout the summer it is seen in small parties; when the breeding season is over these begin to move about, accompanied by the young birds, and join with other parties, and as the season progresses the flock grows by process of accretion until it may number many hundreds. At this season they are remarkably tame, and will allow a person to approach within a few yards and admire their colours and various motions as they cling to and climb, parrot-like, about the twigs in search of seed and fruit. When flying they call to each other with a loud shrill note, and in late winter and spring both male and female utter a low warbling song.

The nest is placed in a pine-tree, at a distance from the ground of from five to forty feet ; it is formed outwardly of twigs, roots, and dry grass ; the inner part, of wool, hair, and feathers. Four or five eggs are laid, white or greenish white in ground-colour, spotted with reddish brown, with under-markings cf pale brown.

Corn-Bunting.

Emberiza miliaria.

Upper parts yellowish brown with dusky spots ; under parts yellowish white spotted and streaked with dusky. Length, seven and a half inches.

The present species is the largest of our five buntings, and is the most generally diffused throughout the British Islands. It is often called the common bunting, but is scarcely deserving of the name, as in most places it is less common than the yellow bunting. It is certainly more local than that bird, although in some localities, both in the south and north of England, it is more numerous than any other bird of its genus. Nor is its other name of corn-bunting more strictly accurate, for though it is a frequenter of corn-fields in spring and summer, it is equally partial to hay-meadows, commons, and other open places. Like the skylark, it loves an open sky and a wide horizon ; but, not being able to soar, it seeks an elevation of some kind to perch on—a hedge-top, or the summit of a bush, or a tall weed in the middle of a field of corn, will serve it ; but, best of all, it loves a telegraph-wire, where it sits on high above the world, in sunshine and wind, and without the slightest exertion is able to experience agreeable sensations like those of the kestrel, lark, or tern, when suspended motionless in mid-air. On a telegraph-wire it will sit contentedly by the hour, delivering its song at regular intervals.

The buntings—all those included in the genus Emberiza—differ from other finches in their more sedentary habits and heavier motions. The present species is the heaviest and most sedentary of all, and on this account, and also on account of its dull plumage, and because its voice is not melodious, it has been usually described in somewhat depreciatory terms. Yarrell speaks of its droning, harsh, unmusical song; and Warde Fowler thus describes it in his delightful book, 'A Year with the Birds': 'Look at the common corn-bunting, as he sits on the wires or the hedge-top: he is lumpy, loose-feathered, spiritless, and flies off with his legs hanging down, and without a trace of agility or vivacity; he is a dull bird, and seems to know it. Even his voice is half-hearted, and reminds me often of an old man in our village who used to tell us that he had a wheezing in his pipes.' This is a pretty description; but it makes the homely bunting a little too homely, and the critical remarks on its singing are not quite satisfactory: the song is not droning, and not half-hearted. Heard at intervals in the open, sunny fields and pasture-lands, it somehow has a pleasant effect. It is a peculiar sound, not easily describable. The song begins with two or three vigorous and musical chirps, then all at once the bird seems to lose himself as a musician, and throws out all that remains of his song in a burst of confused sound. In character it is somewhat like the sharp note of alarm, or excitement of some kind, often uttered in spring by the skylark as he flies low above the field, but is sharper and more prolonged. Robert Gray wrote: 'It puts you in mind of the jingling of a chain or the sound of breaking glass.' It is certainly like breaking glass. You can imitate it by tightly pressing a handful of polished pebbles together, which produce, as they slide over each other, a variety of sharp and scraping sounds. It is a peculiarity of the song that it is like several sounds emitted simultaneously, as of a note broken up into splinters, or issuing from a bundle of minute windpipes instead of out of one of larger size.

Of all the birds that remain with us throughout the year, the bunting is the latest to breed, the nest being usually built in May. It is placed among grass and herbage close to the ground, and formed of dry grass and fibrous roots, lined with horsehair and fine fibres. Four to six eggs are laid, dull purplish white or pale yellowish in ground-colour, blotched and streaked with dark brown, with some patches of a dull lavender hue.

The bunting feeds on seeds and grain and insects. In autumn it becomes gregarious, and visits the stubbles and rickyards, where it is seen associating with sparrows, greenfinches, and chaffinches.

Yellowhammer.

Emberiza citrinella.

Fig. 51.—Yellowhammer. ⅓ natural size.

Head, neck, breast, and under parts bright yellow, more or less streaked with dusky; flanks streaked with brownish red; upper parts reddish brown spotted with dusky. *Female*: the yellow parts less bright, and spotted with dull reddish brown. Length, six and a quarter inches.

The yellowhammer, or yellow bunting, is one of the most generally diffused species in the British Islands, and, on account of its habit of always perching on the summit of a bush or other elevation, and of its bright yellow head and neck, which make it conspicuous at a distance, it is a familiar object to every person in the rural districts. It differs from the corn-bunting both in a brighter colouring and in a slimmer and more graceful figure. But it is a heavy bird nevertheless, of a sedentary disposition, and during the warm season spends a great portion of its time in sitting upright and motionless on its perch, uttering its song at regular intervals.

This species affects rough commons and waste lands in preference to fields, and where he is found you may hear his song at all times of the day, even during the sultriest hours; for although the yellow hammer remains with us throughout the year, and is able to resist the colds of winter, he is a great lover of heat. The song is very different from that of the species last described: it is composed of half a dozen or more short, reedy notes, all exactly alike, and shaken out, as it were, in a hurry, followed by a long, thin note, or by two notes, slightly melodious in character. It may be described as a trivial and monotonous song, but it is a summer sound which most people hear with pleasure, and the yellowhammer, or 'little-bit-of-bread-and-no-c-h-e-e-s-e,' as it is called in imitation of its note, is something of a favourite with country-people. The rustics have a story about the origin of the bread-and-no-cheese name, which they think very laughable; and one is certainly very much amused at the manner in which it is usually told. This is ponderous and slow, and strikes one as highly incongruous, the subject being only a childish legend about a little bird.

According to Yarrell, the Scotch peasants have some curious superstitions about the yellow yoldring, as they call it. To them its song sounds like the words 'Deil, deil, deil tak ye,' and the bird itself is supposed to be on very familiar terms with the evil being whose name it invokes so freely, and who supplies it on a May morning with a drop of his own blood with which to paint its curiously marked eggs.

About the middle of April the yellowhammer builds its nest, on or above the ground, among furze and bramble bushes, or at the roots of a hedge, or in a bank among grass and nettles. The nest is large but neatly made, outwardly of dry grass, stalks, roots, and moss, the inside being lined with fibres and horsehair. The eggs are four or five in number, purplish white in ground-colour, streaked and veined with deep reddish purple, with violet-grey under-markings.

The young males acquire the bright yellow head of the adult bird at the autumn moult.

Although this bird remains with us throughout the year, it has a partial migration. In autumn and winter it is seen in small flocks, often feeding in company with the common bunting and other finches. In winter its food consists principally of seeds; in summer it subsists largely, and feeds its young exclusively, on insects.

Cirl Bunting.

Emberiza cirlus.

FIG. 52.—CIRL BUNTING. ⅓ natural size.

Crown olive streaked with black; throat, neck, and band across the eye black; gorget and band above and below the eye bright yellow; breast olive-grey, bounded at the sides by chestnut; belly dull yellow; back brownish red with dusky spots. *Female*: the distinct patches of black and yellow wanting; the dusky spots on the back larger. Length, six and a half inches.

This bird, in its dress of many colours—chestnut-brown, olive, black and white, and lemon-yellow—is the handsomest of the British buntings. It is an uncommon species, being restricted to the southern and western counties of England, and exceedingly local in its distribution. It is, moreover, of a shy disposition, and hides from sight in tall trees; consequently it is seldom seen, and is known to few persons. It is resident all the year. Its winter movements, if it has any, are not known. The curious fact about this bunting is that its breeding-places, which form small isolated areas, chiefly on or near the south-western coast, remain year after year unchanged. The birds do not nest outside of the old limits, nor do they form fresh colonies in other suitable places.

Hedgerow-elms, and other large trees growing near fields, are favourite resorts of the cirl bunting, and the male takes his stand to sing on a tree-top, just as the yellowhammer does on a furze-bush or hedge-top. His song comes nearest in character to that of the species just named, being composed of several rapidly uttered, short notes, only brighter and more vigorous; but the song is without the long, thin note with which the more common species ends his slight strain. In its nesting habits and in the colour of its eggs it is like the yellowhammer, but its young are fed almost wholly on young grasshoppers.

In summer the cirl bunting lives chiefly on insects, but in autumn and winter it is, like other finches, a seed-eater, and at this season unites in small flocks, and occasionally associates with birds of other species.

Reed-Bunting.

Emberiza schœniclus.

FIG. 53.—REED-BUNTING. ¼ natural size.

Head, throat, and gorget black (in winter speckled with light brown); nape, sides of the neck, and a line extending to the base of the beak white; upper parts variegated with reddish brown and dusky; under parts white streaked with dusky on the flanks. *Female*: head reddish brown with dusky spots; the white on the neck less distinct; under parts reddish white, with dusky spots. Length, six inches.

The reed-bunting, although by no means an uncommon bird, is not nearly so common as either the corn-bunting or yellowhammer. It is a bird of the waterside, and its spring and summer life is passed among the reeds and aquatic herbage and willows and alders growing on the margins of streams and marshes. It is widely distributed, and, where suitable localities exist, may be looked for with some confidence. In most districts it is known as the reed-sparrow, and in its colouring and general appearance it is undoubtedly more sparrow-like than the other buntings. From its black head, which is very conspicuous by contrast with the white collar, it is often called the black-headed bunting, a name which more properly belongs to a continental species to be noticed later on as an accidental visitor to this country. The male is a persistent singer in the spring months, and, perched near the top of a reed, or on the topmost branch of an alder tree, he will repeat at intervals his slight reedy song of four or five notes, the last somewhat prolonged. If disturbed, he will fly a little distance ahead and perch again; and this action he will repeat two or three times if followed up; then, doubling back, he will return to the first spot. He is a sprightlier bird than the other buntings. The slender reed-stems he perches on, which bend and sway beneath the slightest weight, have taught him easier and more graceful motions, although in that respect he cannot compare with the bearded tit.

The nest is made near the water, on or close to the ground, under a bush or bunch of rushes, and is composed of dry grass and leaves and stems of aquatic plants, and lined with fibrous roots and horse-hair. The eggs are four or five in number, in ground-colour dull white or grey, spotted and streaked with purplish brown and dull grey.

The reed-bunting remains in this country all the year, but in severe weather leaves the wet, low ground, and is then seen among the flocks of mixed finches in fields and in the neighbourhood of farmhouses.

Snow-Bunting.

Plectrophanes nivalis.

Head, neck, portion of the wings and under parts white; upper parts black, tinged here and there with red. In winter the white of the head and the black on the back mixed with reddish brown. *Female*: the white on the head and upper parts mottled with dusky, and her colours not so pure. Length, six inches and three-quarters.

The snow-bunting, or snowflake, as it is also called, breeds regularly in some localities in the Highlands of Scotland, and may there-tore be regarded as an indigenous species; but the birds breeding within British limits are only a few pairs, and the snow-bunting is best known as a winter visitor from more northern regions. They appear on our coasts in the month of October, sometimes in immense flocks, to pass the winter, for the most part in the neighbourhood of the sea, seeking their food in fields and on waste lands. Occasionally these flocks penetrate to the more inland districts. Being very pretty and lively little birds, they are great favourites in the places they visit; and their appearance is all the more welcome on account of the desolate aspect of nature in the districts where they are most abundant. Many ornithologists have written lovingly about the snow-bunting. Thus, Saxby says: ' Seen against a dark hillside or a lowering sky, a flock of these birds presents an exceedingly beautiful appearance, and it may then be seen how aptly the term " snowflake " has been applied to the species. I am acquainted with no more pleasing combination of sight and sound than that afforded when a cloud of these birds, backed by a dark grey sky, descends, as it were, in a shower to the ground, to the music of their own sweet, tinkling notes.'

The fullest, and by far the most interesting, account ever given of the snow-bunting is by Seebohm. He says that in its habits it is the most arctic of the small birds, breeding as far north as latitude 82° 33'. Its appearance is thus described: ' In sledging over the snow across the steppes of South-western Siberia from Ekaterranburg to Tomsk, a distance of about a thousand miles, the snow-bunting was the only bird we saw, except a few sparrows, jackdaws, and hooded crows near the villages. The snow-buntings were in small flocks, and many of them had almost lost their winter dress. It was a charming sight to watch them flitting before the sledge, as we disturbed them at their meals. Sometimes, in the sunshine, their white bodies were invisible against the white snow, and we could almost fancy that a flock of black butterflies was dancing before us. The flight of the snow-bunting is peculiar, and is somewhat like that of a butterfly, as if the bird altered its mind every few seconds as to which direction it wished to take.'

Of its song he says: ' Whilst the female is busy with the duties of incubation the male sings freely, sometimes as he sits upon the top of a rock, but often flinging himself into the air like a shuttlecock, and then descending in a spiral curve, with wings and tail expanded, singing all the time. The song is a low and melodious warbling, not unlike that of the shore-lark.'

The nest is placed in crevices of rocks, and is made of dry grass, roots, and moss, lined with root-fibres, hair, wool, and feathers. Five or six, sometimes seven, eggs are laid, in ground-colour greyish white or pale blue, spotted and blotched with reddish brown, with under-markings of pale brown and pale grey.

The young are fed on the larvæ of gnats. In winter the snow-buntings feed on seeds of grass and weeds.

Besides the five buntings described, five more species figure in the list of British birds, and these may now be briefly noticed:—

Black-headed bunting (*Emberiza melanocephala*), inhabiting South-eastern Europe; a single specimen has been obtained in this country.

Ortolan bunting (*Emberiza hortulana*).—A summer visitor to Europe. Several specimens have been obtained in the British Islands, mostly in the south and east of England.

Rustic bunting (*Emberiza rustica*).—Breeds in North-eastern Europe and Northern Siberia. A rare straggler to Britain.

Little bunting (*Emberiza pusilla*), from North-eastern Europe and Siberia. Has been taken once in England.

Lapland bunting (*Calcarius lapponica*).—A circumpolar species breeding in the arctic regions. Occasionally straggles to this country.

Starling.

Sturnus vulgaris.

Black with purple and green reflections, the upper feathers tipped with pale buff; under tail-coverts edged with white; beak yellow; feet flesh-colour tinged with brown. *Female*: spotted below as well as above. *Young*: uniform ash-brown, unspotted. Length, eight and a half inches.

A compactly built bird with a short, square tail, strong legs and feet, and a long, sharp beak, the starling does not excel in beauty of figure or grace of carriage; his lines are rather indicative of strength; he looks what he is—a plodding digger in the meadows and pastures, a hardy bird of rook-like habits, able to stand all weathers. But he has a beautiful coat. As in the case of the large corvine species he so frequently associates with when feeding, his richly coloured plumage has a gloss which causes it to shine at times like polished metal in the sunlight. The starling has an added distinction in the spangling of white and buff on the upper parts.

During the greater portion of the year his food consists almost entirely of insects in their different stages. Like the rook, he searches at the roots of the grass for worms and grubs; and there is no doubt that he deserves his reputation of one of the farmer's feathered helpers. He attends the sheep and cattle in the meadows, and is often seen perching on their backs; the animals take it quietly, and perhaps know that he is on the look-out for ticks, which are a source of irritation to them.

Although a digger and plodder, the starling is very different from his companion, the rook, in manner. The rooks are seen soberly marching about, quartering the ground, each one intent on finding something for himself. The starlings are not nearly so methodical; they run about a great deal on the feeding-ground, and watch and interfere with each other. When one by chance finds a rich treasure, the others are eager to share it, and there are occasional scolding matches, and sometimes downright quarrelling, among them.

The starling is also a fruit-eater, particularly of cherries; and in winter, when insect food is scarce, he will eat berries, seeds, and grain, and, like the blackbird and blue tit, may be easily attracted to the house with scraps of animal food.

The nesting habits of the starling contribute to make it one of our most familiar birds. He breeds in holes, and a hole in a tree or rock, in a cliff or quarry, suits him very well; but he more often finds a suitable place under the eaves of a house, or in a barn, or church-tower, or other building; and, unless disturbed, he will continue to use the same site year after year. As early as January the starlings begin to pay occasional visits to the breeding-site, but they do not build until April. The nest is composed of a large quantity of dry grass, small twigs, moss, and other materials, and is sometimes lined with wool or feathers. Four to seven eggs are laid—five being the usual number—of a delicate pale greenish blue colour, and unspotted.

The starling sings more or less all the year, but his song is at its best in the spring months. He has no such melodious notes as distinguish the warblers; his merit lies less in the quality of the sounds he utters than in their endless variety. In a leisurely way he will sometimes ramble on for an hour, whistling and warbling very agreeably, mingling his finer notes with chatterings and cluckings and squealings, and sounds as of snapping the fingers and of kissing, with many others quite indescribable. On account

M

of this variety of language he has always been reputed a mimic;
but he does not mock as the mocking-bird does: he never reproduces the song of any other songster. Notes and phrases, and
calls and alarm-notes, he has apparently picked up, and, listening,
you recognise this or that species; but the imitations are seldom
perfect, and in the end you are almost inclined to believe that he
is called a mimic only because his variety is so great.

After the breeding season the young and old birds feed together
in the pastures, where they unite with other families; and the
flocks thus formed, as they increase in size, extend their wanderings over the surrounding country. Like rooks, they have favourite
roosting-places, to which they return annually; these are reed and
osier beds, thickets of holly and other evergreens, and fir-planta-
tions. But they are not so constant in their attachment to one
locality as the rook. They are more vagrant in their habits, and
shift their ground, and migrate, and their numbers may vary
greatly from year to year in the same district. In a district
where they are abundant, they are seen at the end of each day
gathering from all directions to the roosting-place; and it is then
that the 'cloud of starlings' may be seen at its best, and it is
certainly one of the finest sights that bird life presents in England.
At intervals, after the birds have been steadily pouring in their
flocks for a couple of hours, the whole vast concourse rises, and,
seen from a distance, the flock, composed of tens and hundreds of
thousands, may then be easily mistaken for a long black cloud suspended above the wood. In a few moments it is seen to grow
thin, as the flock scatters, until it almost fades away. Suddenly it
darkens again; and so on, alternately, the form, too, changing
continually, now extending to an immense length across the sky,
like a long bar of vapour, and now gathered into a huge oval or
oblong black mass; and by-and-by the cloud again empties itself
into the trees, and the sky is clear once more. These evolutions
are repeated many times, until, as the evening draws on, the birds
finally settle down in their places, but not to sleep; for an hour
longer the wood is filled with an indescribable noise—a tangle of
ten thousand penetrative voices, all together whistling, chattering,
scolding, and singing.

We have but one starling; an allied species, the beautiful rose-
coloured pastor (*Pastor roseus*), which breeds in Western Asia, is an
irregular visitor to all parts of England.

Chough.

Pyrrhocorax graculus.

FIG. 54.—CHOUGH. ⅛ natural size.

Black with purple and green reflections; beak and feet coral-red. Length, sixteen inches.

It is melancholy to think that this interesting and extremely handsome bird has been diminishing in numbers for a long period, and is now become so rare that, unless strong measures to secure its protection be at once taken, its eventual extinction in this country must be regarded as merely a question of time. Formerly it bred in many inland localities in England, Wales, Scotland and Ireland; but from all its ancient nesting-cliffs in the interior of these countries it has long vanished, and, like the raven, which has also fallen on evil days, is now only found in a few spots on the rock-bound coasts where high, precipitous cliffs afford it some chance of hatching its eggs and continuing the species for a few years longer.

A few pairs are still found breeding each year on the coast of Cornwall, where it was formerly abundant, and on this account was called the Cornish chough. It also breeds in limited numbers in a few other situations:—at Lundy Island, the rocks of the Calf of

Man, on the coast of Wales, and at Islay and a few other situations on the coast of Scotland.

In size, flight, language, habits, and general appearance, the chough comes nearest to the jackdaw, but is a much handsomer bird, its uniform intense black plumage and long, curved, coral bill, and red legs and feet, giving it a distinguished and somewhat singular appearance. Its cry, uttered both when perched and on the wing, differs only from that of the daw in its more ringing and melodious sound. The flight is easy and buoyant, and the birds are fond of aërial pastimes, similar to those of the jackdaw, during which the members of the company pursue one another in play, and frequently tumble down from a great height through the air as if disabled. They feed inland, often going long distances from the cliffs they inhabit to seek their food, like rooks, in the meadows and pasture-lands. They also follow the plough to pick up the worms and grubs, like the rook and black-headed gull, and are said to eat carrion, berries, and grain. On the sands and rocks they feed on the animal refuse left by the tides.

The chough, like the daw, lives always in communities ; the two species may often be found breeding near each other and associating in flocks. The nest is placed in a hole or crevice in the rocks in the least accessible part of the cliff. It is built of sticks and twigs, and lined with grass, fur, wool, and other soft substances. Four to six eggs are laid, in ground-colour white, faintly tinged with blue or yellowish, and spotted and blotched with various shades of grey and pale brown.

Jay.

Garrulus glandarius.

Crest greyish white streaked with black ; a black moustache from the corners of the beak ; general plumage reddish grey, darker above ; primaries dingy black ; secondaries velvet-black and pure white ; inner tertials rich chestnut ; winglet and greater coverts barred with black, white, and bright blue ; upper and under-tail-coverts pure white ; iris bright blue ; beak black ; feet dark brown. Length, thirteen and a half inches.

The jay is nearly equal to the daw in size, and has a variegated and beautiful plumage, and when seen flying across an open sunlit space is nearly as conspicuous as a magpie. But among the dense

foliage of the woods and thickets he inhabits it is as difficult to
see a jay as a wood-wren; and it is doubtless owing to this fact, and
to his extreme wariness and cunning, that he still survives in
many parts of England where the magpie has now been extirpated,
although both species are pursued by gamekeepers with the same
stupid and deadly animosity. In Scotland he is said to be decreasing more rapidly than in England, probably because the Scotch
are more thorough than the Southrons, especially in the process of
stamping out: in Ireland it is found only in the southern half of
the island, where it is somewhat scarce.

The most striking characteristic of the jay is its tireless energy,
and a liveliness of disposition and alertness almost without a
parallel among British birds; even the restless, prying, chattering
magpie seems a quiet creature beside it; and as to the other corvine
birds, they are by comparison a sedate family. Like the magpie,
he is an excitable and vociferous bird, and has a curious and varied
language. When disturbed in his woodland haunts he utters a
scream that startles the hearer, so loud and harsh and piercing is it.
Richard Jefferies well describes it as being like the sound made in
tearing a piece of calico. He also has a lower, monotonous, rasping
note, which he will continue uttering for half an hour at a time
when his curiosity or suspicion has been excited. In the love
season he utters a variety of sounds by way of song, and as they
resemble the notes of the starling, sparrow, and other birds, he is
supposed to be a mocker. In captivity he can be taught to speak a
few words; but it is possible that the various sounds composing his
vocal performance in the woods are his own.

In spring he becomes somewhat social, and unites in noisy
parties; at other times he is solitary, or lives with his mate.

Owing to an excessively wary and suspicious habit, engendered
by much persecution, it is difficult to observe him narrowly for any
length of time. In the woods and plantations, few and far between,
where jays are not persecuted, and do not associate the human
figure with a sudden shower of murderous pellets, he will allow a
nearer approach, and it is then a rare pleasure to study him on his
perch. He does not, as a rule, rest long in one place, and when
perched is of so active and excitable a temper that he cannot keep still
for three seconds at a stretch. The wings and tail are raised, and
depressed, and flirted, the crest alternately lowered and elevated,
the head turned from side to side, as the wild, bright eyes glance in
this or that direction. If he should by chance place himself where

a stray sunbeam falls through the foliage on him, lighting up his fine reddish brown plumage, variegated with black and white and beautiful blue, he shows as one of the handsomest birds that inhabit the woodlands.

The jay makes his nest in a bush or sapling at no great height from the ground; the lower branch of a large tree is sometimes made choice of, where the nest is well concealed by the close foliage; a thick holly or other evergreen is also a favourite site. The nest is built of sticks and twigs, sometimes mixed with mud, and the cup-shaped cavity is lined with fine roots. Four to seven eggs are laid, pale greyish green in ground-colour, thickly freckled, and spotted all over with pale olive-brown. The young birds follow their parents for some weeks after leaving the nest.

The jay is omnivorous, but in summer feeds mainly on slugs, worms, grubs, and insects of all kinds; in this season he devours berries and fruit—plums, cherries, also peas and currants; and in autumn, nuts, beech-mast, and acorns. He also plunders the smaller birds of their eggs and young, and is said to carry off pheasant and partridge chicks. He is a keen mouser, and after killing a mouse with two or three sharp blows on the head, strips the skin off before devouring it. Like the nuthatch and some other species, he has the habit of concealing the food he does not want to eat at once.

Magpie.

Pica rustica.

Head, throat, neck, and back velvet-black; scapulars and under plumage white; tail much graduated, and, as well as the wings, black, with lustrous blue and green reflections; beak and feet black. Length, eighteen inches.

In spite of his evil reputation, the magpie is regarded by most persons who are not breeders of pheasants with exceptional interest, and even affection. He has some very attractive qualities, and is one of that trio of corvine birds—pie, chough, and jay—from which it is difficult to single out the most beautiful. The most conspicuous he undoubtedly is, in his black and white plumage; and his figure, with its long, graduated, tail, is also the most elegant. In his habits there is abundant variety, and in sagacity he is probably unsurpassed by any member of the corvine family, which counts so many wily brains. His excessive cunning and rapid rate of increase have probably served to save him from the fate that has overtaken the hen harrier and marsh-harrier, and many another beautiful member of the British avifauna. As it is, he has been almost extirpated throughout a large part of England and Scotland. In Ireland, however, he is still a common species, but, oddly enough, he is not indigenous to that country. It is believed that he first appeared

FIG. 55.—MAGPIE. ½ natural size.

there about, or a little more than, two centuries and a half ago. How he got there is not known. According to Yarrell, there is a widespread belief in Ireland that the magpie was imported into that island by the English out of spite.

The magpie is as singular in his motions, gestures, and flight as he is beautiful in colour and elegant in form. On the wing he appears most conspicuous when the white webs of the quills are displayed. The wings are very short, and the flight is slow and somewhat wavering, and at every three or four yards there is an interval of violent wing-beats, during which the black and white of the quills mix and become nearly grey. High in the air he has a most curious appearance; as a rule he flies low, passing from tree to tree, or along the side of a hedge. He seeks his food on the ground, and his movements are then utterly unlike those of any other ground-feeder. His manner of running and hopping about, flinging up his tail; his antics and little, excited dashes, now to this side, now to that, give the idea that he is amusing himself with some solitary game rather than seeking food. Richard Jefferies has given so accurate and vivid a picture of the bird in his ' Wild Life in a Southern County ' that I cannot refrain from quoting it in this place. ' To this hedge the hill-magpie comes; some magpies seem to keep entirely to the downs, while others range the vale, though there is no apparent difference between them. His peculiar uneven, and, so to say, flickering flight marks him out at a distance, as he jauntily journeys along beside the slope. He visits every fir-copse and beech-clump in his way, spending some time, too, in and about the hawthorn hedge, which is a favourite spot. Sometimes in the spring, when the corn is yet short and green, if you glance carefully through an opening in the bushes, or round the side of the gateway, you may see him busy on the ground. His rather excitable nature betrays itself in every motion : he walks, now to the right a couple of yards, now to the left in quick zigzag, so working across the field towards you ; then, with a long rush, he makes a lengthy traverse at the top of his speed ; turns, and darts away again at right angles ; and presently up goes his tail, and he throws his head down with a jerk of the whole body, as if he would thrust his beak deep into the earth. This habit of searching the field, apparently for some favourite grub, is evidence in his favour that he is not so entirely guilty as he has been represented of innocent blood. No bird could be approached in that way. All is done in a jerky, nervous manner. As he turns sideways, the white feathers show with a flash above the green corn ; another moment, and he looks all black.'

In disposition the magpie is restless, inquisitive, excitable, and loquacious. Where he is greatly persecuted by gamekeepers—as, indeed, is the case almost everywhere in England—he grows so wary that, in spite of his conspicuous colouring, it would be almost impossible to get a glimpse of him, were it not for his outbursts of irrepressible excitement and garrulity. The sight of a stoat, fox, or prowling cat will instantly cause him to forget the more dangerous keeper and his gun, and to fill the coppice with cries of alarm. The feathered inhabitants of the wood hurry from all sides to ascertain the cause of the outcry, and assist in driving out the intruder. But the keeper, too, hears; this is the opportunity he has been long watching and waiting for ; and if he approaches the scene of excitement with due caution, poor beautiful Mag, dead, and shattered with shot, will soon be added to his festering trophies.

The usual sound emitted by the magpie is an excited chatter—a note with a hard, percussive sound, rapidly repeated half a dozen times. It may be compared to the sound of a wooden rattle, or to the bleating of a goat; but there is always a certain resemblance to the human voice in it, especially when the birds are unalarmed, and converse with one another in subdued tones. But it is more like the guttural voice of the negro than the white man's voice. Their subdued chatter has sometimes produced in me the idea that I was listening to the low talking and laughing of a couple of negroes lying on their backs somewhere near. It is well known that this bird can be taught to articulate a few words.

The magpie is a notable architect, and as a rule builds his nest in a tall tree in or on the borders of a wood; sometimes in a low, isolated tree or large bush, or in the centre of a thick hedge. It is large, and formed of sticks and mud, with a hollow in the centre, plastered with mud and lined with fibrous roots; over this solid platform and nest a large dome of loosely interwoven thorny sticks is built, with a hole in the side just large enough to admit the bird.

Magpies pair for life, and the nest may serve the birds for several years, a little repairing work being bestowed on it each spring. The eggs are usually six in number, but in some cases as many as nine are laid. In colour they are pale bluish green, very thickly spotted and freckled with olive-brown, and faintly blotched with ash-colour.

The magpie may be easily tamed; even the wild birds, when not persecuted, become strongly familiar with man, and come about the house like fowls. In a state of nature he subsists on grubs, worms, snails, slugs, and various insects, and will eat any kind of animal food that offers, not excepting carrion; he also devours young birds and eggs, and is fond of ripe fruit. He is supposed to be a deadly enemy of the poultry-yard, and a stealer of pheasant and partridge chicks; but it is certain that his depredations have been greatly exaggerated.

Jackdaw.

Corvus monedula.

Crown and upper parts black with violet reflections; back of the head and nape grey; iris white; under parts dull black. Length, fourteen inches.

It is hard to pronounce which of our indigenous corvine species is the most interesting. They are all wonderful birds ; and to those who have made pets of, and studied them, and know them intimately as most of us know our dogs, they appear to excel other feathered creatures in the quality of *mind*, just as thrushes, larks, and warblers do in that of melody, and as terns and others of the more aërial kinds excel in graceful motions. If the jackdaw is not the first of his family in intelligence, he is certainly not behind any of them. In beauty he does not compete with the three species already described—chough, jay, and pie—and at a distance is only a lesser rook or carrion crow in appearance ; but there is a peculiar look about this bird when seen closely that engages and holds the atten- tion more than mere beauty or grace. When he is sitting in repose, his head drawn in and beak inclining downwards, and turns his face to you, it does not look quite like a bird's face : the feathers puffed out all round make the head appear preternaturally large, and the two small, bright, whitish grey eyes set close together in the middle have an expression of craft that is somewhat human and a little uncanny.

The jackdaw is one of the birds that the gamekeeper wars against without ruth, shooting and trapping them in the breeding season, especially when they are occupied in feeding their young, and can be seen and easily shot in their frequent journeys to and from the nesting-tree. But the jackdaw is not so easy to extirpate as some of its congeners. He is probably just as common as he ever was, while the chough is rapidly dying out, and crow and jay and pie are yearly diminishing in numbers, and the raven, driven from its inland haunts, clings to existence in the wildest and most inaccessible parts of the coast. The reason of this is that the jack- daw is more adaptive than the other species. He has been com- pared in this respect to the house-sparrow, for he can exist in town as well as country, and readily adapts himself to new surroundings. The variety of sites he uses for breeding purposes shows how plastic are his habits. He breeds apart from his fellows, like the carrion crow ; or in communities, like the rook and chough. He builds in hollow trees in parks and woods, in rabbit-burrows, in ruins, church- towers, and buildings of all kinds ; and in holes and crevices in cliffs, whether inland or facing the sea, where he lives in company with the rock-pigeon and the puffin. ' At Flamborough,' Seebohm says, ' the jackdaws are very abundant. A republican might call them the aristocracy of the cliffs. Like the modern noble, or the

ROOKS. JACKDAWS. STARLINGS.

monks of the Middle Ages, they contrive to eat the fat of the land without any ostensible means of living. They apparently claim an hereditary right in the cliffs ; for they catch no fish, and do no work, but levy blackmail on the silly guillemots, stealing the fish which the male has brought to the ledges for the female, upsetting the egg of some unfortunate bird who has left it for a short time, and devouring as much of its contents as they can get hold of, when the egg is broken, on some ledge of rock or in the sea.'

The social disposition of the jackdaw, and its friendliness towards other species of its family, is no doubt favourable in the long run to it ; for by mixing with the rooks, both when feeding and roosting, he comes in for a share of the protection extended to that bird in most districts. There is also a sentiment favourable to the jackdaw on account of its partiality for churches and castles : the ' ecclesiastical ' daws are safe and fearless of man while soaring and playing round the sacred buildings in villages and towns ; when they go abroad to forage, and are not with the rooks, there is danger for them, and they are, accordingly, wary and shy of man.

At all seasons the jackdaw loves to consort with his fellows, and to spend a portion of each day in aërial games and exercises : the birds circle about in the air, pursuing and playfully buffeting one another, and tumbling downwards, often from a great height, only to mount aloft again, to renew the mock chase and battle and downward fall. They are loquacious birds, and frequently call loudly to one another, both when perched and when flying ; the usual callnote has a clear, sharp, querulous sound, something like the yelping bark of a small dog.

The nest is a rude structure made with sticks, dry grass, leaves, wool, and other materials heaped together, and is large or small according to the situation ; when in a church-tower or hollow tree an enormous quantity of material is sometimes used to fill up the cavity. The eggs are four to six in number, and vary much in size, shape, and markings. They are very pale blue, varying to greenish blue, in ground-colour, and are spotted and blotched with blackish brown and olive-brown, with pinkish grey under-markings.

The jackdaw is omnivorous, but subsists principally on worms, grubs, and insects, which it picks up in the pastures where it feeds in company with rooks and starlings. In spring it will eat the newly sown grain, in autumn devours acorns and beech-mast, and in winter will stoop to carrion.

In captivity the jackdaw makes a clever and amusing pet, and may be taught to repeat a few words.

Carrion Crow.

Corvus corone.

Black with green and violet reflections; iris dark hazel; lower part of the beak covered with bristly feathers. Length, nineteen inches.

The common, black, or carrion crow so closely resembles the rook in form, size, and colouring as to be indistinguishable from it when seen at a distance. Viewed nearer it is seen to have the base of the beak clothed with feathers, instead of naked and grey, as is the case in the more common bird. The young rook may, however, be mistaken for a crow even when very near, as its face is feathered like the crow's. In voice the two birds differ, that of the crow being louder and very much harsher—more like the raven's croak than the familiar hoarse, but not disagreeable, caw of the rook. In summer he may be identified by his solitary habits. He has a very much worse reputation than the species he so nearly resembles: both game-preserver and farmer regard him as a pest, and he is said to be the most persecuted bird in this country. But somehow, in spite of all that is done to extirpate him utterly, he manages to keep a pretty strong hold on life, although he is not common. He inhabits all of the British Islands, chiefly England and Wales; in the central and northern parts of Scotland, and in Ireland, he is rarely met with, his place in those countries being taken by the hooded crow. When not engaged in breeding the crow is to some extent gregarious, and is also social, associating both in the fields and at roosting-time with rooks and jackdaws. And it is probable that this habit has been of great advantage to him, and may even have saved the species from extermination, for while among the rooks he easily passes for a rook. That he is exceptionally sagacious, and very careful to keep out of reach of his deadly human enemies, goes without saying; he is a member of a family ranking high in intelligence; and being so large and conspicuous a bird, his life is one of incessant danger. In selecting a site for his nest his intelligence is sometimes at fault. Not only is the nest a large structure, but, with a strange fatuity, the bird will at times build in a conspicuous place near a house. On the coast he is, like the raven and jackdaw, a nester in cliffs; inland he usually builds in or on a large tree, and if the nest is allowed to remain he will use it for several years. The nest is a large plat-form, made of sticks, weeds, pieces of turf, and other materials, with a hollow in the centre neatly lined with fine grass, wool, hairs, and feathers. The eggs are four to six in number, in ground-colour pale bluish green, spotted and blotched with various shades of olive-brown, with purplish grey underlying blotches.

When there are young to feed the crow is exceedingly active; he is then most destructive to young pheasants and other game, and is a troublesome neighbour to the poultry. Young and weakly birds are dropped upon and picked up with astonishing adroitness and rapidity. He will pounce upon and carry off any small and easily conquered animal to satisfy his nestful of voracious young. At other times he is omnivorous: a carrion-eater like the raven, and devourer of dead stranded fish and other animal refuse cast up by the sea; in the pastures he searches for worms and grubs with the rooks; and when occasion offers he feeds on grain, berries, wal-nuts, and fruit. He appears to have a greater appetite than most species: he is said to be the first bird astir in the morning, and from dawn until sunset he is engaged incessantly in seeking food.

His flight resembles that of the rook, but is somewhat heavier.

Hooded Crow.

Corvus cornix.

Head, throat, wings, and tail black; the rest of the plumage ash-grey; iris brown. Length, nineteen and a half inches.

This bird, which is also known as the hoodie, Royston crow, grey or grey-backed crow, and by other names, is now regarded by some of our first authorities on such subjects as a form of the carrion crow. In England and Wales it is very rare. In Ireland, where the black crow is almost unknown, it is common; it is also found throughout Scotland and the Western Islands as a resident breeding species. In winter, hooded crows visit the east coast of England in large numbers, and are specially abundant on the Lin-colnshire coast, where they feed on shellfish and animal refuse left by the tide on the extensive mud flats. These seaside crows that wait on the tide come to us from the north of Europe, and leave our shores in spring.

Excepting in the matter of colour—one bird being wholly black and the other grey on the back and under parts—the black and grey crows are identical in size, language, and in all their habits, and what has been said of the carrion crow applies to the present species.

Rook.

Corvus frugilegus.

Black with purple and violet reflections; base of the beak, nostrils, and region round the beak bare of feathers, and covered with a white scurf; iris greyish white. Length, eighteen inches.

The rook is common throughout the British Islands, and is our best-known large land bird, being everywhere the most abundant species, as well as the most conspicuous, owing to his great size, blackness, gregariousness, and habits of perching and nesting on the tops of trees, and of feeding on open grass spaces, where it is visible at a long distance. Without being a favourite of either the gamekeeper or the farmer, he is, in a measure, a protected species, the rookery being looked on as a pleasant and almost indispensable appanage of the country-house. It was not always so. In former times the rook was regarded as a highly injurious bird, and in the reign of Henry VIII. an Act of Parliament was passed to ensure its destruction. But this is ancient history. The existing sentiment, which is so favourable to the bird, probably had its origin centuries back in time, and the rook has everywhere come to regard the trees that are near a human habitation as the safest to build on. It is surprising to find how fearless of man he is in this respect, while retaining a suspicious habit towards him when at a distance from home. I recall one rookery on a clump of fir-trees so close to a large house that, from the top windows, one can look down on the nests and count the eggs in many of them ; yet for miles round the area is a well-wooded park, where the birds might easily have found scores of sites as well or better suited to their requirements.

The birds usually return to the rookery in February, and in March, or even earlier if the weather should prove mild, they begin to repair the old nests and build new ones. The nests are placed on the topmost branches of the tree—elm, oak, birch, or fir ; but an elm-tree is generally made choice of. The tree to suit the rook must be tall—if possible, the tallest tree in the place —for it is the

Fig. 56.—Rooks and Nest.

instinct of the bird not only to have his house far out of reach of all possible terrestrial enemies, but so placed that a wide and uninterrupted view of earth and sky may be obtained from it. As things now are his winged enemies do him little hurt, but it was not always so. In the next place, the branches must afford a suitable foundation to build on : they must be strong, and forked, so as to hold the fabric securely during high winds and sudden violent storms ; furthermore, there must be a clear space above or at the side, to enable the bird to approach and leave it without striking against the surrounding boughs. It is a well-known fact that rooks will desert a rookery when the trees are decaying, even when, to a human eye, they appear sound. The most probable explanation which has yet been offered of this fact is, that a considerable amount of pliancy in the branches is necessary for the safety of the nest ; for if the branches do not yield and sway to the force of the wind, the nest is in danger of being blown bodily out of its place : in the decaying tree the upper branches become too stiff, from the insufficient supply of sap.

The building and repairing time is one of great and incessant excitement in the rookery ; and it is curious to note that birds of such a social disposition, and able to live together in concord at all other times, are at this period extremely contentious. As a rule, when one bird is abroad foraging for sticks, his mate remains on guard at the nest. Among these watchers and the birds that are leaving and arriving there is much loud cawing, which sounds like ' language,' in the slang sense of the word ; and it might appear that they were all at strife, and each one fighting for himself. But it may be observed that a majority of the birds respect each other's rights, and never come into collision, and that there are others, in most cases a very few, who depart from these traditions, and are, like freebooters, always on the watch to plunder sticks from their neighbours' nests, instead of going afield to gather them. The presence of these objectionable members of the community may account for some of the curious episodes in the life of the rookery—as, for instance, the fact that all the birds will sometimes combine to persecute one pair, and demolish their nest again and again as fast as it is made.

The nest, when completed, is a large structure, two feet or more in diameter, made of sticks, and lined with dry grass. The eggs are four to six in number, and are bluish green, spotted and blotched with greyish purple and dull brown.

During incubation the male assiduously feeds his sitting mate, and occasionally changes places with her ; and after the young are out of the shells both parents are engaged incessantly in collecting food for them. From early morning until dark they may be seen flying to and from the rookery, on each return journey carrying a cluster of worms and grubs in the mouth.

When the young are fully fledged they are seen perching awkwardly on the branches near the nest, occasionally making short, tentative flights, and apparently anxious to go forth into that wide green world spread out beneath their cradle and watch-tower. They are, happily, ignorant of the doom that awaits them ; for the time is now near when the blood-tax must be levied on the community—the price which is paid for protection ; and, the young only being eatable, the slaughter must fall on them. As a rule, a few of the young escape death, as, when the shooting begins, and the old birds rise in haste to scatter in all directions, a few of the most advanced young birds that are already strong on the wing follow their parents to a place of safety.

After the breeding season, which is usually over at the beginning of June, the rookery is forsaken ; in some cases the birds disappear, and do not return until the next spring ; more often they pay an occasional visit to the rookery, and some rookeries are visited almost daily by the birds. But for the rest of the year their roosting-place is elsewhere, often at a considerable distance. In districts where rooks are abundant there is generally one great roosting-place, where the communities inhabiting the country for many miles around are accustomed to congregate at the end of each day. As the evening draws near the birds begin to arrive from two, or three, or more directions, in detachments or long, loose trains, flying steadily, at an equal height above the ground. Where they settle the tree-tops are black with their numbers ; and as fresh contingents pour in the noise of the cawing grows louder and more continuous, until it is in volume like the sound of a surging sea. At intervals large numbers of birds rise up, to hang like a black cloud above the trees for some minutes, but as the evening darkens they all finally settle down for the night ; still, in so vast an assemblage there are always many waking individuals, and a noise of subdued cawing may be heard throughout the hours of darkness. With the returning light there is a renewal of the loud noise and excitement, as the birds rise up and wheel about in the air before setting out on their journey to their distant feeding-grounds.

Raven.

Corvus corax.

FIG. 57.—RAVEN. $\frac{1}{12}$ natural size.

Black with purple reflections; tail black; iris with two circles, the inner grey, the outer ash-brown.   Length, twenty-five inches.

The raven has the reputation, true or false, of being one of the longest-lived birds; certainly it is one of the hardiest, and capable of adapting itself to the greatest extremes of temperature.   Its range in the northern hemisphere extends from the regions of 'thick-ribbed ice' to the damp, hot woods and burning coasts of Southern Mexico and Central America.   The tropical jaguar may help it to a meal at one extremity of its range, the polar bear at the other.   Compared to such diversities of climate and of other conditions, those of the British Islands are as nothing.   From the Isle of Wight and the southern coast to the northern extremity of Scotland, and beyond, to 'utmost Kilda's lonely isle,' the raven has lived in what, to a bird of his grit, must have been a very pleasant garden with a mild and equable temperature throughout the year. Formerly he was a fairly common bird in all parts of our island, and it is probable that some protection was accorded to him by owners of large estates, in spite of his evil reputation, on account of some such sentiment as now exists with regard to the rook. A pair of ravens in a woodland district, Seebohm says, ' was often considered the pride and pest of the parish.' But the sentiment, if it existed, was not strong enough, and the constant persecution of the bird by its two principal enemies, the gamekeeper and the shepherd, joined by a third during the present century in the ' collector,' has gradually driven it from all, or well-nigh all, its ancient inland haunts, and it now exists in its last strongholds, the rugged iron-bound sea-coast on the northern coasts of Scotland and the neighbouring islands. A few—a very few—pairs are still to be met with on some of the cliffs on the south and south-west coasts of England, and on the Welsh coast; but even in the rudest and most solitary localities inhabited by it the bird can keep its hold on life only by means of a wariness and sagacity exceeding that of most other wild and persecuted species.

Like most of the members of its family, the raven is omnivorous, feeding indiscriminately on grubs, worms, insects, grain, fruit, carrion, and animal food of all kinds. Being so much bigger and more powerful than other crows, with a larger appetite to satisfy, he is more rapacious in his habits, and bolder in attacking animals of large size. He will readily attack a small lamb left by its dam, and pick out its eyes; but, as a rule, his attacks on lambs and sheep are confined to the very young and to the sickly or dying. He also attacks hares, rabbits, and birds of various kinds, when he finds them ailing or wounded by shot. He is fond of eggs, as well as of nestlings, and plunders the nests of the sea-birds that inhabit the cliffs in his neighbourhood. But the greatest part of his food consists of dead animal matter cast up by the sea, and carrion of all kinds : a dead sheep will afford him pasture for some days, and keep him out of mischief—for he can be hawk or vulture as occasion offers.

In appearance the raven is a larger rook or carrion crow; he is a fine bird, and his large size, the uniform blackness of his plumage, and his deep, harsh, and human-like, croaking voice, strongly impress the imagination. But the effect produced on the mind by the raven is, doubtless, in part due to the bird's reputation, to its ancient historical fame, its large place in our older literature, and to the various sombre superstitions connected with it. When feeding on a carcase his appearance is not engaging: there is a lack of dignity in his sidling or 'loping' motions, and savage haste in tearing at the flesh, with a startled look round after each morsel. When disturbed from his repast the slow, cumbrous, flapping flight as he rises strongly reminds you of the vulture. He makes a nobler figure when soaring high in the air, or along the face of some huge beetling cliff that fronts the sea; for then his flight has power and ease as he falls and rises, playing, like a giant chough or jackdaw, with his mate.

The raven pairs for life, and uses the same nest year after year. A pair or two may still breed in a tree somewhere in Scotland or in the north of England, but, in almost all cases, the bird now makes his nest on a ledge of rock on some cliff on the sea-coast. It is a rude, bulky structure, formed of sticks and heather, and lined with grass and wool. The eggs are four to six in number, bluish green in ground-colour, more or less thickly spotted and marked with dark olive-brown.

The raven is the earliest bird to breed in this country: the nest-building begins in January, and the eggs are laid in February or March.

Besides the eight species described, a ninth member of the corvine family has been included among British birds; this is the nutcracker (*Nucifraga caryocatactes*), a very irregular straggler to our shores from northern Europe.

Skylark.

Alauda arvensis.

Upper parts varied with three shades of brown, the darkest of which lies along the shaft of each feather; a faint whitish streak over the eye; throat white; under parts yellowish white tinged with brown; the throat and sides of neck with dark brown lanceolate spots, which form a gorget just above the breast. Length, seven inches and a quarter.

The skylark is so universally diffused in these islands, and so abundant, well known, and favourite a species, that anything beyond a brief and prosaic account of its habits would appear superfluous. His image, better than any pen can portray it, already exists in every mind. A distinguished ornithologist, writing of the sparrow, declines to describe its language, and asks his reader to open his window and hear it for himself. In like manner, I may ask my reader to listen to the lark's song, which exists registered in his own brain. For he must have heard it times without number, this being a music which, like the rain and sunshine, falls on all of us. If someone, too curious, should desire me not to concern myself with the images and registered sensations of others' brains, but to record here my own impressions and feelings, I could but refer him to Shelley's 'Ode to a

Fig. 58.—Skylark. ⅓ natural size.

Skylark,' which describes the bird at his best—the bird, and the feeling produced on the listener. Some ornithologist (I blush to say it) has pointed out that the poet's description is unscientific and of no value; nevertheless, it embodies what we all feel at times, although we may be without inspiration, and have only dull prose for expression. It is true there are those who are not moved by nature's sights and sounds, even in her 'special moments,' who regard a skylark merely as something to eat with a delicate flavour. It is well, if we desire to think the best that we can of our fellows, to look on such persons as exceptions, like those, perhaps fabled, monsters of antiquity who feasted on nightingales' tongues and other strange meats.

The skylark inhabits open places, and is to be met with on pastures, commons, downs, and mountain slopes; but he prefers arable land, and is most abundant in cultivated districts. In winter his song may be occasionally heard in mild weather; in February it becomes more frequent, and increases until the end of March, when it may be said that his music is at full flood; and at this high point it continues for several months, during which time successive broods are reared. A more inexhaustible singer than the lark does not exist; and when we consider how abundant and widely diffused the bird is, the number of months during which he is vocal, and the character of the song—a rapid torrent of continuous sound—it is almost possible to believe that the melody from this one species actually equals in amount that from all the other song-birds together.

The nest, made in April, is a slight hollow in the ground in a cornfield, or among the grass of a meadow, or any open place, and is composed of dry grass and moss, lined with fine grass and horse-hair. The eggs are four or five in number, greyish white, spotted and clouded with greenish brown. Two or three broods are reared.

In September the skylarks begin to assemble in flocks and shift their ground. At this season they migrate in large numbers; but many remain throughout the year, except in the more northern districts. Large flocks of migrants from the Continent also appear during the winter months.

In winter the lark feeds chiefly on seeds; in summer he is an insect as well as a seed eater.

Woodlark.

Alauda arborea.

Upper parts reddish brown, the centre of each feather dark brown; a distinct yellowish white streak above the eye, extending to the back part of the head; under parts yellowish white streaked with dark brown. Tail very short. Length, six and a half inches.

In appearance the woodlark is a lesser skylark, with a shorter tail in proportion to the body, and no apparent difference in colour, except that the spots on the breast and the pale streak over the eye are more conspicuous. It ranks with the six or eight finest British songsters, but is the least known of all. The tree-pipit, sometimes called woodlark, is a much better known songster. When the woodlark is seen and heard he is taken by most people for the skylark. The mistake is easily made, the song having the same character, and is a continuous stream of jubilant sound, delivered in the same manner; for the woodlark, too, soars, ' and soaring, sings.' He differs from the skylark in his manner of rising: that bird goes up and up, not quite vertically, but inclining now to this side, now to that, with intervals of suspension, but still as if drawn heavenwards by an invisible cord or magnet; the woodlark ascends in circles, and finally does not attain to so great a height. He also sings on his perch on a tree, and rises from the tree to sing aloft, and in this habit he is like the tree-pipit. Although the woodlark's song resembles that of the larger bird in character, there is more sameness in the flow of sounds, and it is not so powerful; on the other hand, the sounds are sweeter in quality. Of the two, he is the more constant singer, and may be heard in mild weather throughout the autumn and winter months. His usual call is a melodious double note.

The woodlark is very local in its distribution; it is nowhere common, and its range in this country is a somewhat limited one. In the north of England it is very rare, and in Scotland it has only once been observed breeding. In Ireland it breeds in some localities. It inhabits wooded parks and the borders of woods and commons, and grass-lands in the vicinity of trees and hedgerows; for although it feeds, roosts, and nests on the ground, it must, like the tree-pipit, have trees to perch on; and, like that bird, it has a favourite perch, where it may be confidently looked for at any hour of the day during the spring and summer months.

The nest is placed in a slight hollow in the ground, under a bush, or sheltered by grass and herbage, and is formed of dry grass and moss, and lined with finer grass and hair. The eggs are four or five in number, buffish or faint greenish white in ground-colour, freckled and spotted with reddish brown, with purple-grey under-markings. Three, and even four, broods are said to be reared in the season.

In autumn and winter the woodlarks unite in families or small flocks, and at this season they have a partial or internal migration, the birds that breed in the northern counties moving south. In the southern and south-western counties they remain stationary, and it is observed that during a spell of mild weather in winter these small flocks break up, but re-form at the return of cold.

Besides the two indigenous larks, we have as rare stragglers the following four species : the crested lark (*Alauda cristata*), an inhabitant of Europe and Asia; the short-toed lark (*Calendrella brachydactyla*), from southern Europe; the white-winged lark (*Melanocorypha sibirica*), a Siberian species, obtained once in England ; and the shore-lark (*Otocorys alpestris*), an irregular winter visitor from North Europe, Asia, and America.

Swift.

Cypselus apus

Sooty brown; chin greyish white; tarsi feathered; bill, feet, and claws shining black. Length, seven and a half inches.

The swift arrives in this country about the end of April or early in May, and from that time onwards, throughout the spring and summer months, day after day, from morning until evening, he may be seen overhead, in twos, threes, and half-dozens, pursuing his mad, everlasting race through the air. Even as late as ten o'clock in the evening, or later, when his form can no longer be followed by the straining sight, his shrill, exulting cry may be heard at intervals, now far off, and now close at hand, showing that the daylight hours of these northern latitudes are not long enough to exhaust his wonderful energy. It has even been supposed by some naturalists that, when not incubating, he spends the entire night on the wing. This is hard to believe ; but if we consider his rate of speed, and the number of hours he visibly spends on the wing, it would be within the mark to say that the swift, in a sense, ' puts a girdle round the earth ' two or three times a month. Year after year the swifts return to the same localities to breed, and there are few towns, villages, hamlets, or even isolated mansions and farmhouses in the British Islands where this bird is not a summer guest. The bunch of swifts to be seen rushing round the tower of every village church are undoubtedly the same birds, or their descendants, that have occupied the place from time immemorial ; and it is probable that the annual increase is just sufficient to make good the losses by death each year. It is hard to believe that a life so strenuous can last very long, and impossible to believe that birds so free of the air are subject to many fatal accidents. A spell of intense frost is very fatal to them in spring, but the cold is their only enemy in this country.

The black swift, or ' develing,' or ' screecher,' as he is sometimes named, with his exceedingly long, stiff, scythe-shaped wings, still ' urging his wild career' through the air, is a figure familiar to everyone. And his voice, too, is a familiar sound to every ear. It is usually described as a harsh scream. Wild and shrill and piercing it certainly is, but it varies greatly with the bird's emotions, and is at times a beautiful silvery sound, which many would hear with delight if uttered by the song-thrush or nightingale.

The swift breeds in holes in church-towers and in houses, its favourite site being under the eaves of a thatched cottage; it also nests in crevices in the sides of chalk-pits and sea-cliffs, and sometimes in hollow trees. A slight nest of straw and feathers, made to adhere together with the bird's saliva, is built, and two eggs are laid; they are oval in form, white in colour, and have rough shells. One brood only is reared in the season, and the birds depart at the end of August, but stragglers may be met with as late as October.

The white-bellied swift (*Cypselus melba*) is known in England as a rare straggler from Central and Southern Europe. A still rarer straggler from Eastern Siberia, where it breeds, is the needle-tailed swift (*Acanthyllis caudacuta*); of this species not more than two or three specimens have been obtained in this country.

Nightjar.

Caprimulgus europæus.

Ash-grey spotted and barred with black, brown, and chestnut ; first three primaries with a large white patch on the inner web, the two outer tail-feathers on each side tipped with white. Length, ten and a quarter inches.

The nightjar, or goatsucker, is the representative of a type widely distributed on the earth ; we have only one species, just as we have but one swift, one kingfisher, one wryneck, and one cuckoo. And, having but one, and this being so singular a bird, unlike all other species known to us, in structure, colouring, language, and habits, he excites a great deal of interest, and is very well known, although a night-bird, nowhere abundant, and a sojourner with us for only about four months and a half out of the twelve. He arrives in this country about the middle of May, and inhabits commons, moors, and stony places, and is also to be met with in woods. He is found in all suitable localities throughout Great Britain, but is more local in Ireland. Year after year he returns to the same spot to breed, faithful as the swift to its church-tower and the wryneck to its hollow tree, although the unforgotten spot may be on level waste land with a uniform surface. During the daylight hours he sits on the ground among bracken or heather, or by the side of a furze-bush, or in some open place where there is no shelter ; but so long as he remains motionless it is all but impossible to detect him, so closely does he resemble the earth in colour. And here we see the advantage of his peculiar colouring—the various soft shades of buff

FIG. 59.—NIGHTJAR. ⅕ natural size.

and brown and grey, which at a short distance harmonise with the surroundings, and render him invisible. When perching on a tree he makes himself invisible in another way: his habit is to perch, not crossways on a branch, but lengthways. He rises from the ground when almost trodden on, and goes away with a silent flight, darting this way and that in an eccentric course, and looking more like a great grey mottled and marbled moth than a bird. After going a short distance he drops to earth just as suddenly as he rose. After sunset he may be seen on the borders of woods, by the side of hedges, and in meadows near the water, pursuing his insect prey, dashing rapidly along, with quick turns and doublings, as of a lap-wing at play. At this hour his curious reeling, spinning, or whirring song may be heard, a little like the song of the grasshopper warbler in character; but the warbler's song is a whisper by comparison. 'The sound,' Yarrell truly says, 'can be easily imitated by vibrating the tongue against the roof of the mouth; but the imitation, excellent as it may be close to the performer, is greatly inferior in power, being almost inaudible to anyone twenty yards off, while the original can be heard in calm weather for half a mile or more.' Of the other curious vocal performance of the nightjar the same author says : 'On the wing, while toying with his mate, or executing his rapid evolutions round the trees, . . . the cock occasionally produces another sound, which, by some excellent observers, has been called a squeak, but to the writer is exactly like that which can be made by swinging a whipthong in the air.' Most of the names the bird is called by have reference to its summer song—spinner, wheelbird, night-churn, and churn-owl.

The nightjar deposits its two eggs on the bare ground; their colour is white or cream, blotched, mottled, clouded, and veined with brown, blackish brown, and grey. One brood is reared in the season. The return migration is in September.

A single specimen of the red-necked nightjar (*Caprimulgus ruficollis*), an inhabitant of South-western Europe, has been obtained in this country; and (in 1883) one specimen of the Egyptian nightjar (*Caprimulgus ægyptius*), was shot in Nottinghamshire.

Spotted Woodpecker.
(Great Spotted Woodpecker.)
Dendrocopus major.

Crown and upper parts black; a crimson patch on the back of the head; a white spot on each side of the neck; scapulars, lesser wing-coverts, and under parts white; belly and under tail-coverts crimson. *Female*: without crimson on the head. Length, nine and a half inches.

The present species is less common than the green woodpecker; and as it seldom goes to the ground, and usually confines its food-seeking to the higher branches of trees, it is rarely seen. Nor is it nearly so loquacious as the larger bird, nor so richly coloured, although handsome and conspicuous in its black-and-white dress,

with a touch of glossy crimson on the nape.   It frequents woods,
hedgerows, and plantations, also pollard willows growing by the side
of streams.   It may be met with in most English counties, but in
the northern counties and in Scotland it is very scarce.   In Ireland
it does not breed, although occasionally seen there as a migrant
in winter.   These migrants come from northern Europe, sometimes
in considerable numbers, and are diffused over the British Islands;
the birds of British race are believed to remain in this country
throughout the year.

FIG. 60.—SPOTTED WOODPECKER.   ⅕ natural size.

Like most woodpeckers, this species feeds principally on insects
found in crevices of the bark and decayed wood of trees.   In the
season he becomes a fruit and seed eater, and visits gardens and
orchards to steal the cherries; and also feeds on berries, nuts, acorns,
and fir-seeds.   He is, for a woodpecker, a silent bird; his usual call
is a sharp, quick note, repeated two or three times.   The most
curious sound he makes is instrumental: it is the love-call of the
bird, produced by striking the beak on a branch so rapidly as to
produce a long jarring or rattling note.

The eggs are laid in a hole in a tree, not always made by the
bird; they are six or seven in number, and creamy white in colour.

Barred Woodpecker.
(Lesser Spotted Woodpecker.)
Dendrocopus minor.

Forehead and lower parts dirty white; crown bright red; nape, back, and wings black with white bars; tail black, the outer feathers tipped with white and barred with black; iris red. Length, five and a half inches.

When Yarrell wrote that the neglect of the name of barred woodpecker, which had been used by some authors for the present species, was to be regretted for brevity's sake, it was a pity that he did not go so far as to reintroduce it in his great work. For doubtless many a writer on birds has groaned in spirit at the necessity laid upon him to use two such cumbrous names as great, or greater, spotted woodpecker, and lesser spotted woodpecker. Partly on this account I lament Yarrell's timidity, and partly for a personal reason, since my boldness in using the neglected name will be taken by some readers as an exemplification of the familiar truth that fools rush in where angels fear to tread. But no one will deny that the book-names of these two woodpeckers are bad, and to some extent misleading, since the birds are as unlike in markings as they are in size. The first is as big as a fieldfare, and is spotted; the second is scarcely larger than a linnet, and is distinctly barred.

The barred woodpecker is found in most English counties as far north as York; in Scotland and Ireland it is a rare straggler. It is nowhere common, and appears to be even rarer than it is, owing to its small size and its habit of frequenting tall trees. Its usual note is a sharp chirp, resembling that of the blackbird when going to roost; its love-call, as in the case of the spotted woodpecker, is instrumental, and produced in the same manner. The sound varies in tone and pitch according to the character of the tree performed on, and has been compared to the sound made by an auger when used in boring hard wood; also to the creaking of a branch swayed by the wind.

The barred woodpecker in most cases makes a nesting-hole for itself in the branch or trunk of a soft-wooded tree. Six or seven smooth, creamy white eggs are laid.

Green Woodpecker.

Gecinus viridis.

Fig 61.—Green Woodpecker. ⅙ natural size.

Upper parts olive-green; rump yellow; under parts greenish grey; crown, back of the head, and moustaches crimson; face black. *Female*: less crimson on the head; moustaches black. Length, thirteen inches.

The chief characteristic of this beautiful woodland bird is his extraordinary energy. His entire structure, from the straight, sharp, powerful bill, and long, barbed tongue, to the climbing feet and stiff tail-feathers, used as a support to the body when clinging vertically to the trunk of a tree, is admirably adapted to the laborious trade he follows. And this peculiar form has its correlative in a strength, boldness, and determination in attacking a hard piece of work that are nothing less than brilliant. One is astonished at the force of the sounding blows he delivers on the tough bark and wood in his search for hidden insects; yet this is one of the common, small, everyday tasks of his life, and not comparable to the huge labour of digging a breeding-hole deep into the heart of a large branch or trunk of a tree. This energy and intensity of life shows itself also in his motions, gestures, and language. His very qualities of eagerness and determination in splitting up the wood in which his prey lies concealed, and the loud racket he is compelled to make at such times, call upon him the undesirable attentions of the species that are his enemies: he must, when hammering on a tree, be exceedingly vigilant all the while, less some prowling sparrow-hawk or swift-descending falcon shall take him unawares. The wood he exerts his strength on does not absorb his whole attention: his eyes are all the time glancing this way and that, and on the slightest appearance of danger he is nimble as a squirrel to place the trunk or branch between himself and a possible enemy. After a few moments of hiding his red head becomes visible as he peeps cautiously round the trunk, and if the danger be then over he goes back to his task. In the presence of a winged enemy he finds his safety in clinging to the trunk, round which he can move so rapidly, as on the wing he is a heavy bird; but hawks are now rare in England, and his chief persecutors are men with guns.

The language of the green woodpecker, or yaffle, as he is called in the southern counties, adds greatly to his attractiveness; his ringing cry is a sound to rejoice the hearer. Many of the woodpeckers have extremely powerful voices, and the cry of the great black woodpecker of continental Europe has been described by one familiar with it as being like the ' yell of a demon.' This ' demon ' must, I imagine, be a very blithe-hearted one, and its ' yell ' an expression of wild, joyous, woodland life which we should be glad to listen to in England. Our bird's voice is not so powerful; but who has not been made happier for a whole day by hearing his ' loud laugh,' as one of our old poets has called his cry? It is a clear, piercing sound, so loud and sudden that it startles you, full of wild liberty and gladness; and when I listen for and fail to hear it in park or forest, I feel that I have missed a sound for which no other bird cry or melody can compensate me.

This species is found in woods and parks throughout England as far north as Derbyshire and the south of Yorkshire; farther north he is very rare as a breeder, and in Ireland is only known as a straggler. In seeking his food he climbs obliquely up the trunk, until, having mounted to the higher branches, he passes with a dipping flight to the next tree, invariably alighting near the roots. In summer he feeds a great deal on the ground, especially on ants, of which he is very fond. The breeding-hole is usually made in a soft-

o

wooded tree; it is carried straight to the heart of the wood, and is then extended downwards to the depth of about a foot. In most cases it is found that the heart of the tree selected by the birds is rotten, although outwardly no signs of decay may appear. The hole ends in a chamber in which the eggs are deposited on a slight bed of chips; the eggs are four to seven in number, are oval in form and have pure white polished shells. The young when fledged come out of their cell in the tree's heart, and creep about the bark for some days before they are able to fly.

The same breeding-hole is used for several years, if not taken possession of by a pair of marauding starlings, which not unfrequently happens.

Wryneck.

Iÿnx torquilla.

FIG. 62.—WRYNECK. ⅓ natural size.

Upper parts reddish grey, irregularly spotted and lined with brown and black; a broad black and brown band from the back of the head to the back; under parts dull white, tinged with buff, and barred with dark brown, except on the breast and belly, where the markings become arrow-headed in form; outer web of the quills marked with rectangular, alternate black and yellowish red spots; tail-feathers barred with black zigzag bands; beak and feet olive-brown. Length, seven inches.

The wryneck is placed by anatomists next to the woodpeckers, and is like them in the form of its feet and the habit of perching vertically on the trunks of trees; but he does not dig into the wood with his beak, nor does he support himself with his tail, the feathers of which are soft, as in most perching birds. He is a singular bird, differing from all others in form, colouring, language, and habits. His variously coloured plumage, so curiously and beautifully barred and mottled, is most like that of the nightjar; but his beauty appears only when he is seen very near. At a distance of twenty-five or thirty yards he is obscure in colouring, and is more remarkable for his attitudes and gestures, when seen on a tree trunk deftly and rapidly picking up the small ants on which he feeds. When thus engaged he twists his neck, turning his head from side to side in a most singular manner; hence the name of wryneck. When taken in the hand he twists his neck about in the same manner, and hisses like a snake, as he also does when disturbed during incubation; and on this account he has been called snake-bird. When held in the hand he sometimes swoons, and appears to be dead until released, whereupon he quickly recovers and makes his escape. Even more characteristic than his contortions, hissings, and ' death feignings,' is his voice. It is an unmistakable and familiar sound of early spring, as distinctive as the shrill cry of the swift and the cuckoo's call—a clear, high-pitched, far reaching note, reiterated many times—a sound that makes itself heard at a distance of a quarter of a mile. As a rule, this note is heard a few days before the cuckoo's call, and on this account the wryneck is known in the southern counties, where he is most common, as the cuckoo's mate, or messenger, or boder, and is also called the cuckoo's maid.

The wryneck feeds chiefly on ants and their larvæ, and, like the green woodpecker, he goes to the anthills on commons and uncultivated grounds; the insects are taken with the long, retractile tongue, which is covered with an adhesive saliva, and which the bird, when feeding, darts out and withdraws with lightning rapidity.

A hole in the trunk of a tree, often near the roots, is a favourite nesting-place. The eggs are seven to ten in number, and are deposited, without any nest, on the rotten wood. They are pure white, and have glossy shells. The same breeding-hole is used year after year.

The wryneck is most common in the southern and south-eastern counties; in the West of England and in Wales it is rarer. In the northern counties of England it is also rare and local; in Scotland it does not breed, and in Ireland it is not known.

Kingfisher.

Alcedo ispida.

Fig. 63.—Kingfisher. ¼ natural size.

Back azure-blue; head and wing-coverts bluish green spotted with azure-blue; under and behind the eye a reddish band, passing into white, and beneath this a band of azure-green; wings and tail greenish blue; throat white; under parts rusty orange-red. Length, seven and a half inches.

The kingfisher is by far the most brilliantly coloured bird in the British Islands; and those who see it living and moving with the sunlight on it can form an idea of the wonderful lustre of many tropical species, which certainly cannot be done by gazing on the labelled pellets of dead and dimmed feathers, called 'specimens,' in cabinets and museums. Unhappily, this rare splendour of the kingfisher, which gives it value, has served only to draw destruction upon it. As Yarrell long ago said, it is persecuted chiefly because of its beauty, and the desire to possess a stuffed specimen in a glass case. It is found in suitable localities throughout Great Britain where it has not been exterminated to gratify the vile taste that prefers a mummy to a living creature. In Ireland it is rare and local as a breeding species, but as an autumn and winter visitor is found throughout the country. It frequents streams and rivers, and the margins of lakes, and, more rarely, the seaside. It is a solitary bird, and, like the dipper, restricts itself to one part of the stream where it gets its food. Day after day it returns to the same perch, where it sits watching the surface, silent and immovable as a heron. It looks out for its prey both when perched and when flying at a height of a few feet above the surface, and often hovers motionless for a few moments before darting down into the water. With the minnow it captures held crossways in the beak it flies to a perch, and, after beating it against the branch or stone, swallows it, head first, sometimes tossing it in the air and catching it as it falls. It also preys on aquatic insects and small crustaceans. The pairing-time is early, and in February or March the birds make choice of a breeding place, usually near their fishing-ground, but sometimes at a distance of a mile or more from the water. A hole is dug in a bank to a depth of from one to three or four feet ; but sometimes the birds find a hole suited to their purpose, or a cavity under the roots of a tree growing on an overhanging bank, which they occupy. The hole made by the birds has an upward slope, and ends in a chamber about six inches in diameter. Here is formed the nest, of the strangest material used by any nest-making bird. The kingfisher, like the owl and cuckoo and many other species, casts up the indigestible portions of its food—the minute bones of minnows in this case—in the form of small pellets. The pellets are thrown up in the nest-chamber, and, when broken up and pressed down by the sitting-bird, are shaped into a cuplike nest. The eggs are six to eight in number, pure white and translucent, and globular in form.

Probably the kingfisher pairs for life, as the same breeding-hole is used year after year, although the two birds are not seen together out of the breeding season.

The cry is a shrill but musical piping note, two or three times repeated, somewhat like the sandpiper's cry.

Two specimens of the belted kingfisher (*Ceryle alcyon*), an American species, have been obtained in Ireland.

Three other birds remain to be noticed in this place ; they are members of three distinct families, and are amongst the most beautiful of the rare occasional visitors seen in our country :—

The roller (*Coracius garrula*), a jay-like bird, blue and chest-nut-brown in colour. It breeds in Southern and Central Europe, and is known only as a rare straggler in the British Islands.

The bee-eater (*Merops apiaster*)—A good many examples of this elegant and richly coloured bird have been obtained in England. It is an abundant species in Southern Europe, where it breeds in colonies in sandbanks, like our sand-martin.

The hoopoe (*Upupa epops*).—This species has some claim to a place among British birds, as it is an annual visitor to our country,

Fig. 64.—Hoopoe.

although in small numbers. It is a singular and beautiful bird, and it is sad to think that, but for the persecution it has encountered year after year, it would most probably have established itself as a regular breeding species in the southern counties of England.

Cuckoo.

Cuculus canorus.

Upper parts bluish ash, darker on the wings, lighter on the neck and breast; under parts whitish with transverse dusky streaks; quills barred on the inner webs with oval white spots;

tail-feathers blackish, tipped and spotted with white; beak dusky, edged with yellow; orbits and inside of mouth orange yellow;

FIG. 65.—CUCKOO. ⅙ natural size.

iris and feet yellow. *Young*: ash-brown barred with reddish brown; tips of feathers white; a white spot on the back of the head. Length, thirteen and a half inches.

There are many cuckoos in the world, and in some countries it would be possible to see three or four, or even half a dozen, distinct species in the course of a single day. We have but one, and have made much of it. 'Perhaps no bird,' says Yarrell, 'has attracted so much attention, while of none have more idle tales been told.' And he might have added, that of no other bird so much remains to be known. Our cuckoo interests us in two distinct ways: he charms us, and he affects the mind with his strangeness. He is a visitor of the early spring, with a far-reaching, yet soft and musical, voice, full of beautiful associations, prophetic of the flowery season. To quote Sir Philip Sidney's words, applying them to a feathered instead of to a human troubadour : ' He cometh to you with a tale to hold children from their play and old men from the chimney-corner.' Seen, this melodist has the bold figure, rough, feathered legs, and barred plumage of a hawk. This fierce, predacious aspect is deceptive: he is a timid bird, with the climbing feet of the wood-pecker and wryneck. Strangest of all, the female has the habit of placing her eggs in other birds' nests, forgetting her mother-hood, a proceeding which, being contrary to nature's use, seems unnatural. It reads like a tale from the 'Thousand and One Nights,' in which we sometimes encounter human beings, good, or bad, or merely fantastic, who wander about the world disguised as birds. Only when we see and handle the cuckoo's egg placed in the hedge-sparrow's, or pipit's, or wagtail's nest, when we see the large hawk-like young cuckoo being fed and tenderly cared for by its diminutive foster-parent, do we realise the extraordinary nature of such an instinct. In spite of this 'naughtiness' of the cuckoo, to speak of it in human terms, it is to all a favourite, 'the darling of the year,' and from the days when the oldest known English lyric was written—

> Summer is icumen in,
> Loud sing cuckoo,

to the present time the poets have found inspiration in his fluting call; and musicians, too, owing to that unique quality of his voice which makes it imitable and harmonious with human music, vocal and instrumental.

The cuckoo does not usually arrive in this country before the middle of April, but he is sometimes two, and even three weeks earlier. The males arrive first, and it is they that utter the well-known double call that gives the bird its name. The cry of the female, a curious prolonged bubbling sound, is heard less frequently.

One of the strangest facts in the strange history of this bird is that its egg is not laid in the nest in which it is found, but is carried by the cuckoo in her bill and placed there. It is very small for so large a bird, although much larger, in most cases, than the eggs it is placed with, as its favourite nests in this country are all of small birds—the hedge-sparrow, reed-warbler, pied wagtail, and meadow-pipit. The eggs are very variable, being dull greenish or dull reddish grey, with spots and mottlings of a deeper shade. In some instances the cuckoo's egg resembles in colour the eggs it is placed with, and it is thought by some naturalists that the female cuckoo invariably deposits her eggs in the nests of one species. As a rule, only one egg is laid in a nest, and a few days after the eggs are hatched the young cuckoo gets rid of his foster-brothers by getting them on to his back, which is broad and hollow, and throwing them over the side of the nest. If any unhatched eggs remain in the nest, he gets rid of them in the same way.

The food of the cuckoo is exclusively insectivorous, and consists in large part of hairy caterpillars, which most birds refuse to touch. The indigestible portions of the food he swallows are cast up in small pellets.

By August the old birds take their departure ; the young migrate one to two months later.

No fewer than three exotic cuckoos have been placed on the list of British birds. Two of these are American species: the yellow-billed cuckoo (*Coccyzus americanus*) and the black-billed cuckoo (*C. erythrophthalmus*). The third is the great spotted cuckoo (*Coccystes glandarius*), an African species, which visits Spain in summer, and, like our bird, is parasitical, but has the habit of depositing its eggs in the nests of various species of the crow family.

Barn-Owl.

Strix flammea.

Beak yellowish white; upper parts light tawny yellow minutely variegated with brown, grey, and white; face and lower plumage white, the feathers of the margin tipped with brown. Length, fourteen inches.

The barn-owl is one of the very few species that have almost a world-wide range. It is resident throughout the British Islands, and inhabits the greater part of Europe; it extends to Africa, including Madagascar; to India and America, and to the Malaysian, Australian, and Polynesian regions ; and is found in islands so widely separated and far removed from the mainland as the Azores, Madeira, the Canaries, and Cape de Verde. The short-eared owl has a distribution just as wide, or even wider ; but that bird, wherever found, is of a wandering habit, making his home and breeding-place wherever food is abundant, and staying not where it fails him. His action resembles, only on a vaster scale, that of the nomads of the human race, who break up their camp and move away from the district that no longer affords pasture to their cattle. Thus, in the case of this species, the vagrant habit may be held to

account for so extensive a range. But the barn-owl's universality
cannot be accounted for in the same way, since he is, in most

countries, a stay-
at-home bird, and
spends his whole life,
from year's end to
year's end, in the
same spot. We can
only conjecture that
at some former and
very remote period
in the history of his
species he, too, had a
vagrant disposition ;
or else that he is a
very ancient bird on
the earth, and has
had unlimited time
to get so widely dis-
persed ; also, that the
barn-owl is one of
those rare types that
can exist unaltered
in a great variety of

FIG. 66.—BARN-OWL. ⅐ natural size.

conditions. One of our domestic birds, the goose, affords an instance
of the unchangeableness of some types in all regions of the globe ;
but the goose has been carried everywhere by adventurous white men,
while the barn-owl, by means unknown to us, has distributed himself over the earth.

Another general remark about this most strange and fascinating
fowl may be made in this place. The barn-owl, being so widely
distributed, and in many countries the most common species, and
being, furthermore, the only member of its order that attaches
itself by preference to human habitations, and is a dweller in towns
as well as in rural districts, is probably the chief inspirer and object of
the innumerable ancient owl superstitions which still flourish in all
countries among the ignorant. His blood-curdling voice, his whiteness, and extraordinary figure, and, when viewed by day on his
perch in some dim interior, his luminous eyes and great round face,
and wonderful intimidating gestures and motions, must powerfully

affect the primitive mind, for in that low intellectual state whatever is strange is regarded as supernatural.

Before sitting down to write this little history I went out into the woods, and was so fortunate as to hear three owls calling with unearthly shrieks to one another from some large fir-trees under which I was standing, and, listening to them, it struck me as only natural that in so many regions of the earth this bird should have been, and should still be, regarded as an evil being, a prophet of disaster and death.

The barn-owl takes up his abode by preference in a building of some kind—an old ruin, a loft in a barn or an outhouse; but above most sites he prefers an ivyclad church-tower, on which account he has been called the church-owl. He also inhabits caves and holes in cliffs, and hollow trees in woods. He spends the daylight hours, standing upright and motionless, dozing on his perch; and, where he is persecuted, he does not stir abroad until dark. When he is not molested he leaves his hiding-place before sunset, and is so little suspicious of man as to appear like a domestic bird in his presence. He preys on mice, rats, moles, insects, and even fish, which he has been observed to take in his claws from lakes and ponds. The indigestible portions of the small animals he swallows—the fur, feathers, bones, wing-cases, and scales—are disgorged in compact round pellets about the size of a cob-nut; and from an examination of a vast number of such pellets, it would appear that about nine-tenths of the food of this owl consists of mice.

This fact is now so generally known that the owl, from being one of the most persecuted of birds, is becoming a general favourite; and farmers who formerly shot it, and nailed it, with outspread wings, to their barn-doors, in order that all might see and admire their zeal in ridding the earth of so misshapen a pest, are now only anxious to have the 'feathered cats' living in their barns again.

The owl makes no nest, and lays from two to six eggs, which are white and nearly round. It has the curious habit of laying two or three eggs, and, long after incubation has begun, laying others, and then others again, so that young of different ages and eggs not yet near hatching may be found in the nest together. The young make a curious snoring noise, which is their hunger cry; and it has been said that this cry is also occasionally uttered by the old bird on the wing.

Long-eared Owl.

Asio otus.

Beak blackish; eyes orange-yellow; upper parts buff, finely mottled with brown and grey, and streaked with dark brown, especially on the ear-tufts; facial disk buff, with a greyish black margin and outer rim; under parts warm buff and grey, with blackish streaks and minute transverse bars. Length, fifteen inches.

The long-eared owl may be described as a bird of beautiful plumage. The hues of the upper parts—various shades of yellow, buff, and brown, harmoniously disposed—and something, too, in the indeterminate pattern, remind us of the colouring of some of the very handsome cats. This cat-like colouring, long tufts of ear-like feathers, and large, round, fiery, yellow eyes, give the bird a singular and uncanny appearance. As a vocalist he is less interesting than the two other most common British species—the white owl, with its sepulchral shriek, and the tawny owl, with its mellow hoot—that mysterious sound of the deep woods at eventide. The commonest note of the present species is a mewing cry, heard when the birds begin to stir from their hiding-places before going out to forage. It also emits at times a short, barking cry.

The long-eared owl appears to be more gregarious than other species, except, perhaps, the short-eared owl. Mr. Abel Chapman writes: 'A peculiarity of the habits of these owls after the breeding-season deserves a remark. As soon as the young were fledged the whole of the owls associated together, perhaps three or four broods, old and young, in a single family, and chose a thick black Scotch fir for their abode. Here they all passed the day. To this particular tree the whole of the owl-life of these woods resorted regularly at dawn, and in it slept away the hours of daylight, hidden amongst the deep evergreen recesses. At the particular tree of their choice (it varied in different years) the owls could invariably be interviewed during the summer and autumn, though to a casual eye it was difficult, amidst the deep shadows of the foliage, to distinguish their slim forms, pressed closely against the brown branches of the pine. Towards dusk their awakening was notified by the querulous cat-like cry; ten minutes later their

LONG-EARED OWL. CHAFFINCH. GREAT, BLUE, AND COAL TITS. GOLDCREST.

silent forms appeared outside the wood, and, after a few rounds of preliminary gyrations, it was dark enough to commence operations in earnest.'

Field-mice and rats are its principal food; it also preys a good deal on insects, and kills more small birds than does the white owl. It is an early breeder, laying its eggs in the deserted nest of a crow, magpie, rook, or heron, or in a squirrel's drey, or even making use of the slight platform-nest of the wood-pigeon. The eggs are four to six in number, nearly round in shape, and have smooth white shells.

Short-eared Owl.

Asio brachyotus.

Face whitish; beak black; iris yellow; tufts on the head small, composed of black feathers; eyes encircled by brownish black; upper parts dusky brown edged with yellow; under parts dull yellow streaked with brown. Length, fifteen inches.

In its habits the short-eared owl offers a strong contrast to the species last described. It is a bird of the moors and fens, laying its eggs on the ground, and never, or very seldom, perches on trees. In appearance it is less owl-like and uncanny-looking than the long-eared owl, the colouring and markings being less rich, the head smaller, and the ear-tufts so small that at a distance of twenty-five yards they are scarcely visible. It is migratory in its habits, and as it arrives on the east coast at the same time as the woodcock, it is often called the woodcock-owl.

As a winter visitant it is found in most places in the British Islands, but it breeds with us only in Scotland and a few localities in the north of England. As I have said in the history of the barn-owl, the present species ranges over a large portion of the globe, and on the continent of America it is found from Greenland to the Straits of Magellan. It is not so nocturnal in its habits as the majority of owls, and may often be seen, an hour or two before sunset, beating over the rough ground like a hen harrier in search of prey. It feeds on small rodents of all kinds, and on birds. The eggs are three to five in number, and in some instances as many as seven or eight are laid, and are placed in a slight clearing among the herbage on marshy ground, or under the heather on a moor.

There is some variety in the language of this species: it hisses and makes a sharp clicking sound when angry, and has a loud, startling cry, a note repeated three or four times, like a ghostly laugh ; and it also hoots, this performance sounding like the baying of a dog in the distance.

An interesting and curious fact in the history of this owl is that it is known to appear, often in considerable numbers, in any district where, owing to a great increase of field-mice or other small rodents, its favourite food is for the time abundant. This pheno-menon has been observed in various parts of the world, in this country on several occasions ; and during the late great plague of short-tailed voles in the south of Scotland (1891–92), large numbers of short-eared owls appeared, and remained to breed in the district. As long as the plague lasted they remained in the country, and were most prolific. When the voles disappeared the owls departed.

Tawny Owl.

Syrnium aluco.

Beak greyish yellow ; iris bluish dusky ; upper parts reddish brown, variously marked and spotted with dark brown, black, and grey ; large white spots on the scapulars and wing-coverts ; primaries and tail-feathers barred alternately with dark and reddish brown ; under parts reddish white, with transverse brown bars and longitu-dinal dusky streaks ; legs feathered to the claws. Length, sixteen inches.

The tawny owl, named also brown owl and wood-owl, is by a little the largest of the four British species. In his colouring, as well as his woodland habits, he comes nearest to the long-eared owl, but he has no ear-tufts like that bird to add to his strangeness, nor is he in appearance so ghostly and grotesque as the white owl. This species alone of the British owls is unknown in Ireland. In England, Wales, and the south of Scotland it is to be met with in all well-wooded districts, and in some localities it is said to be the most common owl. But, unhappily, in many places where it was formerly common it has been extirpated by gamekeepers. Owls are not very social birds, and the tawny owl is the most unsocial of all. He inhabits the deep wood, where he lives solitary or with his mate, and he is said to be very jealous of the intrusion of another individual of his species into his hunting-grounds. His chief distinction is his powerful, clear voice : heard in the profound silence of the woods at eventide the sound is wonderfully impressive, and affects us with a sense of mystery. This may be due to imagination, or to some primitive faculty in us, since the feeling is strong only when we are alone. If we are in a merry company, then the wood-owl's *too-whit, too-who*, may even seem to us ' a merry note,' as Shakespeare described it.

The tawny owl sometimes breeds, like the barn-owl, in ruins, outhouses, disused chimneys, and such places ; but the usual site is a hollow tree, all the more liked if it is overgrown with ivy. Sometimes he takes possession of a deserted nest of a magpie or crow to breed in. The three or four eggs laid are white, and nearly round in shape.

The tawny owl is strictly nocturnal in habits, and preys on mice, rats, moles, young rabbits, squirrels, and birds ; and he also, like most owls, occasionally takes fish.

Besides the species described, no fewer than seven others have been included in books on British birds, and if these seven were not rare accidental visitors to our island we should indeed be rich in owls. It will be sufficient to give their names :—

Snowy owl (*Nyctea scandiaca*).

European hawk-owl (*Surnia ulula*).

American hawk-owl (*Surnia funeria*).

Tengmalm's owl (*Nyctala tengmalmi*).

Scops owl (*Scops giu*).

Eagle owl (*Bubo ignavus*).

Little owl (*Athene noctua*).

It is possible that the last species may one day come to be ranked as a British bird, like the pheasant and red-legged partridge, as several attempts have been made to introduce it into this country. first by Waterton, in 1843 ; and, in recent years, by Mr. W. H. St. Quintin in Yorkshire, and Mr. Meade-Waldo in Hampshire.

Hen Harrier.

Circus cyaneus.

Upper parts of adult male bluish grey ; lower parts white ; beak black ; irides reddish brown ; legs and feet yellow ; claws black. *Female* : upper parts reddish brown ; under parts pale reddish

P

yellow, with deep orange-brown, longitudinal streaks and spots. Length : male, eighteen inches ; female, twenty inches.

This very handsome and graceful hawk was fairly common within recent times in the British Islands. But the incessant persecution of all birds of prey by game-preservers is having its effect. It is plain to see that as British species they are being extirpated ; and the first to vanish are the harriers, owing to their fatal habit of breeding in the open country on the ground. For while most birds have a close time allowed them, the hawks are sought out and destroyed, old and young, during the breeding season. Thus the marsh-harrier, which should have come first in this place, is now extinct in this country, and cannot be introduced into a work on British birds which does not include the great auk, the bustard, the spoonbill, and many other species which have been exterminated in England. The hen harrier is at the present time very nearly in the same case ; it is only included here because a few pairs probably still breed on the wildest and most extensive moors in Wales, the north of England, and the Highlands of Scotland.

The nest is a slight hollow in the ground, scantily lined with a little dry grass ; and the eggs are four or five, and rarely six, in number. These are pale bluish white in colour, and in some cases have pale brown markings.

The male hen harrier, seen on the wing when quartering the ground in quest of prey, keeping but a few feet above the surface, is certainly one of our handsomest hawks. Its flight, although not wavering, is as buoyant as that of the common tern, and the pale colouring—soft blue-grey above and white beneath—seems in harmony with its slender figure and airy, graceful motions. On account of its blue colour it has been called the dove-hawk. It preys on small birds, mammals, and reptiles, dropping suddenly upon them in the manner of the kestrel, but from a less height. The origin of its name of hen harrier is not known. Yarrell conjectured that it was on account of its predilection for the produce of the farmyard ; which seems unlikely, as the harriers are usually hunters of very small deer. A more probable explanation is that the male bird was formerly supposed to be the female of the ringtail-harrier ; but we know now that the hen harrier is the cock bird, and the ringtail the hen.

Montagu's Harrier.

Circus cineraceus.

Fig. 67.—Montagu's Harrier. ⅑ natural size.

Upper parts bluish grey; primaries black; secondaries with three transverse dark bars; lateral tail-feathers white barred with reddish orange: under parts white variously streaked with reddish orange. *Female:* upper parts brown of various tints; under parts pale reddish yellow, with longitudinal bright red streaks. Beak black; legs and feet yellow. Length, eighteen inches.

This hawk was named by Yarrell after the well-known ornithologist, Colonel Montagu, who was the first to distinguish between this species and the hen harrier, which it so closely resembles. Seen on the wing at a distance of two to three hundred yards, the sharpest-sighted ornithologist would probably be unable to say whether the bird was a hen harrier or a Montagu's harrier. The present species is slimmer bodied; but, owing to the greater comparative length of its wings, it appears, when flying, as large as the hen harrier. It is a spring and summer visitor to this country, and in its flight, and preying and breeding habits, closely resembles the species last described. Small birds, mammals, reptiles, and insects form its prey. It breeds, or formerly bred, in suitable localities in most English counties from the south coast northwards to Norfolk, making its slight nest on the ground, among the furze-bushes or heather. The eggs resemble those of the hen harrier in colouring, but are smaller in size.

Buzzard.

Buteo vulgaris.

FIG. 68.—BUZZARD. $\frac{1}{10}$ natural size.

Upper parts, neck, and head dark brown mottled with brown of a darker shade; tail marked with twelve transverse bands; beak lead-coloured; cere, irides, and feet yellow. Length: male, twenty inches; female, twenty-two inches.

It is impossible for anyone who loves wild bird life to write about the buzzard without a feeling of profound melancholy. For this hawk, too, like the harriers, although once common, and still called in books the common buzzard, is a vanishing species. Howard Saunders writes : ' Fifty years ago it used to breed in Norfolk and in other counties abounding in partridges and ground game, without being considered incompatible with their existence ; but with the increase of pheasant-worship the doom of the buzzard was sealed, for, the larger the " hawk," the worse it must necessarily be ! '

My one consolation in this sad portion of my work, which tells of the noble and useful species whose ' doom is sealed,' is, that I am not writing for grown men, but for the young, who are not yet the slaves of a contemptible convention, nor have come under a system which has been only too mildly described as ' stupid ' by every British ornithologist during the last five or six decades.

This once common bird is now almost unknown in England, and must be sought for in the wildest forest districts of Wales and Scotland. It is of a somewhat sedentary disposition, and in seeking its food displays little of the dashing and courageous spirit of the falcons. Small mammals, especially moles, reptiles, birds of various kinds, and insects, are its prey, which in all cases it drops upon and seizes on the ground. It is strongly attached to one favourite spot, and will return day after day to the same perch, where it will sit for hours at a stretch. All the buzzards show best when flying, and the appearance of the present species was thus described by Sir William Jardine : ' The flight is slow and majestic ; the birds rise in easy and graceful gyrations, often to an immense height, uttering occasionally their shrill and melancholy whistle. At this time, to a spectator underneath, and in particular lights, they appear of immense size ; the motions of the tail when directing the circles may be plainly perceived, as well as the beautiful markings on it and the wings, sometimes rendered very plain and distinct by the body being thrown upwards, and the light falling on the clear and silvery tints of the base of the feathers. The buzzard is a fine accompaniment to the landscape, whether sylvan or wild and rocky.'

It nests both on crags and in forest trees, and sometimes makes use of the old nest of some other bird. The nest is of sticks, and is sometimes very large, lined with wool or some other soft material, and often with green leaves. Two to four eggs are laid, but three is the usual number. They vary from white, suffused with reddish brown, to bluish green, spotted, streaked, and clouded with reddish brown, with purple-grey under-markings.

Golden Eagle.

Aquila chrysaëtus.

Head, back of the neck, and legs lustrous reddish brown; the rest of the body dark brown; primaries nearly black; secondaries brownish black; tail dark grey, barred and tipped with brownish black; beak bluish at the base, black at the extremity; iris brown; cere and feet yellow; claws bluish black. Length of male, three feet.

This noblest of the British birds of prey used at one time to breed in some localities in England and Wales, but it has gradually retreated farther and farther north, and is now restricted (as a breeder) to the Highlands and the western islands of Scotland. Fortunately, it now receives protection from the owners of large deer-forests in its northern habitat, and there is reason to hope that it will long continue to exist as a British species.

This species is very dark in hue, and is known in Scotland as the ' black eagle.' The colour is a very deep brown, the feathers of the head and nape tinged with reddish gold—hence its name of golden eagle. It preys on hares, rabbits, grouse, ptarmigan, and other birds, and occasionally destroys lambs and fawns, and will even attack full-grown ewes and deer.

The nest is a bulky structure of sticks, placed, as a rule, on a crag, sometimes in a tree, and the same nest is used year after year. Two or three eggs are laid, white or pale bluish green in ground-colour, blotched, spotted, and clouded with reddish brown and purple-grey under-markings.

Owing to his great size, dark colour, and power of wing, this eagle makes a very noble figure when flying. But he is noble in appearance at other times as well, and in this he differs from many of the larger species that are equally strong on the wing, or even much stronger—condors, vultures, albatrosses, and others. These, when they fold their pinions, lose all their majesty. But the golden eagle has just as grand a presence when perched as when soaring. The pleasure produced in us by the sight of this creature appears to differ in character from that which we find in contemplating such species as excel in elegance and grace, or in rich colouring—the mute swan glassed in the water it floats upon, and the peacock with splendid starry train. He is built on different lines, that indicate power and rapine ; but his appearance in repose is not less attractive than theirs, and, in a sense, not less beautiful. Tennyson, in a few well-known lines, has described it better, perhaps, than any other writer—the majestic bird and the nature it inhabits, and is in harmony with—its sublimity and desolation :—

> He grasps the crag with hooked hands ;
> Close to the sun in lonely lands,
> Ringed by the azure world he stands.
>
> The wrinkled sea beneath him crawls :
> He watches from his mountain walls,
> And like a thunderbolt he falls.

White-tailed Eagle.

Haliaëtus albicilla.

Upper parts brown, head and neck lightest; under parts chocolate-brown ; tail white ; bill, cere, and feet yellowish white ; claws black. In the young the tail is brown. Length of the male, two feet four inches ; of the female, two feet ten inches.

Immature specimens of the white-tailed, or sea-eagle, or erne, are from time to time obtained in England during the autumn and winter months. They are, probably, in nearly all cases migrants from northern Europe on their way south. The British race—the sea-eagles that bred formerly in many localities on the coasts of Scotland and Ireland, and in the northern islands—is now all but extinct. The bird no longer breeds anywhere on the mainland, and but one or two pairs are known to inhabit the islands.

The sea-eagle has a more varied dietary than the species last described, and he hunts for food both on sea and land. In his habits he is by turns osprey, falcon, and raven. Like the osprey, he drops from a considerable height on to a fish seen near the surface, and, striking his talons into it, bears it away to land. But he preys more on puffins, guillemots, and other sea-fowl, than on fish. Like the golden eagle, he destroys mountain hares, grouse, and ptarmigan, and is regarded by the shepherd as the worst enemy to the flock. But the shepherd has his revenge, for the erne is a great lover of carrion, and may be easily poisoned.

The breeding habits of this species are similar to those of the golden eagle. The eggs, two in number, are white, without markings.

Its yelping cry is very powerful, and shriller than the scream of the golden eagle.

Sparrow-Hawk.

Accipiter nisus.

Upper parts dark bluish grey, with a white spot on the nape; under parts reddish white, transversely barred with deep brown; tail grey, barred with brownish black; beak blue, lightest at the base; cere, irides, and feet yellow. *Female*: upper parts brown, passing into blackish grey; under parts greyish white, barred with dark grey. Length of male, twelve inches; of female, fifteen inches.

The sparrow-hawk is found in wooded districts in all parts of Great Britain and Ireland, and is, perhaps, the most generally diffused species of the diurnal birds of prey in this country, and, compared with most other species, may be said to be almost common. In reality it is becoming rare; which is not strange considering that, next to the carrion crow, it is the most persecuted of all the feathered creatures whose existence is an offence to the gamekeeper. In Yarrell's ' British Birds ' it is said that the female sparrow-hawk is, indeed, the only bird of prey which the game-preserver nowadays need fear; and there is no doubt that it is immeasurably more destructive to the chicks of pheasant and partridge than any other raptor. It preys by preference on birds, as the kestrel does on mice, and in pursuit is capable of rapid flight and quick doublings; but its chases are short and near the surface of the earth. In habits it is a prowler, a stealthy flier among woods, by coppices and hedges, and takes its victims by surprise. It also dashes suddenly on them from its perch, where it has stood concealed by the foliage, keeping a sharp watch on the feathered creatures in its vicinity.

The sparrow-hawk is said to make a nest for itself, but it is more probable that in nearly all cases it takes possession of an old nest of some other bird. The eggs are four or five in number, and sometimes six, pale bluish white in ground-colour, blotched and spotted with various shades of reddish brown.

Kite.

Milvus ictinus.

FIG. 69.—KITE. $\frac{1}{12}$ natural size.

Upper parts reddish brown; the feathers with pale edges, those of the head and neck long, and tapering to a point, greyish white, streaked lengthways with brown; under parts rust-colour with longitudinal brown streaks; tail reddish orange, barred indistinctly with brown; beak horn-colour; cere, irides, and feet yellow; claws black. *Female*: upper parts a deeper brown, the feathers pale at the extremity; head and neck white. Length, twenty-five inches.

The kite, or glead, is another melancholy example of the effect of the pitiless persecution of some of our finest birds by game-preservers, and, as the species became rare, by collectors of ' British-killed ' specimens and ' British-taken ' eggs. Once a common species in the British Islands, it is now reduced to a miserable remnant, composed of a few breeding pairs in Wales and Scotland.

Among the various types of diurnal birds of prey, the kite is one of the finest; the great extent of his sharp-pointed wings and his long, forked tail, fit him for an aërial life. In appearance he is a swallow-shaped eagle; and few birds equal him in grace and majesty of motion when he soars at a vast height. Like the eagles, buzzards, and other strong-fliers among the raptors, he soars for exercise and recreation; but, vulture-like, when soaring he is ever on the watch for a meal. And, like the vulture, he will feed on garbage; for though of so noble an appearance, and possessed of such great power, he has, compared with the falcons, a poor spirit, and his name is a term of reproach that signifies cowardice and rapacity. A carrion-eater, he also preys on small mammals, reptiles, and birds, in most cases the young, the sickly, or wounded.

The nest of the kite is placed in a tree, and is a bulky structure of sticks, mixed with much rubbish—bones, turf, scraps of paper, and old rags—and is lined with wool and moss. Two to four eggs are laid, three being the usual number. In size, colour, and markings they closely resemble those of the buzzard.

Peregrine Falcon.

Falco peregrinus.

Upper parts dark bluish grey, with darker bands; head bluish black, as are also the moustaches descending from the gape; under parts white; breast transversely barred with brown; beak blue, darker at the point; cere yellow; iris dark brown; feet yellow; claws black. *Female*: upper plumage tinged with brown, the under parts with reddish yellow. Length, fifteen inches; female, seventeen inches.

This famed bird is of a handsome appearance, not swallow-like as is the kite, nor so massive as the eagle; but nature in fashioning it has observed the golden mean, and the result is a being so well-balanced in all its parts and so admirably adapted for speed, strength, and endurance, that to many minds it has seemed the most perfect among winged creatures. When standing perched on a crag, erect and motionless, as its custom is, its smooth and compact figure looks as if carved out of a stone or marble of a beautiful soft grey tint. The wings are sharp-pointed, and the flight is exceedingly rapid. In South America, where I first observed its habits, it used always to seem to me that the peregrine, alone among hawks, possessed a courage commensurate with its strength ; and, in hunting, an infallible judgment. However swift of wing its quarry might be, it was almost invariably overtaken and

Fig. 70.—Peregrine. $\frac{1}{10}$ natural size.

struck to the earth ; and the bird thus vanquished was in many cases the equal, and sometimes even the superior, in weight to the falcon. All other hawks make frequent mistakes, and often fail in their efforts : they chase birds they cannot overtake, and attack others that are too strong for them ; and occasionally their courage fails, and they pass by the healthy and strong to attack the wounded or weak that are incapable of making an effort.

In the British Islands the peregrine is an inhabitant of the iron-bound coasts, where it is still able to find comparatively safe breeding-sites. It makes no nest, the eggs being deposited in a slight hollow scratched in the soil on a ledge of a cliff. When it breeds in a tree it makes use of the deserted nest of some other bird. Two to four eggs are laid, yellowish white in ground-colour, mottled and spotted with reddish brown and orange-brown.

The peregrine preys almost exclusively on birds—ducks, waders, pigeons, grouse, partridges—and it has been seen to kill kestrels, jays, and magpies.

It has a sharp, powerful cry, uttered two or three times in rapid succession on the wing.

Hobby.

Falco subbuteo.

Upper parts bluish black; under parts reddish yellow with longitudinal brown streaks; moustaches broad, black; lower tail-coverts and legs reddish; beak bluish, dark at the tip; cere greenish yellow; iris dark brown; feet yellow; claws black. *Female*: colours less bright, and the streaks below broader. Length, twelve to fourteen inches.

The hobby in appearance is a lesser peregrine, being about one-fifth smaller than that bird. It differs from the peregrine in having a softer plumage and a comparatively greater length of wing. It is probably the fastest flier among rapacious birds, being capable of the marvellous feat of capturing swallows and martins in the air. It is a summer visitant to this country, and is most often met with in the southern counties of England, where, however, it is a rare species; and the farther north we go the rarer it becomes. In Scotland it is not known to breed, and it does not range to Ireland. It inhabits woods, and breeds in an old nest of the carrion crow, jay, or some other bird, which it does not re-line. Three eggs are usually laid, and in some rare instances four or five. In size and colour they are not distinguishable from those of the kestrel.

The hobby is a spirited bird, but in courage and power greatly inferior to the peregrine. He preys principally on dragon-flies, beetles, and other large insects, and on small birds, such as skylarks and buntings. In falconry, the hobby was trained to fly at such small game as larks, snipe, and quail.

Merlin.

Falco æsalon.

Upper parts greyish blue; under parts reddish yellow with longitudinal dark brown spots; tail barred with black; beak bluish, darker at the tip; cere yellow; iris dark brown; feet yellow; claws black. *Female*: upper parts tinged with brown; lower parts yellowish white. Length, eleven to twelve inches.

FIG. 71.—MERLIN. ⅛ natural size.

The merlin is a third less than the peregrine in size, and has the distinction of being the smallest of the British birds of prey, But in courage it is second to none, and Yarrell relates an instance in which this small bird, weighing itself no more than six ounces, struck down and killed a partridge twice as heavy. It is a resident throughout the year of the British Islands, from the north of Yorkshire to the Shetlands, and the mountainous parts of Ireland.

The merlin is an inhabitant of the moors and mountains, and nests on the ground among the tall heather. The eggs are laid in a slight hollow with little or no lining, and are four or five in number, smaller than those of the kestrel, but similar in colour. It sometimes, but very rarely, breeds in the nest of a carrion crow or other bird, in a tree.

It preys chiefly on small birds, and it was formerly trained to pursue snipe, pigeons, larks, blackbirds, &c.

Kestrel, or Windhover.

Tinnunculus alaudarius.

Fig. 72.—Kestrel. ⅑ natural size.

Upper plumage, neck, and breast dark lead-grey; sides, under tail-coverts, and thighs light yellowish red, with longitudinal, narrow, dark streaks; beak blue; cere and feet yellow; irides brown; claws black. *Female*: upper plumage and tail light red, with transverse spots and bars of dark brown; lower parts paler than in the male. Length, fifteen inches.

The kestrel is the best known of the British hawks, not only because it is the most common species, but also because its peculiar preying habits bring it more into notice. It is resident and found throughout the United Kingdom, but undoubtedly possesses a partial migration, as it wholly disappears from some northern districts in the winter, and at the same season becomes more abundant in the southern counties.

When in quest of prey the kestrel has the habit of stopping suddenly in its rapid flight, and remaining for some time motionless in mid-air, suspended on its rapidly-beating wings, usually at a height of twenty or thirty yards above the surface. This habit, which has won for the species the appropriate name of windhover, is unique among British hawks. It is this peculiar aërial feat which makes the kestrel, when seen on the wing, so familiar a figure to country-people. The instant that the bird pauses in his swift-rushing flight you know that it is a kestrel, although it may be at such a distance as to appear a mere spot, a small moving shadow, against the sky. It has shorter wings than other falcons, and, by consequence, a more rapid and violent flight.

The kestrel preys chiefly on mice and field-voles; occasionally it takes a small bird, and carries off young, tender chicks, if they come in its way; but it certainly does not deserve its scientific name of *alaudarius* (a feeder on larks), which would have fitted the hobby better. It also preys on frogs and coleopterous insects. Selby relates that a kestrel was observed late one evening pursuing the cockchafers, dashing at them and seizing one in each claw, eating them in the air, and then returning to the charge. When on the wing the kestrel's downward-gazing eyes are constantly on the look-out for the mice that lurk on the surface, and as mice are usually well concealed by the grass and herbage, the eyes must indeed be wonderfully sharp to detect them. After remaining suspended for some seconds, sometimes for half a minute, or longer, during which the bird watches the ground below, he dashes down upon his prey, or flies on without descending, as if satisfied that what had been taken for a mouse had turned out to be something different.

When thus hovering motionless the wings are seen to beat rapidly for a few seconds, then to become fixed and rigid for a moment or two, after which the beating motion is renewed. A short time ago I watched a kestrel thus hovering in the face of a very violent wind, and it struck me that this suspension of the wings' motion in such circumstances was very extraordinary and hard to explain. One can understand that, even in the face of a violent gale, the bird is able to maintain its motionless position by sheer muscular power; but how happened it that in the short intervals, when the outspread wings became fixed and motionless, the bird was not instantly blown from its position?

In its breeding habits the kestrel, like the starling and jackdaw, has a partiality for towers and lofty ruins, and it also nests in holes in rocks and hollow trees. In woods it frequently takes possession of a disused nest of a crow or magpie. The eggs are four or five, blotched with dull red on a reddish white ground; and in many eggs the ground-colour is quite covered with red.

The kestrel, among British birds of prey, is a favourite with the ornithologist in virtue of its interesting habits; and it deserves to be equally esteemed by the farmer on account of its usefulness. It is, indeed, the only bird of diurnal habits that wages incessant warfare against the prolific and injurious mice, and thus carries on by day the task of keeping down a pest which those ' feathered cats,' the owls, so efficiently pursue at night.

The kestrel is easier to tame, and, when tame, more docile and affectionate, than most hawks, and many accounts have appeared in print of the bird and its ways in the domestic condition; but, to my mind, not one so interesting as the history of a pet kestrel kept a few years since by some friends of mine. The bird was young when it came into their hands, and was lovingly cared for, and made free of a large house and park, and of the whole wide country beyond. And it made good use of its liberty. As a rule, every morning it would fly away and disappear from sight until the evening, when, some time before sunset, it would return, dash in at the open door, and perch on some elevated situation—a cornice, or bust, or on the top of a large picture-frame. Invariably at dinner-time it flew to the dining-room, and would then settle on the shoulder of its master or mistress, to be fed with small scraps of meat. This pleasant state of things lasted for about three years, during which time the bird always roosted in, or somewhere near, the house, flew abroad by day, to return faithfully every evening to his loving human friends to be caressed, and fed, and made much of; and it might have continued several years longer, down to the present time, if the bird's temper had not suffered a mysterious change. All at once, for no reason that anyone could guess, he became subject to the most extraordinary outbreaks of ill-temper, and in such a state he would, on his return from his daily wanderings abroad, violently attack some person in the room. Up till this time he had preferred his master and mistress to any other member of the household, and had shown an equal attachment to both; now he would single out one or other of these his best friends for his most violent attacks; and, very curiously, on the day when he attacked his master he would display the usual affection towards his mistress, but on the next day would reverse the process. And his hostility was not to be despised : rising up into the air to a good height, he would dash down with great force on to the obnoxious person's head, often inflicting a lacerating blow with his claws. More than once, the lady told me, after one of these cutting, ungrateful blows on her forehead her face was bathed in blood.

It is pleasant to be able to relate that no feeling of resentment or alarm was excited by this behaviour on the part of the bird ; that he was never deprived of his sweet liberty or treated with less gentleness than before. It was hoped and believed that he would outgrow the savage fit, and if he had confined his virulent attacks to his master and mistress it would have been well with him. Unfortunately for him, he attacked others who were made of poorer clay. One evening at dinner the butler, while occupied with his duties, was struck savagely on the wrist by the kestrel. Like a well-trained servant, he did not wince or cry out, but marched stolidly round the table, pouring out wine, anxious only to conceal the blood that trickled from his wounds. But on the following day the bird was missing, and was never afterwards seen or heard of.

Osprey.

Pandion haliaëtus.

Feathers of the head and neck white with dark centres; on each side of the neck a streak of blackish brown, extending downwards; upper plumage generally deep brown; under parts white, tinged here and there with yellow, and on the breast marked with arrow-shaped spots; tail-feathers barred with dusky; cere and beak dark grey; iris yellow. Length, two feet.

The osprey, like the sea-eagle, hen harrier, and kite, is one of the species that linger with us on the verge of extinction; and it may linger for many years, as in the case of the avocet, the black-tailed godwit, and the ruff, after these species had been reduced to a few breeding pairs; and, on the other hand, it may be gone to-morrow. That it will remain permanently as a member of the British avifauna is scarcely to be hoped.

The osprey, like the peregrine falcon and the short-eared owl, has an immense range, and inhabits Europe, Africa, the greater part of Asia, Japan, Formosa, the Australian region, New Guinea, and America. With us it appears in autumn as a migrant in small numbers; but the birds of the British race are now reduced to one or two pairs that breed annually in the Highlands of Scotland, and are strictly protected in their summer haunts.

The osprey feeds exclusively on fish, which it drops upon like a tern or gannet; but, falcon-like, it strikes with its feet, and, with its slippery prey gripped firmly in its sharp, crooked talons, it flies back to land.

The nest is usually placed in a tree, and is very large, formed of sticks, and lined with moss. Two or three eggs are laid, white or buff in ground-colour, blotched with rich chestnut-red, and purple-grey underlying marks.

Besides the twelve species of the order Accipitres described, all of which breed in the British Islands, there are fourteen others, which, although described as British in the standard ornithological works, are only occasional or accidental visitors or stragglers to our shores. There are two vultures to be mentioned : the griffon vulture (*Gyps fulvus*), an inhabitant of Southern Europe, Africa, and Asia, once obtained in Ireland ; and the Egyptian vulture (*Neophron percnopterus*), an inhabitant of Southern Europe and Africa, twice obtained. The next species is the marsh-harrier (*Circus æruginosus*), once abundant throughout Great Britain and Ireland, now, unhappily, extinct as a British species. This harrier, which was also called the moor-buzzard, is a graceful, handsome bird : the head creamy white ; upper parts brown ; beneath, buff, streaked with brown and chestnut ; part of the wing and the tail silvery grey. In its buoyant flight and preying and nesting habits it resembles the hen harrier, but frequents fens and marshes instead of moors and uplands.

The rough-legged buzzard (*Archibuteo lagopus*) is an irregular visitor, chiefly in autumn and winter, from the northern parts of Europe. It differs from the common buzzard in having its legs feathered to the toes—hence the specific name, *lagopus*—rough-footed like a hare. This species is of more frequent occurrence in the British Islands than any other occasional visitor among the diurnal raptors, and in some years it appears in considerable numbers.

The spotted eagle (*Aquila clanga*), known to us as a rare occasional visitor, breeds in the forests of central and south-eastern Europe. More interesting to us is the goshawk (*Astur palumbarius*), since this fine bird of prey, although now a very rare straggler to Great Britain, is believed to have been formerly an indigenous species, and to have bred in Scotland down to the beginning of the present century. In form, colouring, and manner of preying it resembles the sparrow-hawk, but is nearly double the size of that bird, and flies at very much larger game.

The American goshawk has been included in the list of British birds on ' somewhat slight evidence,' as the author of the ' Manual of British Birds ' says. The black kite (*Milvus nigrans*) is an African species, a summer visitant to Europe south of the Baltic, and has once been obtained in Great Britain. The swallow-tailed

kite (*Elanoïdes furcatus*), an American species, which I once had
the pleasure of seeing (not in a glass case, but sitting on a tree, and
soaring in the air), has also been found as a straggler in this
country. The honey-buzzard (*Pernis apivorus*) is a third species
of hawk in this list which has disappeared from this country. Like
the hobby and the osprey, it is (or was) a summer visitant, and has
been known to breed in most English and Scottish counties from

FIG. 73.—HONEY-BUZZARD. $\frac{1}{12}$ natural size.

Hampshire to Aberdeenshire. Up to within four or five years ago
a few pairs continued to return to us each summer, but these, too,
have now vanished. This fine large hawk, in size the equal of the
common buzzard, lived almost entirely on insect food, wasps and
wild bees especially—hence its name of honey-buzzard.

The remaining species to be noticed are all true falcons: the
gyrfalcon (*Hierofalco gyrfalco*), an inhabitant of arctic Scandinavia,
only once obtained in this country; the Greenland falcon (*Hierofalco candicans*), a wanderer to this country from north-west
America and Greenland; the Iceland falcon (*Hierofalco islandicus*),
a wanderer from Iceland; the red-footed falcon (*Tinnunculus
vespertinus*), an occasional visitor from the warm countries of
Europe; and the lesser kestrel (*Tinnunculus cenchris*), a visitor
from southern Europe, where it breeds.

Cormorant.

Phalacrocorax carbo.

Fig. 74.—Cormorant. $\frac{1}{11}$ natural size.

Upper head and neck black, striated with hair-like white feathers, those on the occiput being elongated, and forming a crest in spring; throat white; gular pouch yellow; mantle black and bronze-brown; all the other parts black, except a white patch on the thigh, assumed early in spring and lost in summer; iris emerald-green. *Female*: larger than the male, brighter in colour, and with longer crest.   Length, three feet.

To those who know it slightly the cormorant is a big, sombre, ugly bird, heavy and awkward in his motions out of the water, and, when breeding, disgusting in his habits.   He improves on a closer acquaintance.   He may be easily tamed, and makes an intelligent, and sometimes very amusing, pet, and is capable of being trained

to catch fish for his keeper. He is most frequently met with on the
sea and seashore, but is an inhabitant of inland waters as well,
and sometimes breeds beside them, making his nest on the ground
or in a tree. He feeds exclusively on fishes and eels, which he
captures by diving and pursuing them under water, sometimes for
considerable distances. The bird is proverbial for its voracity. Its
'swallow' is probably the largest of any bird of its size—a fish
fourteen inches long has been taken from its gullet. When swimming he presents a curious appearance : his body, as if too heavy for
the element it floats in, sinks like a waterlogged boat, until the
flat back is on a level with the surface. When alarmed, he sinks
his body deeper and deeper at will, until the head and long neck
alone appear, looking like the head and neck of a serpent swimming
with body submerged. When resting on a rock after feeding cormorants stand very erect and motionless, their long, hooked beaks much
raised, and at such times they present a heavy, ungainly appearance.
They are fond of opening their wings out to their greatest extent to
dry their feathers, and remain for a long time in this attitude, looking like birds with spread wings carved out of black stone. The
cormorant watches the water at times from a rock, and dives after
its prey ; but it more often swims, when fishing, with head and neck
submerged. When taking wing it rises heavily and with great
labour, but when once fairly launched the flight is powerful. Cormorants are gregarious and social birds at all seasons, and, like
gulls and herons, they breed in communities. Very early in spring,
or shortly after the winter solstice, the bird's nuptial ornaments—a
crest on the head and a white patch on the thigh—begin to appear ;
both crest and white mark disappear at the end of the breeding
season. The same nesting-place is resorted to year after year, as
in the case of most species that breed in communities. The summit
of a crag not easily accessible, or a ledge of rock on a cliff fronting
the sea, or a rocky island, are favourite sites. Here the birds, sometimes in hundreds, live together in the greatest harmony, building
their nests close together, in some cases almost touching. The nest
is pyramidal in form, built up from the rock to a height of from six
or seven inches to a couple of feet, and is composed of sticks, coarse
grass, and seaweed. Three to five eggs are laid, very small for the
bird's size, narrow and long in shape, of a pale greenish blue colour,
overlaid with a thick coat of a chalky substance. This substance
is quite soft when the egg is first laid ; it is then white, but soon
hardens, and becomes stained, in the always wet and filthy nest, to

a dirty yellowish colour. The young birds are hatched blind, and have a naked, bluish black skin, but they soon grow a thick, sooty black down. They are at all stages strange and repulsive-looking creatures, and when handled or approached by a person they become sick with fear or anger, and roll and sprawl about on their nests, screaming harshly, and vomiting their half-digested food.

The young are fed with fish that has already been partially digested in the maw of the parent. It is not disgorged; the young bird thrusts his head and neck deep down into his parent's gullet, and feeds as a horse does from his nose-bag.

The young are said not to assume the adult or breeding plumage until the third year.

Shag, or Green Cormorant.

Phalacrocorax graculus.

Bill black; base of the under mandible yellow, the black skin about the gape thickly studded with small yellow spots; iris emerald-green; crown, neck, upper and under parts dark green with purple and bronze reflections; wing and tail-feathers, legs and feet, black; a crest, curling forwards, grows on the forehead in early spring, and is lost by the end of May. Length, twenty-seven inches.

The shag may be easily mistaken for the cormorant, which it closely resembles, but when near at hand is seen to differ in its smaller size and its prevailing green colour, which appears black at a distance; and, in the breeding season, by the absence of the white patch on the flank. In its habits it is more strictly marine than the cormorant, but resembles that bird in its manner of swimming and flight. It prefers bays and inlets to the open sea, and deep water near rocks to the shallow sea, where there is a low beach. In diving after fish it springs upwards almost out of the water, and goes down head first. Beneath the water it propels itself wholly by its feet; the auks, and some other diving birds, use their wings as fins to assist progression. After capturing a fish the shag brings it to the surface to swallow it, then swims on for a space, and dives again, and so on, and finally returns to the rock, where it proceeds to disgorge its prey, to devour it at leisure. The shag breeds on sea-cliffs, sometimes building on the ledges or in crevices, but caves,

GANNETS. GUILLEMOTS. HERRING-GULLS.

where they exist, are preferred. The eggs are three in number, in shape and colour like those of the cormorant, and the nests, which are placed close together, are also like those of that bird.

The shag is found in certain localities all round the coasts of Great Britain and Ireland, but is less numerous and more local than the cormorant.

Gannet.

Sula bassana.

Adult: head and neck buff-colour; all the rest of the plumage white, except the primaries, which are black. Young of the first year: upper parts blackish brown flecked with white; under parts mottled with dusky ash and buff. The dark markings diminish until the sixth year, when the adult colouring is assumed. Length, thirty-four inches.

One of the most notable seafowls inhabiting the British coasts is the gannet, or solan goose, a species which forms a connecting-link between the cormorants and the pelicans. The origin of its two common names is not precisely known, although it seems probable that gannet is derived from *gans*, the ancient British name for goose. The young birds from the Bass Rock, which are largely used as food in the neighbouring counties, are called, I do not know why, 'Parliamentary geese.' The world will have it that the bird is a goose, although as little like a goose, except in size, as a guillemot is like a sheldrake. The scientific name, *bassana* (of the Bass Rock), had its origin in the belief that the rock at the entrance to the Firth of Forth was the gannet's only breeding-place. There are several other colonies: one, now greatly diminished, on Lundy Island; another, also small, on the coast of Pembrokeshire; on the West Coast of Scotland there are four stations, and others exist on the Irish coast. None of these, however, can compare in importance with the Bass Rock, where it has been calculated that as many as ten thousand pairs congregate each year to breed.

The gannet is an exclusively marine bird, and an inhabitant throughout the year of the seas round the British Islands. Its flight is easy and powerful, and its appearance on the wing more pelican-than cormorant-like. It feeds entirely on fish, and follows the shoals of such species as swim near the surface—mackerel, herrings, pilchards, and sprats. When fishing it sails at a considerable height, and on catching sight of its prey rises to a greater height, and then, with wings nearly closed, drops straight down, with great force, into the water. Its appearance when falling has been likened by one observer to 'a brilliant piece of white marble.'

The gannets begin to assemble at the breeding-rock in March. Their nesting habits are similar to those of the cormorant, but only one egg is laid, which is, like the cormorant's egg, pale blue in colour and thickly coated with a white, chalky material. Mr. Charles Dixon, in ' Our Rarer Birds,' thus describes a visit to the great gannet settlement on the east coast : ' By far the best locality for studying the nesting economy of the gannet is the Bass, that wide-famed mass of basaltic rocks standing like a sentinel in the Firth of Forth. . . . Upon reaching the Bass a few gannets may be seen sailing dreamily about, but you have no idea of the immense numbers until you have climbed the rugged hill. . . . But when the summit of the cliff is reached the scene that bursts upon our gaze is one that well-nigh baffles all description. Thousands upon thousands of gannets fill the air, just like heavy snowflakes, and on every side their loud, harsh cries of " carra-carra-carra " echo and re-echo among the rocks. The gannets take very little notice of our approach, many birds allowing themselves to be actually pushed from their nests. Others utter harsh notes, and with flapping wings offer some show of resistance, only taking wing when absolutely compelled to do so, and disgorging one or two half-digested fish as they fall lightly over the cliffs into the air. On all sides facing the sea gannets may be seen. Some are standing on the short grass on the edge of the cliffs, fast asleep, with their heads buried under their dorsal plumage ; others are preening their feathers ; whilst many are quarrelling and fighting over standing-room on the rocks.'

Describing another great breeding-place of the gannet on the island of Borreay, about four miles from St. Kilda, he says : ' The flat, sloping top of one of these stupendous ocean rocks, called by the natives " Stack-a-lie," looks white as the driven snow, so thickly do the gannets cluster there, and the sides are just as densely populated wherever the cliff is rugged and broken. So vast is this colony of birds that it may be seen distinctly forty miles away, looking like some huge vessel under full sail heading to windward.'

Heron

Ardea cinerea.

Crest bluish black; upper parts slate-grey; forehead, cheeks, and neck white, the latter streaked with bluish grey and terminating in long white feathers; under parts greyish white; bill yellow. Length, thirty-six inches.

The heron is sometimes spoken of as our largest wild bird. It is not meant that he is really larger than the golden eagle, or wild swan, or grey lag goose, but only that he is the biggest of the comparatively common birds. The heron has two very different aspects —when in repose, or standing, and when on the wing. On the ground, or, as we more often see him, standing knee-deep in the water, watching the surface, he presents a sorry appearance—a bird lean and ungraceful in figure, white and ghostly grey in colour, awkward in his motions when he moves. No sooner does he open his wings than this mean aspect vanishes, and he is transfigured. At first the flight appears heavy on account of the slow, measured beats of the broad, rounded vans; but as he rises higher, and soars away to a distance, it strikes the beholder as wonderfully free and powerful. The appearance of the bird is then majestic, and its flight more beautiful than that of any other large wading bird with which I am acquainted—ibis, wood-ibis, stork, flamingo, or spoonbill. When pursued by a falcon the heron is capable of rising vertically to a vast height, while the hawk rushes after in a zigzag course, striving to rise above his quarry so as to strike. This aërial contest of hawk and heron forms a very fascinating spectacle, and formerly, when falcons were trained for this sport, the heron was as much esteemed as the pheasant—which has been called the ' sacred bird '—is at the present day. With the decline of falconry the heron ceased to be protected by law, and diminished greatly in numbers; but he is an historical bird, and there is a feeling, or sentiment, that has served to prevent his extermination. It is still considered a fine thing to have a heronry on a large estate; and so long as this feeling endures the bird will receive sufficient protection, although the existing heronries, when we come to count them, are not many.

The heron breeds in communities, and when the heronry is

well-placed and safeguarded the birds return to it year after year. As a rule the nests are built on the tops of large trees in a sheltered part of the wood. The nest is a bulky, rudely built platform structure of sticks and weeds, lined with rushes, wool, and other soft materials. Three or four eggs are laid, very pale dull green in colour. The young are fed in the nest five or six weeks before they fly. Two broods are reared in the season.

The heronry is a most interesting place to visit when the young birds are nearly old enough to fly, and are most hungry and vociferous, and stand erect on the nests or neighbouring branches, looking very strange and tall and conspicuous on the tree-tops. The nests are of various sizes, and have a very disordered appearance, some of them looking like huge bundles of sticks and weed-stalks flung anyhow into the trees. At this period the parent birds are extremely active, and if the colony be a large one, they are seen arriving singly, or in twos and threes, at intervals of a few minutes throughout the day. Each time a great blue bird with well-filled gullet is seen sweeping downwards the young birds in all the nests are thrown into a great state of excitement, and greet the food-bearer with a storm of extraordinary sounds. The cries are powerful and harsh, but vary greatly, and resemble grunts and squeals and prolonged screams, mingled with chatterings and strange quacking or barking notes. When the parent bird has settled on its own nest, and fed its young, the sounds die away; but when several birds arrive in quick succession the vocal tempest rages continuously among the trees, for every young bird appears to regard any old bird on arrival as its own parent bringing food to satisfy its raging hunger.

The cry of the adult is powerful and harsh, and not unlike the harsh alarm-cry of the peacock.

Common Bittern.

Botaurus stellaris.

Crown and nape black; general colour buff, irregularly barred above and streaked below with black; feathers of the neck long, and forming a ruff; bill greenish yellow; legs and feet green. Length, thirty inches.

The bittern, formerly a common bird, is hardly entitled to a place in this book, since it has long been extirpated as a breeding

PLATE IX.   BITTERN. $\frac{1}{5}$ NAT. SIZE.

species. It is, however, a noteworthy fact that, whereas other species that have been driven out, such as the great bustard, spoon-bill, avocet, black tern, and several more, appear now as only rare occasional visitors in our country, the bittern comes back to us annually, as if ever seeking to recover its lost footing in our island. And that he would recover it, and breed again in suitable places as in former times, is not to be doubted, if only the human inhabitants would allow it; but, unhappily, this bird, like the ruff, hoopoe, and kingfisher, when stuffed and in a glass case, is looked upon as an attractive ornament by persons of a low order of intelligence and vulgar tastes.

The bittern is a bird of singular appearance. On the wing he resembles the heron, but it is a rare thing to see him abroad in the daytime. He is strictly nocturnal in habits, and passes the daylight hours concealed in thick reed-beds in extensive marshes. His buff and yellow and chestnut colour, mottled and barred and pencilled with black and brown, gives him a strange tigrine or cat-like appearance; it is a colouring well suited to his surroundings, where yellow and brown dead vegetation is mixed with the green, and the stems and loose leaves of the reeds throw numberless spots and bars of shade beneath. Secure in its imitative colouring, the bittern remains motionless in its place until almost trodden upon. Its active life begins in the evening, when it leaves its hiding-place to prey on fishes, eels, frogs, voles, small birds, and insects, and every living thing it finds and is able to conquer with a blow of its sharp, powerful bill.

When flying he utters a harsh, powerful scream, and he has, besides, a strange vocal performance, called ' booming '—a sound that resembles the bellowing of a bull. Formerly, when the bittern was a common bird in England, this extraordinary evening performance was the subject of some superstitious notions, and it was commonly believed that, to produce so great a volume of sound, the bird, when screaming, thrust its beak and head into the water. Thus, in Thomson's ' Seasons ' we read:—

> The bittern knows his time, with bill submerged,
> To shake the sounding marsh.

In March or April the nest is made on the ground, among the thick reeds, and is formed of weeds, sticks, and rushes. The eggs are four in number, of an olive-brown colour, sometimes with a greenish shade.

Besides the two species described there are no fewer than eight herons in our list of British birds, most of these being very rare stragglers to our shores:—

Purple heron (*Ardea purpurea*) is a straggler from the continent of Europe ; it breeds in Holland.

Great white heron (*Ardea alba*).—Eight examples of this species, a straggler from South-eastern Europe, have been obtained in this country.

Little egret (*Ardea gazetta*).—A waif from Southern Europe ; it also inhabits Africa, Asia, and Australia.

Buff-backed heron (*Ardea bubulcus*).—Inhabits Southern Europe ; three examples have been obtained.

Squacco heron (*Ardea ralloïdes*).—From Southern Europe ; occasionally seen on migration in England.

Little bittern (*Ardetta minuta*).—This bittern almost deserves to rank as a British species, as it is of somewhat frequent occurrence, and has been known to breed in the Broads of Norfolk, and in other localities in Great Britain. It is a summer visitor to most countries in Europe.

Night heron (*Nycticorax griseus*).—This heron has a range almost as extensive as that of the barn-owl, and breeds in many localities throughout the continent of Europe. The question as to whether or not it has ever bred in England has not been settled ; but it, is now an almost annual spring and autumn visitor to our country, and it is hardly to be doubted that it would breed with us if unmolested, or, in other words, allowed to live.

American bittern (*Botaurus lentiginosus*).—A few examples of this North American bittern have been obtained in this country.

Two other families in the present order (Herodiones) are represented by occasional visitors in the list of British birds—two storks (Ciconiidæ), and a spoonbill, and an ibis (Platalaidæ) :—

White stork (*Ciconia alba*).—Common in Holland, and an occasional visitor to the east coast of England.

Black stork (*Ciconia nigra*).—A rare straggler from continental Europe.

Spoonbill (*Platalea leucorodia*).—Now an occasional straggler to Great Britain ; formerly a regular breeder in heronries in several localities in England.

Glossy ibis (*Plegadis falcinellus*).—A very rare straggler from Southern Europe.

Grey Lag Goose.

Anser cinereus.

FIG. 75.—GREY LAG GOOSE. $\frac{1}{14}$ natural size.

Head, neck, and upper parts greyish brown; lower breast and abdomen dull white with a few black spots; bluish grey rump and wing-coverts; bill flesh-coloured, with a white nail at the tip; legs and feet flesh-coloured.   Length, thirty-five inches.

Eight species of geese are counted among British birds; two of these—the snow-goose (*Chen albatus*) and the red-breasted goose (*Bernicla ruficollis*)—may be dismissed at once as rare stragglers to the British Islands.   The other six are all winter visitors to our coasts, and are divisible into two natural groups—the grey geese (counting four species), all large birds, brownish grey in colour, and feeders on land; and the black, or dark-coloured geese (two species), very dark in colour, very much smaller in size, and feeders on the tidal flats.

The grey lag is the largest species in the first group, and the only goose that breeds within the limits of the United Kingdom. It was formerly a common summer resident, and bred in the eastern counties of England; it is now confined as a breeding species to a few localities in Scotland and the Hebrides, and in all these last refuges it is said to be rapidly diminishing. That it will diminish still further, until the vanishing-point is reached, hardly admits of a doubt. As a winter migrant from northern Europe it will long continue to visit our coasts, and as a domestic bird we shall have it always with us; for the grey lag is supposed to be the species from which our familiar bird has descended.

The grey lag goose pairs for life, and is gregarious, but is said not to associate with geese of other species. It feeds on grass and young shoots, and in the autumn on grain, and spends nearly the whole day in feeding, and resorts at dark to some open level space to roost, where it is almost impossible to approach within gunshot of the flock, owing to its watchfulness. The grey lag makes a large nest of reeds and grass, lined with moss, and lays six eggs, sometimes a larger number. During incubation the gander keeps guard over his mate, and afterwards assists her in rearing the young. These are led back to the nest every evening by the goose, and sleep under her wing. The male begins to moult a month earlier than the female, and when the time comes he leaves her in sole charge of the young, and withdraws to some hiding-place, or spends the daylight hours on the water, coming to the land in the evening to feed. The goose begins her moult after the young are able to take care of themselves.

The grey lag goose does not range so far north as the allied species; it is only in Norway, where the summer is longest, owing to the influence of the Gulf Stream, that it is found nesting north of the arctic circle.

Bean-Goose.

Anser segetum.

The bean-goose differs from the preceding species in its more slender shape and longer bill, which is orange-colour in the middle, black at the base and on the nail; and in its darker colour and the absence of black marks on the breast, and the bluish grey colour on the shoulder of the wing; legs and feet orange-yellow. Length, thirty-four inches.

This species is more arctic in its range than the grey lag, and has not been known to breed in this country, except in a domestic state. It visits Scotland, Ireland, and the north and east coasts of England, in winter. It is less in size than the grey lag, but its habits are similar: by day it feeds on the wolds and stubbles, and its love of grain has won for it the common name of bean-goose, as well as its scientific name, *segetum*. Its flight is somewhat laboured, with measured wing-beats, but powerful and rapid, and the birds travel in skeins, or in a phalanx formation. It breeds in extensive marshes and lakes, making its nest on the ground among the rushes on small islands. The nest is a slight hollow lined with dead grass and moss, and down from the parent bird: three or four eggs are laid, creamy white in colour, with a rough granular surface. Before the young are able to fly the moulting season begins, when the birds lose the power of flight, as is the case with all the geese ; and according to Seebohm's interesting account, even in the remote and desolate districts in Siberia, to which this bird resorts to breed, the moulting season is one of great danger to it. He says : 'The Samoyades in the valley of the Petchora gave us glowing accounts of the grand battues which they used to have at these times, surrounding the geese, killing them with sticks, and collecting sacks full of down and feathers.'

Pink-footed Goose.

Anser brachyrhynchus.

Colour of plumage as in the bean-goose, but with the bluish grey on the shoulder of the wing as in the grey lag goose; upper mandible pink in the centre; base, edges, and nail black ; legs and feet pink. Length, twenty-eight inches.

This goose very closely resembles the bean-goose in habits, colour, and general appearance ; the only difference of any importance between the two species consists in the smaller beak of the pink-foot, from which it takes its name of *brachyrhynchus* (short-billed), and in its legs being pink instead of yellow. It was first described as a distinct species about fifty years ago, but is still regarded by some authorities as only an ' island form ' of the bean-goose. The

R

pink colour of the bill and feet is found not to be constant, and Seebohm says, ' It looks very much as if the pink-footed geese had been long enough in the arctic climate of Spitzbergen to change the colour of their feet, but not long enough to make the new colour permanent, and that when bred in the warmer climate of this country they had a tendency to hark back to their ancestors.'

White-fronted Goose.

Anser albifrons.

White on the forehead and at the base of the lower mandible ; upper parts brownish ash ; breast and belly brownish white broadly barred with black ; bill orange-yellow, with a white nail at the tip ; legs and feet orange. Length, twenty-seven inches.

The white-fronted goose is the fourth and last on our list of grey geese—four forms of one species, as some hold—and, like the others, it comes to us from the north in winter, but is more common in Ireland than in Great Britain. It is like the bean-goose in size, but differs from it in its white front, and from the grey lag goose in having the under parts more speckled with black feathers. Its voice is most like that of the grey lag, but is more trumpet-like in sound, and the rapidly repeated notes give its cry a laughter-like character ; laughing goose is one of its common names. It breeds farther north than the bean-goose, and its nest is described as a hollow in the ground lined with dead grass. It lays five to seven creamy white eggs.

Brent Goose.

Bernicla brenta.

Bill, head, throat, and neck black, except a small white patch on each side of the latter ; mantle brownish black with rufous-brown edges ; wing-feathers, rump, and tail black ; coverts white ; upper breast black ; lower breast and belly slate-grey ; legs black. Length, twenty-three inches.

The brent goose arrives in our islands in the autumn, and remains through the winter in suitable localities in various parts of the coast, from the Orkneys and Shetlands in the north to the

Channel Islands; it is, however, most abundant on the north-east coast of England. In most years old and young birds arrive to-

FIG. 76.—BRENT GOOSE. $\frac{1}{10}$ natural size.

gether in flocks; in other years only adults appear, and it is supposed that in such seasons exceptionally cold weather has prevented the eggs from hatching. The brent differs from its nearest ally, the barnacle goose, in its slightly smaller size, darker plumage, which is nearly black, and its more marine habits. With us it spends most of the time out at sea, visiting the tidal flats early and late in the day, and at night, to feed on the wrack grass (*Zostera marina*). Mr. Abel Chapman has graphically described this goose in his 'Bird Life on the Border.' It is, he says, the last of our winter visitors to arrive, seldom coming in force until the new year. Their affections are so hyperborean that they will come no farther south than they are actually compelled by food requirements, being driven reluctantly southwards, point by point, before the advancing line of the winter's ice. He writes: ' On alighting at the feeding-grounds the geese at once commence greedily to pull up and devour the blades of the sea-grass, the whole flock advancing in the closest order over the green oozy mud, all heads down except the sentries, of which an ample number are always discernible. . . . After finishing their morning meal, about noon, the geese are disposed to rest, and spend the middle of the day floating about on the water, preening themselves, and, in mild weather, splashing about, and chasing each other in sheer exuberance of spirit. . . . Towards evening the geese recommence feeding, and so intensely eager are they about sunset to utilise the few remaining minutes that they then, perhaps, offer the most favourable chance to get within shot. . . . Just at dark the whole host rise on wing together, and make for the open sea. In the morning they come in by companies and battalions, but at night they go out in a solid army ; and a fine sight it is to witness their departure. The whole host, perhaps ten thousand strong, here massed in dense phalanxes, elsewhere in columns, tailing off into long skeins, V's, or rectilinear formations of every conceivable shape, but always with a certain formation—out they go ; . . . while their loud clanging *honk honk*, and its running accompaniment of lower croaks and shrill bi-tones, resound for miles around.'

Barnacle Goose.

Bernicla leucopsis.

FIG. 77.—BARNACLE GOOSE. $\frac{1}{10}$ natural size.

Head, neck, and throat black ; forehead, cheeks, and chin white ;
a black stripe between the eye and bill ; mantle lavender-grey
barred with bluish black and white ; wing and tail feathers blackish ;
breast and belly greyish ; vent and tail-coverts pure white ; flanks
barred with grey ; bill, legs, and feet black. Length, twenty-five
inches.

The present species is not nearly so abundant as the brent, and
not so exclusively marine in its habits. It sometimes visits inland
districts, and although it feeds on the mud-flats like the brent, it
leaves them as soon as the tide rises, and repairs to some grassy
bank of a river or lake, where it feeds. The breeding habits of this
species are not known ; it is believed to have its nesting-grounds in
Spitzbergen and Nova Zembla.

Mute Swan.

Cygnus olor.

Bill reddish orange ; the nail, nostrils, lores, and basal tubercle
black ; plumage pure white ; legs and feet black. Length, sixty
inches ; weight, about thirty pounds.

The mute, or tame swan, is as well known to most people as the
turkey, goose, and pheasant, and, like the pheasant, is supposed to
be a foreign species, said to have been first brought from Cyprus to
this country, by Richard I., about the end of the twelfth century.
As a semi-domestic species it exists throughout the British Islands,
but whether wild birds of its species visit us or not is not known,
since wild and semi-wild birds are indistinguishable. The wild mute
swan breeds in Denmark and South Sweden, in South Russia and
the valley of the Danube, and many other localities, and in winter
visits the Mediterranean. The breeding habits of the wild and tame
bird are the same, but, according to Naumann, the wild bird in the
pairing season has a loud, trumpet-like note, resembling the cry of
a crane or whooper swan.

The cygnet is sooty grey in colour, but in the so-called ' Polish
swan ' (*Cygnus immutabilis*) of Yarrell, which is now regarded by
most ornithologists as a variety of the mute swan the cygnets are
white.

Whooper Swan.

Cygnus musicus.

Beak : anterior part depressed and black, basal part quadrangular and lemon-colour; plumage white ; legs and feet black. Length, sixty inches ; weight, about twenty-four pounds.

The whooper, also called the wild swan and the whistling swan, is a not uncommon visitor to our coasts in winter, and a little over a century ago had a breeding-station in the Orkneys. It is very closely related to the mute swan, but it ranges very much farther north in summer, its breeding-grounds being north of the arctic circle. The nest is bulky, composed of sedge and coarse herbage, and the eggs are four or five in number, and white. Seebohm, who observed its habits in its breeding-grounds, says : ' The whooper is a ten times handsomer bird than a tame swan in the eyes of an ornithologist, but is not really so graceful—its neck is shorter, and its scapulars are not so plume-like. Instead of sailing about with its long neck curved in the shape of the letter S, bent back almost to the fluffed-up scapulars, the whooper seemed intent on feeding with his head and neck under water.' He compares the notes of the whooper to a bass trombone ; but the notes are short—three or four trumpet-blasts, keeping time with the upward and downward beat of the wings. He adds : ' The extermination of the whooper in so many of its breeding-places has arisen from the unfortunate habit, which it evidently acquired years ago, before men came upon the scene—a habit which it shares with the goose. Most birds moult their quills slowly, in pairs, so that they are only slightly inconvenienced by the operation, and never without quills enough to enable them to fly. Swans and geese, on the other hand, drop nearly all their flight-feathers at once, and for a week or two, before the new feathers have grown, are quite unable to fly. In some localities the whoopers have had the misfortune to breed where the natives have been clever enough to surround them at the critical period of their lives, and stupid enough to avail themselves of the opportunity thus afforded of killing the geese that laid the golden eggs.'

Bewick's swan (*Cygnus Bewickii*), named by Yarrell after Thomas Bewick, author of a well-known ' History of British Birds.'

is of frequent occurrence in the British Islands in severe winters, but is not a regular visitant. It is a third smaller than the whooper, which it resembles in figure and habits.

Common Sheldrake.

Tadorna cornuta.

Fig. 78.—Sheldrake. $\frac{1}{10}$ natural size.

Beak and basal knob bright red; head and upper neck dark glossy green, followed by a white collar, below which is a chestnut band; wing-coverts white; speculum green; scapulars, part of the secondaries, and the primaries black; rump, upper tail-coverts, and tail-feathers white, the latter tipped with black; lower, central line of the breast and belly dark brown, the rest of the under parts white; legs and feet pink. Length, twenty-six inches. The female is without the knob at the base of the bill, and her colours are not so bright.

The sheldrakes, or sheld-ducks, are curious and interesting birds, and form a connecting-link between the geese and ducks; but they are more like the former than the latter, and sheld-gander, or sheld-goose, would perhaps be a more suitable name. The common sheldrake is, perhaps, the most duck-like in appearance of all the birds of this genus, and the common name, sheld, which means parti-coloured, really applies to this species only. As in the geese, the male and female sheld-ducks are nearly alike in plumage, and the male does not change colour; and, like the gander, he assists his mate in rearing the young. In the true ducks the drake changes his plumage in summer, becoming like the female in colour, and in most cases (for there are exceptions) he remains apart from the duck from the time that incubation begins until the young are fully grown. Of the seven known species of sheldrake, only one is indigenous to the British Islands. A second species, the ruddy sheldrake (*Tadorna casarca*), is a rare visitor, or straggler, to our coasts, and it is probable that most of the sheldrakes of this species that are shot from time to time in England are escaped birds.

The common sheldrake is a bird that, once seen, cannot be easily forgotten, its strange guinea-pig arrangement of three colours—black white, and red—making it one of the most strikingly conspicuous fowls in this country. On account of its handsome and singular colouring it is much persecuted, and as a breeding species is becoming increasingly rare with us. It inhabits sandy sea-coasts, and is only seen as a rare straggler on inland waters. It feeds close to the shore where the sea is shallow, and is partial to coasts where wide stretches of sand, mixed with rocks, are uncovered at low water. It feeds, both in the water and on the flats, on marine insects and molluscs, and breeds in the sandhills along the coast. The nesting-hole is in most cases a deserted rabbit-burrow, but it also burrows for itself, and is known as the 'burrow-duck' on many parts of the coast. The hole is six to twelve feet in length, ending in a chamber lined with dry grass and moss. Seven to twelve creamy white eggs are laid, sometimes a larger number. The eggs are enveloped in a quantity of down, which the bird plucks from her own body. It is said that the male takes no part in incubation, but remains near the burrow on guard, and gives timely warning of danger, and when the young are hatched and taken to the sea, assists in rearing and protecting them.

The sheldrake has a harsh cry, but in the breeding season the drake utters a soft, tremulous, whistling note.

Wigeon.

Mareca penelope.

Fig. 79.—Wigeon. ½ natural size.

Bill dull blue; forehead and crown cream-white; chin, neck, and throat chestnut; the cheeks and hind neck minutely spotted with deep green; breast white; under parts grey, the flanks pencilled with dark grey; mantle vermiculated grey; shoulder white, with a terminal bar of black, followed by a green speculum tipped with black below; wing- and tail-feathers dark brown; legs and feet dark brown. Length, eighteen inches. *Female :* above, mottled greyish brown; shoulder whitish; speculum greyish green; under parts mottled buffish white. The drake assumes female plumage in July.

Next to the mallard, the wigeon is the most familiar freshwater duck in the British Islands. Its abundance, handsome plumage, peculiar voice, and interesting habits, to say nothing of its excellence as an article of food, contribute to make it well known. It is a visitor in winter in very large numbers to our coasts, and seeks its food both on the tidal flats and on inland waters throughout the country, but is always most abundant in the vicinity of the sea.

In April and May it migrates to higher latitudes: in Scotland it is partly a resident species, and breeds in many localities; and, in less numbers, it also remains to breed in Ireland. The wigeon differs a good deal from other ducks in its feeding habits: it feeds both by day and night, in the water and on land. On land it is, like the goose, a grass-eater, and in Lapland is known from this habit as the 'grass-duck.' In disposition it is one of the shyest and wariest, and at the same time the most gregarious, among the waterfowl, and often unites in immense flocks. It is also very loquacious: its loud, prolonged whistle in two syllables, strongly accented on the first, is described by Seebohm as being 'very wild and weird, as it startles the ear on the margin of a mountain tarn or moorland lake—a solitary cry, very high in key, not unmusical in tone, but loud and piercing.' It is called 'whew duck' in some localities, from its whistling cry.

The nest is placed amidst coarse grass or heather, and is deeply lined with down. The eggs are seven to ten in number, and cream-coloured.

A few specimens of the American wigeon (*Mareca americana*) have been obtained in various parts of Great Britain.

Pintail.

Dafila acuta.

Head and neck bronze-brown, black on the nape; a white stripe down the neck on each side, extending to the white breast and under parts; back and flanks mottled grey; greater wing-coverts buff; speculum green margined with black and white; tail black, the two middle feathers greatly prolonged; under tail-coverts black; bill, legs, and feet slaty grey. Length, twenty-eight inches. *Female*: mottled brown above and greyish white below; speculum green. In July the male assumes the female dress, and retains it until October.

The pintail, although not so handsomely coloured as the shoveler, mallard, wigeon, and teal, is the most elegant of the freshwater ducks, being slim and graceful in form, with the two slender middle feathers of the tail greatly elongated. Sea-pheasant is one of its local names, but the same name is sometimes given to the long-tailed duck (*Harelda glacialis*) on the north-east coast. The pintail is a winter visitor only to the British Islands, appearing in October, and is most common on the south coast. It is found in small flocks, and prefers shallow waters with muddy bottoms, and feeds on aquatic weeds, insects, and crustaceans. It is always most abundant near the shore, but is also met with on inland waters.

Fig. 80.—Pintail. $\frac{1}{10}$ natural size.

It has a rapid flight, and is a comparatively silent bird by day; its cry by night is a low quack, and in spring, during courtship, the drake utters soft and inward notes, which he accompanies with some curious gestures and antics. The pintail breeds freely in a semi-domestic state, and lays seven to ten eggs, pale buffish green in colour.

Mallard, or Wild Duck.

Anas boscas.

Bill yellowish; head and neck glossy green, followed by a white ring; hind neck and breast deep chestnut; across the secondaries a greenish purple speculum, bordered above and below with white;

rump, upper tail-coverts, and the four middle curled tail-feathers black; the rest of the tail-feathers grey; flanks and belly greyish white; under tail-coverts velvet-black; legs and feet orange-red. Length, two feet. *Female*: smaller; bill greenish; crown dark brown; general plumage mottled brown and buff; speculum green.

The mallard is the most common and best-known freshwater duck in Britain, and is a resident species, breeding in suitable localities throughout the country; but the birds that breed and remain all the year are few in number compared to the migrants that come to us in winter from more northern regions. In the domestic state the mallard is, next to the fowl, the most abundant and familiar bird we possess. The tame duck differs from the mallard only in its heavier body and shorter wings, and in being polygamous instead of monogamous in its habits. The tendency to vary in colour is a result of domestication in all species. It was from observing the annual change in the plumage of the domestic drake that the discovery was made that ducks differ from other birds in the manner of their moult. The period of the moult does not coincide in the drake and duck; and this discrepancy in the sexes has caused ducks to differ in their breeding habits from all other birds. Thus, in most birds, male and female share the labours of incubation, and of rearing and protecting the young; and the moult, which is always a period of danger, during which the bird is obliged to go into hiding, takes place some time after the young are able to shift for themselves—in other words, the family tie is broken after it has ceased to be necessary; and the female of the mallard, and of other ducks, moult in this way. Not so the male. He is smitten by the change after the eggs are all laid and incubation begun; with the result that the marriage tie is dissolved just at the period when his help is most needed. This is one of the strangest things in bird history; for up to the time when the physical change begins the drake is not less loving and solicitous than any other male bird, and if by chance the moulting period is delayed, he continues to guard the nest and share the labours of incubation; so that we may say, without straining a metaphor, that the drake is forcibly torn away from his marital duties, just as the late-breeding swift or swallow is sometimes forced by an overpowering migratory instinct to abandon its helpless young in the nest. The action of the swift in leaving its helpless young to perish of starvation in the nest is

MALLARDS. PEREGRINE FALCON. HERON. COOT.

painful to contemplate, since we are accustomed to look on the parental affection as the most powerful of all; and in this case there is a conflict between this emotion and another—the desire for another climate; and the last conquers, and the young are forsaken. In the drake it is not a case of a conflict between two emotions or two instincts, but of a physical change, which kills or makes nugatory the instinct and emotion; for it is certain that the moulting period in all species that, like the duck, change their whole plumage in a short time, is not only a period of danger, but of suffering. When the change comes the bird acts like the 'stricken deer,' and like animals afflicted with some fatal disease: he goes apart, and remains in hiding until his new plumage has grown, and with renewed health his social instincts are restored. It is only in the case of the male duck that this change from health and strength to sickness and impotence falls in the midst of the breeding season.

Another extraordinary fact about the moulting of the drake is that, in moulting, he puts on the dress of the female. The moult is complete, but only after the whole of the small feathers have been changed are the wing- and tail-feathers shed, and as these are all shed at once, the bird is for some time incapable of flight. But while in this incapable condition he is no longer a drake in appearance—a bird of rich and conspicuous colouring—but has a dull mottled brown like the duck. This annual ' eclipse,' as Waterton called it, lasts for three or four months; and then there is a second, autumnal moult, of the body-feathers only, in which the rich colours of the male sex are recovered.

The duck, in the meantime, moults only once in the year.

A slight difference has been noted between the resident mallard that breeds in the British Islands and the mallard from the north that visits us in winter, the native bird being heavier.

Gadwell.

Chaulelasmus streperus.

Beak lead-colour; head and upper neck light brown with darker mottlings; back marked with crescents of light grey on a dark ground; median wing-coverts chestnut; greater coverts blackish; primaries brown; secondaries brown and black, the outer webs forming a white speculum; rump and upper tail-coverts bluish black; tail-feathers dark brown with pale edges; lower neck dark grey, each feather with a pale grey margin; breast and belly white; flanks and vent grey; under tail-coverts bluish black; legs and feet orange. Length, twenty-one inches. *Female*: head and upper neck light brown mottled with dark; lower hind neck and upper parts brown; speculum and under parts white.

FIG. 81.—GADWELL. $\frac{1}{10}$ natural size.

The gadwell most nearly resembles the mallard, but is not so richly coloured, and is smaller in size. It is a widely distributed species, ranging over a greater portion of the northern hemisphere. In the British Islands it is a winter visitor in small numbers, very few pairs remaining to breed, except in one locality in Norfolk, where it has been strictly protected for the last forty years, with the result that it breeds regularly, and is abundant. Elsewhere it is the rarest of the British freshwater ducks. The wings are long and sharply pointed, and the flight exceedingly rapid. When flying it frequently utters its cry, which resembles that of the mallard, but is shriller in tone. Like the mallard, it is a night feeder; during the daylight hours it usually remains concealed in the closest cover. Its nest, lined with dry grass and a quantity of down, is placed on the ground at some distance from the waterside. Eight to twelve buffish white eggs are laid.

Garganey.

Querquedula circia.

FIG. 82.—GARGANEY. $\frac{1}{11}$ natural size.

Bill black; fore head, crown, nape, and back dark brown; from the eye a white stripe extending to the back of the neck; cheeks and neck light brown with short hair-like lines of white; scapulars black, with central white stripe; wing-coverts bluish grey; speculum green between two bars of white; primaries and tail dull brown; chin black; breast pale brown with dark crescentic bands; belly white; flanks with transverse black lines; under tail-coverts black and white; legs and feet greyish brown. Length, sixteen inches. *Female*: mottled brown; stripe over the eye yellowish white; speculum dull metallic green between two white bars.

The garganey, or summer teal, or cricket teal, as it is sometimes called, on account of the low, jarring note of the male in the pairing season, differs considerably from its nearest relation, the common teal, both in its larger size and its colouring, which a little resembles that of the shoveler. It is an early spring visitor to the British Islands, rare in England, and still rarer in Scotland and Ireland. It remains to breed in suitable localities in this country, and is perhaps most common in the district of the Broads in Norfolk. It flies swiftly, and utters on the wing a sharp, quacking cry, sometimes repeated twice. Its feeding habits are similar to those of the teal, but it is not esteemed a good bird for the table. The nest is made among the coarse grass and herbage in swampy ground; eight or nine creamy white eggs are laid sometimes a larger number.

S

Teal.

Querquedula crecca.

Bill blackish ; crown, cheeks, neck, and throat chestnut ; round and behind the eye an elongated patch of glossy green margined with buff ; upper parts and flanks delicately marked with black and white ; speculum black, green, and purple, tipped with yellowish white ; rump and tail-coverts black ; tail-feathers brown ; front of neck spotted with black on a buff ground ; breast and belly white ; legs and feet brownish grey. Length, fourteen inches and a half. *Female* : mottled brown ; little or no purple on the speculum. The female dress is assumed by the drake in July, and is kept until October.

The handsome and natty little teal is the smallest of our ducks, its weight being only one third that of the mallard. In appearance it is a small wigeon, but whereas the wigeon is the wildest of our wild ducks in disposition, the teal is the tamest. It is chiefly a winter visitor to this country, and from September until spring is found throughout the British Islands. A considerable number of pairs remain to breed in suitable localities throughout England, and more numerously in Scotland and Ireland. The nest is placed on the ground on the borders of a marsh or bog, and sometimes at a distance from water, among heather or herbage ; it is made of dry grass and leaves, and, later on, down from the bird is added. The eggs are creamy-white or pale buff in colour, with a tinge of green, and eight or ten in number, sometimes as many as fifteen. The teal feeds chiefly by night, on aquatic plants, insects, slugs, and small crustaceans. Its call-note is a short, sharp quack, and in the pairing-time the drake emits a low, jarring note. The drake does not moult so early as most ducks, and remains longer with the female during the breeding season, leaving her only when the young are partly grown.

Two American species of teal—the blue-winged teal (*Querquedula discors*) and the green-winged teal (*Q. carolinensis*)—have been obtained in Great Britain, one specimen of each.

PLATE X.

TEAL (MALE AND FEMALE). $\frac{1}{3}$ NAT. SIZE.

Shoveler.

Spatula clypeata.

Bill lead-colour, very broad at the tip; head and upper neck green; lower neck and scapulars white; middle of the back dark brown; shoulders pale blue; greater wing-coverts white; secondaries dark brown with a green speculum; primaries, rump, upper and under tail-coverts, and tail-feathers, blackish; breast and belly rich chestnut; flanks freckled with dark brown on a paler ground; vent white; legs and feet reddish orange. Length, twenty inches. *Female*: brown with dark and light mottlings. In summer, the male in moulting assumes the colours of the female.

The shoveler is the handsomest of the British freshwater ducks, and the most singular in appearance, on account of the great breadth of its spoon-like bill. Its plumage also, although beautiful, strikes one as somewhat singular; for it is rare to find pale and delicate hues, like those on the wings and upper parts of this duck, together with a deep, rich colouring, as on the head, upper neck, and under parts. The pale blue and pure white contrast beautifully with the deep green and chestnut-brown. Another most interesting point in the shoveler's history is its distribution. There is but one shoveler duck in the northern hemisphere, over which it has an immense range, including Europe, North Africa, Asia, and North America from Alaska to Panama. But in the southern hemisphere there are four other species, occupying respectively the four following widely separated regions—South America, South Africa, Australia, and New Zealand.

The shoveler is a winter visitor to the British Islands; it also breeds sparingly in some localities in the Midlands, in East Anglia, and the northern counties; also in the Hebrides, and in one or two spots in Ireland. It is a very early breeder, placing its nest, lined with dry grass and down, on the ground, usually near the water, and it lays eight to fourteen eggs, pale greenish buff in colour.

In the breeding season it utters a low quack, but at other times is a silent bird.

Tufted Duck.

Fuligula cristata.

Fig. 83.—Tufted Duck. ⅟₁₁ natural size.

Black, the head and neck with purplish gloss; speculum, flanks, and belly white; bill pale blue; irides brilliant yellow; legs and feet dark blue. Length, seventeen inches. *Female* : dark brown; under parts brownish grey. Male changes colour in May.

Of sea or diving ducks (including the mergansers) no fewer than twenty species, referable to nine genera, have been described as ' British.' Of this number nine species are irregular visitants or stragglers, and may be dismissed with a mention of their names : Red-crested pochard (*Fuligula rufina*), white-eyed duck (*Nyroca ferruginea*), Barrow's goldeneye (*Clangula islandica*), buffel-headed duck (*C. albeola*), harlequin duck (*Cosmonetta histrionica*), Steller's duck (*Heniconetta Stelleri*) ; king eider (*Somateria spectabilis*) ; surf-scoter (*Œdemia perspicillata*), and hooded merganser (*Mergus cucullatus*).

Of the eleven species, referable to six genera, that breed in, or regularly visit, these islands, and may properly be described as British birds, three are mergansers, the least duck-like of the ducks in their curiously modified beaks and grebe-like habits. Of the other eight species, four only are, strictly speaking, sea-ducks, being (on our coasts) exclusively marine in their habits. These are the eider, the long-tailed duck, the common scoter, and the velvet scoter. The tufted duck, pochard, and goldeneye, are marine and freshwater ducks. The scaup is more of a sea-duck than these three, and may be said to be intermediate in its habits between the two groups.

These eight diving ducks are all interesting, and some of them very handsome birds in their richly coloured and conspicuous plumage. They have stout, heavy-looking figures, and are clumsy walkers on land; but in the water they are as much at home as grebes and guillemots, and are also strong on the wing. But they are not so familiar to us as the mallard, wigeon, and teal, as comparatively few persons have the opportunity of observing them. Mr. Abel Chapman, in his valuable work, ' Bird Life on the Border,' says that these ducks are only well known to those ' who are enthusiastic enough to follow the regular sport of wildfowling afloat, and who alone enjoy the opportunity of becoming acquainted with these wild creatures in their bleak and desolate haunts.'

The tufted duck is a winter visitor to our coasts, also a resident throughout the year, and a regular breeder in various localities in England, Scotland, and Ireland. In winter it is both a sea- and fresh-water duck ; in the breeding season it is exclusively an inhabitant of inland waters, with a preference for small ponds with weedy bottoms. It pairs in March, and male and female thereafter keep company until incubation begins, when the marriage tie is dissolved, as is the case with most ducks. It feeds chiefly by night, and is inactive by day, floating lazily on the water, dozing, or preening its feathers. At sunset it leaves the pool where it has passed the day, to seek its feeding-grounds. Its food consists of weeds growing at the bottom, for which it dives, and, tearing them up, brings them to the surface, to be eaten at leisure.

The nest is placed among the rushes at the waterside, or in the centre of a tuft of aquatic grass, and is composed of dry sedges and grass, to which down is added as incubation progresses. Eight or ten eggs are laid, sometimes more, greenish buff in colour.

When rising from the water it utters a grating cry. In winter it is gregarious, and is often seen associating with the scaup, pochard, and goldeneye.

Scaup.

Fuligula marila.

Head, neck, upper breast, and back glossy black; mantle finely vermiculated with greyish brown and white ; speculum white, terminated with greenish black ; rump, wing- and tail-feathers brown; belly white; bill pale blue; irides straw-yellow; legs and feet dull blue. Length, eighteen inches. *Female*: brown; a broad white band round the base of the bill; upper breast and mantle vermiculated with grey; belly dull white.

The scaup is common with us in winter, and found on most parts of the coast, but never remains to breed. It does not come inland, like the tufted duck and goldeneye, but is met with in estuaries and the mouths of tidal rivers. In its breeding-haunts in the extreme north of Europe it penetrates to lakes and rivers at a considerable distance from the sea. It feeds on shellfish, crustaceans, aquatic insects, also on vegetable food, which it obtains by diving. It is gregarious at all times, and in the breeding season is seen in small flocks, feeding or floating idly on the water. It rises heavily, and flies rapidly, with violently-beating wings. Seebohm, who observed it in its summer haunts, says of its language: ' Of all the cries of ducks that have come under my notice, I think that of the scaup is the most discordant. None of them are very musical, perhaps; but if you imagine a man with an exceptionally harsh, hoarse voice, screaming out the word *scaup* at the top of his voice, some idea of the note of this duck may be formed.'

The scaup makes its nest near the water, and lays from six to nine eggs, of a pale greenish grey colour.

Pochard.

Fuligula ferina.

Head and neck chestnut-red; breast and upper back black; mantle finely freckled with black and white; speculum inconspicuous and grey; under parts greyish white; tail-coverts black: bill black with a blue band across the middle; irides red; legs and feet bluish grey. Length, nineteen and a half inches. *Female*: dull brown; chin white.

The pochard is a common winter duck when it comes to us from northern Europe; it is a resident throughout the year in small numbers, and breeds regularly in many localities in Great Britain and Ireland. As a breeding species it has, however, greatly diminished in numbers, owing to the extensive draining of marshes and meres in recent times. The pochard is more a freshwater than a sea-duck, and comes nearest to the tufted duck in its habits, obtaining its food by diving, and tearing up the grass and weeds from the lake-bottom. It feeds chiefly on vegetable matter, and is considered a better bird for the table than any other diving duck. In its flight it resembles the tufted duck, and also has a harsh, quick cry, like that species, when alarmed. At other times it has a low, whistling call-note. The nest is a hollow among the herbage near the water, or in a tussock of sedge, and is lined with dry grass, and with down from the sitting-bird. Seven to ten or twelve eggs are laid, in colour like those of the scaup.

Goldeneye.

Clangula glaucion.

Head and neck glossy green, the crown-feathers slightly elongated; a white patch at the base of the bill; back black; lower neck, scapulars, speculum, and under parts white; thighs dark brown; bill bluish black; irides golden-yellow; legs and toes yellow, with blackish webs. Length, nineteen inches. *Female*: dark brown above, without the white face-spot; below, white. The female colour is assumed by the male in summer.

The goldeneye is a regular winter visitant to the British Islands, remaining from the middle of October to the middle of April. In language and flight it resembles the scaup and tufted duck, but its flight is more violent, the rapidly-beating wings producing a loud, whistling sound. It passes most of the time on the water, and dives for its food, which consists of small fishes, frogs, shellfish, and insects; also seeds and tender shoots of water-plants. During the winter it inhabits the sea and inland waters indifferently; but in its summer haunts it seeks an inland lake, marsh, or river, where it has the peculiar habit of nesting in the trunk of a hollow tree. The eggs are deposited on the rotten wood at the bottom of the cavity, and a thick bed of down from the sitting-bird is made. As many as nineteen eggs are sometimes laid, but a dozen or thirteen is the more usual number. They are smooth and glossy, and greyish green in colour. The natives in the summer home of the goldeneye place suitable nesting-boxes, with small entrance-holes, in the trees; the ducks readily occupy the boxes, and return to them year after year, although always robbed of their eggs. When the young have hatched the parent bird takes them in her beak, and carries them one by one to the water.

Long-tailed Duck.

Harelda glacialis.

Head and neck, white with brownish grey cheeks, and below, on each side of the neck, an oval patch of dark brown ; back, rump, and tail-feathers blackish ; long scapulars, inner secondaries, short outside tail-feathers, belly, and flanks white; breast, wing-coverts, and primaries brownish black; bill, rose-colour in the middle, base and tip black; irides yellow or red ; legs and feet pale lead-colour. Length, twenty-six inches. *Female* : brown; stripe above the eye and lower parts white.

The long-tailed duck has the most elegant figure of the sea and diving ducks, if we except the mergansers, and although not so richly coloured as some species, is a beautiful bird in its white and brown plumage, bright red irides, and rose-coloured bill. During its winter sojourn on our coasts it is exclusively marine in its habits. To the south and east coasts its visits are irregular ; on the west coast of Scotland and in the Hebrides it is common ; in Ireland it is restricted to the north coast. It is more arctic in its distribution than any other duck, and in summer is only to be met with north of the limit of forest growth. In its summer haunts it goes inland to breed, and Seebohm says : ' Probably the explanation of its almost exclusive attachment to salt water in winter is to be found in the fact that it rarely winters in a climate where all the fresh water is not frozen up.' A charming account is given by the same author of the habits of the long-tailed duck in its summer home in the Siberian tundra—a vast level region of swamps and lakes, gay with bright-tinted moss and lichen, and brilliantly-coloured arctic flowers. The ducks were abundant and very tame, in strange contrast to their excessively shy and wary disposition on our coasts. The smaller lakes were inhabited by single pairs, the larger sheets of water by several pairs. Each pair appeared to be very jealous of any invasion of its breeding-grounds, and severe battles were frequent between the males. The call of the drake was very peculiar, and often heard, and was a loud, clear cry of three syllables, the middle one prolonged and strongly accented. In its summer haunts it feeds on water-plants. The drake does not leave his mate after the eggs have all been laid, but assists in incubation and in protecting the young. The nest is a slight hollow in the ground with down for lining; the eggs are pale buffish green in colour.

Mr. Abel Chapman says that, like other sea-ducks, this species gets its food by diving, but is not a bottom-feeder like the eider and scaup, which cannot feed in water more than two or three fathoms deep. The long-tail feeds on small marine animals floating in the water, and is hence able to feed in deep as well as shallow seas at a distance from land.

Eider Duck.

Somateria mollisima.

FIG. 84.—EIDER DUCK. $\frac{1}{10}$ natural size.

Bill greenish; down its centre, halfway to the nostrils, is a wedge of feathers which are black, like those of the forehead and crown; the latter bisected by a white line running to the pale green nape, and divided by another white line from a green patch on each side of the neck; cheeks, back, and wing-coverts white; long sickle-shaped secondaries yellowish white; wing-feathers, rump, and tail nearly black, with a white patch on each side of the latter; breast rosy buff; abdomen black; legs and feet dull green. Length, twenty-five inches. *Female* : rufous-brown barred with blackish.

The male eider is a large and strikingly handsome duck in its conspicuous and strongly contrasted colours—velvet-black and snowy white, variegated with buff and delicate pale sea-green. But it is exclusively a sea-duck, living most of the time away from land, and most people know it only by name, as the bird that yields the exceedingly light and elastic down with which bed-quilts are stuffed. It inhabits the northern coasts of Great Britain, its most southern breeding-station being on the Farne Islands, off the coast of Northumberland. It is gregarious at all seasons, and is usually seen in small flocks on the sea. It sits lightly on the water, swims and dives well, and flies rapidly near the surface. It feeds much near the shore, but seldom comes to land, except in the breeding season. Its food is obtained at the bottom of the sea, and Mr. A. Chapman says of its feeding habits : ' The eider resembles the scaup in many of its habits, and both ducks are intimately acquainted with the local geography of the sea-bottom : all its depth for miles, and the position of every submerged reef and shallow, are well known to them. But while the scaup contents himself with the smaller shellfish and crustacea, the eider, with his strong hooked beak, can crush and devour dog-crabs nearly as broad as one's fist.' Charles Dixon thus describes its language and love-making : ' It is a remarkably silent bird, except in the breeding season, when I have often heard the male utter a note something like that of the ring-dove, as he swam round and round his mate, bobbing his head rapidly all the time. On one occasion I met with a party of these birds evidently engaged in pairing, my attention being drawn to them by a chorus of grunting notes the males were uttering. It was a most animated sight, and the drakes were constantly chasing each other with angry cries, or swimming excitedly round the ducks, with trembling wings and heads swaying up and down. The noise made by this party of eiders could be distinctly heard a mile across the water.'

The nest, as a rule, is placed near the sea, sometimes on the tops of lofty cliffs, and is usually concealed among the coarse grass, heath, and herbage that grow in such situations. It is a hollow lined with fine grass and seaweed, and a quantity of down plucked from the under parts of the sitting-bird. The eggs are five to seven in number, and are smooth, oval in shape, and of a pale dull green colour. The female continues to pluck down from her body during incubation, until the eggs are enveloped in a large mass of it; and on leaving the nest to feed she covers the eggs with the down. At this time the drake is not wholly forgetful of her, and on her appearance, when she leaves her eggs to feed, he usually keeps company with her, and after she has left the water rejoins his male companions.

The drake is at all times a shy and wary bird; but in the breeding season the ducks, if not molested, are very tame, and at the Farne Islands the sitting-bird will sometimes allow her back to be stroked, without leaving her eggs.

Common Scoter.

Œdemia nigra.

FIG. 85.—COMMON SCOTER. $\frac{1}{12}$ natural size.

Black, the upper parts glossy; central ridge of the upper mandible orange. Length, twenty inches. *Female*: blackish brown above, dark brown below.

The common, or black scoter, is a large, handsome bird, whose handsomeness is due to its uniform blackness, reminding one of those two familiar beauties and favourites, the blackbird and the domestic black cat; and as with these two—one with splendid yellow eyes, the other with a golden dagger for a beak—so is the scoter's blackness relieved, and its handsomeness brought out, by a touch of bright orange on the upper mandible. It is the most marine of the diving ducks, and a deep-sea feeder like the long-tailed duck. Its breeding-grounds are in northern Europe, West Siberia, and Iceland, but a few pairs breed annually in the north of Scotland. The nest is a hollow in the ground near the sea, lined with dead leaves and grass, and with down from the sitting-bird. The eggs are eight or nine in number, and of a pale greyish buff. In winter the black scoter visits our coasts in thousands, and is the most common sea-duck. It does not appear to breed until its second year, as large numbers in immature plumage remain on our coasts throughout the summer. The scoter has a harsh cry like that of the tufted duck, and in spring the drake has a love-call, said to be not unmusical.

Velvet Scoter.

Œdemia fusca.

Plumage velvet-black, except a small white patch behind the eye and a conspicuous white bar across the wing; bill apricot-yellow, with a black tubercle at the base; irides white; legs and toes orange-red; webs black. Length, twenty-two inches. *Female*: sooty brown; a large dull white patch before, and a smaller one behind, the eye; speculum less defined than in the male.

Mr. Abel Chapman, comparing this species with the last described, has given the best picture of it. He says: 'The velvet scoter is a larger and handsomer species, the jet-black plumage of the old drakes being peculiarly rich and glossy, and is easily distinguished at any distance by the broad white speculum on the wings, closely resembling an old black cock, if one could imagine such a bird far out at sea.' It is not known whether the velvet scoter breeds in Scotland or not. In summer it is found on inland lakes in Scandinavia and Northern Russia, and it visits our coasts in winter, but not in such large numbers as the common scoter. It is not so exclusively marine in its habits as that species.

Goosander.

Mergus merganser.

Fig. 86.—Goosander. $\frac{1}{12}$ natural size.

Bill and irides blood-red ; head and upper neck glossy dark green ; lower neck and under parts white tinged with salmon-pink ; upper back and scapulars black ; wing-coverts white ; primaries and some of the secondaries ash-brown ; lower back and tail ash-grey ; legs and feet orange-red. Length, twenty-six inches. The female is less conspicuously coloured, and has a reddish brown head and neck.

The mergansers are sea-ducks of slimmer and more elegant forms than the species already described, and differ from scaups, eiders, and scoters as terns differ from gulls. They have grebe-like necks and long, slender, serrated bills, and a variegated plumage with strongly contrasted colours.

The goosander is the largest of the three British species, and is not uncommon in winter on some parts of the coast, and is abundant in the west districts of Scotland. Its visits to the coasts of England and Ireland occur chiefly in severe seasons. It is also a breeder in the Highlands of Scotland. In its summer haunts in Scandinavia and north of the arctic circle the goosander affects rivers and inland lakes, but is also found on the sea-coast. But whether on sea or lake, the water is its element; and being somewhat grebe-like in form, with the legs placed very far back, it sits erect, and moves with difficulty on land. On the water it submerges its body when swimming like the cormorant, and, like that bird, preys on fish, pursuing and capturing them under water.

The goosander has a habit very singular in a bird of its conform-ation and marine habits during the greater part of the year: it breeds in the hollow trunk of a tree. Seebohm relates that the Finns take advantage of this habit, and of the goosander's readiness to make use of an artificial substitute for the hollow trunk, by fastening hollow boxes, with a trapdoor behind, to the trees. The peasant robs the nest daily until a score or more eggs have been taken; the bird is then allowed to keep and hatch any more that may be laid, so that the following year's harvest may not be spoilt. He adds that if there is no hollow tree, and no boxes are provided, the nest is made in a hole under a rock, and that the bird has been known to breed in an old nest of a crow or bird of prey in a tree. When the nest is at a distance from the ground the parent bird removes her young in her beak, carrying them down one by one, then leading them to the water. The nest is made of weeds and moss, and a quantity of down from the bird is added. Eight to twelve eggs are laid, smooth-shelled, and creamy white in colour.

The call of the goosander is a low whistling cry.

Red-breasted Merganser.

Mergus serrator.

Bill and irides red; head, including crest and upper neck, dark glossy green; below, a white collar, divided on the nape by a narrow black line running to the back, which is also black; the long fal-cated inner scapulars black, the outer ones white; speculum white barred with black; rump, flanks, and tail-coverts vermiculated with grey; lower neck pale chestnut streaked with black, on each side a conspicuous tuft of white feathers edged with black; under parts white; legs and feet reddish orange. Length, twenty-four inches. The female has the head and neck reddish brown, and is less richly coloured than the male, and much smaller.

The present species exceeds the goosander in elegance of form and in handsomeness of colouring and ornament. It is a winter visitor, and also a resident throughout the year on the coast of Scotland north of the Clyde, and of the Orkneys, Shetlands, Hebrides, and St. Kilda. In Scotland and Ireland it inhabits inland lakes and rivers, as well as the sea-coasts. During the cold season it is gregarious, and usually goes in small flocks. In March these companies break up, and male and female are thereafter seen always in close companionship. They are excessively shy and wary birds,

FIG. 87.—RED-BREASTED MERGANSER. $\frac{1}{11}$ natural size.

diving or taking to flight on the least alarm. They feed on small fishes and marine molluscs, which they take by diving; near the shore, where the water is shallow, they are often seen with head and neck almost continuously immersed as they explore among the seaweed at the bottom for food. They swim like the cormorant, having the faculty of sinking the body beneath the surface; and also dive like that bird, springing up and plunging down almost vertically. The favourite nesting-place is on an island, under the shelter of a rock, sometimes in a hole in the ground. The nest is formed of leaves and grass placed in a slight hollow, down being added later by the incubating bird. Six to nine eggs are laid, sometimes as many as twelve. The eggs are glossy, and pale olive-grey in colour. The drake does not assist in incubation or in protecting the young.

Smew.

Mergus albellus.

Forehead, crown, with crest, throat, neck, and under parts satin-white; a black patch before and below the eye, and a greenish black triangular patch on the crest; back black, with a crescentic mottled band of the same colour stretching over each side of the shoulders, and another in front of each wing; scapulars white margined with black; lesser wing-coverts white; greater coverts black, with two narrow white bars; wing- and tail-feathers blackish brown; flanks vermiculated with grey; bill, legs, and feet lead-colour. Length, seventeen inches. *Female*: head reddish brown; collar ash-grey; rest of the plumage much as in the male. In June the male assumes the female plumage, which is retained until the autumn.

The smew, or nun, as it is sometimes called, is usually placed among the irregular visitors to the British Islands, and hardly comes within the scope of this book; but there is reason to believe that it is present every winter, although sometimes in very small numbers, in the seas around our coasts; and it has, therefore, some claim to be described as a British species. Females and immature birds, called red-headed smews by fishermen, are frequently met with on the east coasts of England and Scotland; males in the beautiful mature plumage are very rare, it is supposed because they do not approach the shore, except in very severe weather.

In its breeding habits the smew resembles the goosander, laying its eggs in the trunk of a hollow tree. Finnish Lapland is said to be the western limits of its breeding range.

Wood-Pigeon, or Ringdove.

Columba palumbus.

Head bluish grey; sides and back of neck glossed with violet and green, bounded on each side by a patch of white; upper parts grey, the wing-coverts broadly edged with white, forming a conspicuous bar; tail-feathers dark slate-grey; under parts reddish purple, pale on the belly; bill orange, powdered with white at the base; legs and feet bright red. Length, seventeen inches.

Of the four species of British doves, the wood-pigeon is the most interesting, as well as the best known, on account of its large size, its abundance, and general diffusion throughout the country, and its plaintive music, so familiar to everyone; not in the rural districts only, but even in London town, where this bird exists in a semi-domestic state, and is seen to be actually tamer than the domestic pigeons it frequently associates with. Like most widely diffused and well-known species, it is called by various names: quest and cushat in the north, and, in England, ringdove and wood-pigeon. The last name, which it once shared with the stock-dove, is now becoming the most general.

For many years past the wood-pigeon has been increasing in numbers, and, in Scotland, extending its range; this is no doubt due to the spread of cultivation and the planting of trees, and to the extirpation of its natural enemies, the rapacious birds, by game-keepers. But, in spite of all this, it is really surprising that the wood-pigeon should continue to increase, considering that it is one of the most persecuted of wild birds, and is perpetually being shot at by everyone in possession of a gun, from various motives. It affords good sport, and is a good bird for the table, and is heartily disliked by the farmers. It is an exceedingly voracious feeder, and as it is partial to grain of all kinds, to young turnip buds and leaves, also to the roots in which rooks or other birds have first pecked a hole, the amount of damage it does is very considerable. It also devours gooseberries, green corn, young clover, acorns, beech-mast, and wild fruit of most kinds. But the pigeon is not purely a pest to the farmer; after the harvest, when it resorts to the stubbles, it consumes an immense quantity of seeds of charlock and other noxious weeds.

In autumn and winter the number of wood-pigeons is greatly increased by the arrival of large flocks from the Continent; and at this season, and until March, it is not uncommon to see them congregated in thousands.

The wood-pigeon is the handsomest, as well as the largest, of the British doves, its dove-grey tints being singularly delicate, soft, and harmonious, and their effect heightened by the white marks and touch of iridescent colour on the neck. On the ground its motions are deliberate, and have a graceful dignity which contrasts strongly with the hurried, eager manner of the rock-pigeon and stock-dove. When startled from its perch it rushes out with great violence and loud clapping of the wings. Its flight is easy and

T

powerful; and before alighting, when it sweeps swiftly and silently on its long, sharp-pointed wings through the glades of a wood, it sometimes has a singularly hawk-like appearance. Even the wild birds in the wood may be deceived by it, and thrown for a few moments into a violent commotion.

The wood-pigeon's familiar song may be heard in favourable weather throughout the year, but its voice gains greatly in beauty in the breeding season. In May and June the love-note of this pigeon is one of the woodland sounds that never fail to delight the ear. It commonly happens that birds improve in voice in the season of courtship; and not only do they acquire greater richness and purity in their strains, but there is at this season an increased beauty and grace in their gestures and motions, and in most species the male indulges in pretty or fantastic antics—a kind of love-dance, in which he exhibits his charms to the female he is desirous of winning. All doves have performances of this kind, and that of the wood-pigeon is not the least graceful. On the ground, or on a branch, he makes his curious display before the female, approaching her with lowered head, and with throat and neck puffed out, in a succession of little hops, spreading his tail fanwise, and flirting his wings so as to display their white bars. All at once he quits his stand, and rising in the air to a height of thirty or forty yards, turns, and glides downwards in a smooth and graceful curve. This mounting aloft and circling descent is very beautiful to see, and produces the idea that the bird has been suddenly carried away by an access of glad emotion.

Breeding begins in April, and, in very favourable seasons, even as early as the first week in March. The nest is a slight platform of slender sticks laid across each other on the smaller branches or twigs of a tree, usually at a good height from the ground, and the eggs are two, with pure white, glossy shells. Two, and sometimes three, broods are reared in the season.

The young are fed on a substance called 'pigeon's milk,' a thick white, curd-like fluid, consisting of the partially digested food the parent bird has swallowed, and which is regurgitated from its crop. In feeding, the young bird thrusts its beak deep down into the mouth of its parent and literally drinks. The pigeons alone among birds feed their young in this way; and they also differ from other birds in drinking like mammals, taking a continuous draught instead of a series of sips.

Stock-Dove.

Columba œnas.

Head, throat, wings, and lower parts bluish grey; the lower parts of the neck with metallic reflections; breast wine-red; a black spot on the last two secondaries and some of the wing-coverts; primaries grey at the base, passing into dusky; tail grey, barred with black at the extremity, the outer feather with a white spot on the outer web, near the base; iris reddish brown; bill yellow, red at the base; feet red. Length, thirteen and a half inches.

The stock-dove is a third smaller than the wood-pigeon, and in size, colouring, and appearance when flying, so closely resembles the common pigeon, or rock-dove, as to be often mistaken for it. But it differs from the better-known bird in the uniform blue colour of the back: the rock-dove has a white patch on the rump. It is not so abundant nor so widely diffused as the species last described, being most common in the southern and eastern counties of England; but it is found in suitable localities throughout England and Wales, and is extending its range in Scotland; also, in a less degree, in Ireland. In some localities in the south it is so abundant that its low, monotonous, crooning or 'grunting' voice may be heard all day long in summer like a continuous murmur in the woods. It prefers ancient woods, and breeds in holes in trees and pollard tops, and from this habit it is said to derive its name of stock-dove. It is also an inhabitant of seaside cliffs, like the rock-dove; and at Flamborough Head, on the Yorkshire coast, both species may be found breeding in the same caverns, and sometimes associating in flocks together. In districts with a sandy soil it nests on the ground in a rabbit-burrow, or under a thick furze-bush. A very slight nest is made of twigs and sticks, and in many cases no nest at all. The eggs are two in number, and of a light cream-colour.

Rock-Dove.

Columba livia.

Bluish ash, lighter on the wings; rump white; neck and breast lustrous, with green and purple reflections; two transverse black bands on the wing; primaries and tail tipped with black;

outer tail-feathers white on the outer web ; iris pale orange ; bill black ; feet red.   Length, twelve and a half inches.

The rock-dove, or blue rock, the wild form of the domestic pigeon, is very rarely found breeding in any inland locality in the

Fig. 88.—Rock-Dove. ⅐ natural size.

British Islands ; in Spain and Italy, and other parts of continental Europe, it is an inhabitant of the mountainous districts.   With us it inhabits the rock-bound coasts of Scotland and its islands, and of Ireland, and, very sparsely, the south and east coasts of England, and breeds in caverns, making its nests on the ledges of the rock. In its language, flight, and habits it is indistinguishable from the bird familiar to everyone in a domestic state.

Turtle-Dove.

Turtur communis.

Head and nape ash tinged with wine-red ; a space on the sides of the neck composed of black feathers tipped with white ; neck and breast pale wine-red ; back ash-brown ; primaries dusky ; secondaries bluish ash ; scapulars and wing-coverts rust-red, with a black spot in the centre of each feather ; belly and under tail-coverts white; tail dusky, all but the two middle feathers tipped with white, the outer feather edged with white externally; iris yellowish red; feet red; bill brown. Length, eleven and a half inches.

The turtle-dove differs from other British doves in its much smaller size and in being a summer visitor to England. It arrives in the southern counties at the end of April, and ranges as far north as Westmorland and Cumberland; in the west of England, and in Wales and Ireland, it is a somewhat scarce bird. Like the wood-pigeon and the stock-dove, it is believed to be increasing its

Fig. 89.—Turtle-Dove. ⅙ natural size.

numbers. It inhabits woods and plantations, and being of a shy disposition, is not often noticed. In the autumn it may be seen in small companies, usually composed of a pair of old birds and their young; at other times it goes alone or with its mate. Its spring song is a cooing note, very soft and agreeable, and somewhat plaintive in sound. The nest is made at no great height, a large bush or a hedge being as often selected for a site as a tree. It is a slight structure of slender sticks and twigs laid crosswise, and the two eggs are creamy-white. Two broods are reared in the season.

In September the turtle-doves take their departure to their winter haunts in Africa.

A few specimens of the handsome and elegant passenger-pigeon (*Ectopistes migratorius*), a North American species, once excessively abundant in that continent, but now nearly extinct, have been obtained in this country.

Pallas's sand-grouse (*Syrrhaptes paradoxus*), a curious and handsome bird, related structurally to the pigeons, is also included in works on British birds. Its home is the steppes of Central Asia, but from time to time visitations of this species, sometimes in very large numbers, have occurred in Europe, extending to the British Islands. The last and largest visitation of this kind occurred in 1888.

Pheasant.

Phasianus colchicus.

Head and neck glossed with metallic reflections of green, blue, and yellow; sides of head bare, scarlet, minutely spotted with black; plumage spotted and banded with red, purple, brown, yellow, green, and black. Length, three feet. *Female*: light brown marked with dusky; sides of head feathered.

The pheasant has had a remarkable and a very long history, extending back into the period of myth and fable to the famous expedition of the Argonauts, who brought back this bird, with some other curious and beautiful objects, including the golden fleece, from the banks of the river Phasis, in Colchis. That, at all events, is the tradition which science has preserved in both names of the species. It is not incredible that the pheasant was introduced into Europe twelve and a half centuries before Christ; for we know that our familiar homing pigeon was employed as a letter-carrier by the Egyptians at an even earlier date. When and by whom it was first introduced into England is not known. There is evidence that the bird existed and was held in great esteem in this country before the Norman Conquest; and the belief is that it was brought hither by the Romans, who were accustomed to introduce ' strange animals ' into the countries they conquered, and who gave the fallow-deer to Britain. That the first pheasants brought to Europe were obtained on the banks of the Phasis—now the Riou—is highly probable, since the marshy woods in the neighbourhood of that stream are still the headquarters of the aboriginal wild bird.

JAY. WOOD-PIGEONS. PHEASANTS.

Its habits appear curiously persistent: it must have wood, dense cover, and water in abundance to thrive. In Britain, where it has been permitted to run free in the woods for the last sixteen or seventeen centuries, it is still scarcely able to maintain its existence without the strictest protection and a great deal of attention on the part of man. It is known that when the birds are left to shift for themselves they soon decrease in numbers, and eventually die out, except in a few rare cases where the conditions are extremely favourable. How heavy the cost is of keeping pheasants in numbers sufficient for the purposes of sport is well known to all those who have preserves.

An interesting fact about the pheasant is, that the various species forming the group to which our bird belongs freely interbreed when they come together, and produce hybrids which are fertile. A Chinese species, the ring-necked pheasant, which is a little smaller than the British bird, was introduced into this country at the end of the last century, and everywhere the two species have interbred so freely that it is now scarcely possible to find a bird which does not show traces of hybridism.

An account of the habits of the pheasant would be superfluous here, as this bird, in the nearly semi domestic state in which it exists throughout the country, is as familiar to most persons as the fowl.

Red-legged Partridge.

Caccabis rufa.

Throat and cheeks white, surrounded by a black band, which spreads itself out over the breast and sides of the neck in the form of numerous spots and lines, with which are intermixed a few white spots; upper parts reddish ash; on the flanks a number of crescent-shaped spots; the convexity towards the tail rust-red; the centre black bordered by white; beak, orbits, and feet bright red. Length, thirteen and a half inches.

The red-legged partridge, or French partridge, as it is often called, is, like the pheasant, a naturalised species, introduced by man; but its history as a British bird is comparatively a short one. and devoid of romance. A first attempt to naturalise it was made in the reign of Charles II., but was not successful; on its reintroduction. about a hundred and twenty years ago, it proved well able to maintain existence in its new surroundings. Owing to its swift-ness of foot and excessive wildness it was difficult for the sportsman to get within shooting distance of it, when partridges were shot over dogs. On this account it was disliked; so much so in some cases that attempts were made to extirpate it. But in spite of persecution it continued to increase, and is now found distributed over a large part of England, from the southern counties to Westmorland.

FIG. 90.—RED-LEGGED PARTRIDGE. ½ natural size.

It differs from the common partridge in language and habits, as well as in its more conspicuously marked plumage and bright red legs. It is not a bird of the homestead, being partial to dry, sandy soils, to commons, and uncultivated lands. Its call-note is a musical, piping cry. It breeds early, and makes a slight nest on the ground. The eggs are fifteen to eighteen in number, yellowish white in ground-colour, and blotched with brown.

An allied species, the Barbary partridge (*Caccabis petrosa*), has been included, as a rare straggler to England, among British birds.

Partridge.

Perdix cinerea.

FIG. 91.—PARTRIDGE. ⅛ natural size.

Plumage grey and reddish brown, the male with a chestnut horseshoe patch on the lower breast. Length, twelve and a half inches.

The partridge is a favourite of the ornithologist, and of all lovers of our wild bird life. A handsome and interesting bird, he is the only indigenous gallinaceous species in Britain that is not adversely affected by the reclamation of waste lands and the spread of cultivation. On the contrary, the changes that prove fatal to other game-birds are advantageous to him, since he flourishes most on rich soils, and where agriculture is most advanced. As a bird of the homestead he is made dear by association to those who have passed their early years in rural England; to the sportsman he is more, in the long run, than any other game-bird we possess, on account of his greater abundance and more general distribution.

Except during the breeding season, the partridge is gregarious, keeping in coveys of half a dozen to twenty or more birds. Their feeding-times are early in the morning and in the afternoon. Towards noon they repair to some secluded spot to take their ease and dust themselves; and, if the weather be genial, to lie basking in the sunshine. At dusk they resort to some open place, usually the central part of a field of grass, to roost, or 'jug,' as it is called; and it may then be seen that the covey is not a mere chance assemblage, but a community, under the leadership of one individual, presumably the oldest and most sagacious cock bird among them. At the approach of sunset, and until dark, the call of the leader may be heard from the chosen roosting-ground. It is a familiar sound to everyone in the rural districts—a harsh and powerful cry; but, like the clamour of blackbirds and redwings on going to rest, and the cawing of rooks at eventide, it has a great charm for the lover of nature. In character it resembles the call of the guinea-fowl, but is somewhat more metallic, and is more powerful and far-reaching. When the birds are assembled, they settle down for the night a little distance apart from each other, disposed in a circle, all with faces turned outwards. Disposed in this form, it must be difficult for any prowling animal to come upon them without being detected by some one bird in the covey.

In spring, usually in March, pairing takes place, and the coveys break up; but if snow or frost supervenes the birds pack again, and wait in company for the return of milder weather. In the pairing season the males are jealous and pugnacious, and two cocks are often seen engaged in fierce fight, making the fields resound, meanwhile, with their angry cries.

The nest is placed on the ground, among the growing corn, or under the shelter of an untrimmed hedge, and is a mere hollow scratched in the earth, with a slight lining of dead grass and leaves. The eggs vary in number from six or seven to eighteen, and are of a uniform olive-brown colour. When the young have been hatched by the female the male assists in rearing and protecting them, and both birds display intense anxiety and great boldness in the presence of danger, and will drag themselves over the ground, with flapping and trailing wings, within a few yards of a man or dog, to entice him away from their chicks. The young feed principally on insect food, small caterpillars, and larvæ of ants, of which they are extremely fond. The old birds include green leaves, buds, grain, and seeds of weeds, in their dietary.

Quail.

Coturnix communis.

Fig. 92.—Quail. ⅕ natural size.

Head mottled with black and reddish brown, with three parallel, longitudinal, yellowish streaks; upper parts ash-brown variegated with black and straw-colour; neck reddish yellow, with a double crescent of dusky brown; breast pale reddish brown streaked with white; bill and feet yellowish brown. Length, eight inches. *Female*: paler, and wanting the double crescent on the neck.

The quail is a summer visitor to this country, arriving in May. It is nowhere a common bird, although widely distributed, and it has been found breeding in most parts of the British Islands. Occasionally it is met with in winter, most often in Ireland. Immediately after its arrival the call of the male is heard morning and evening, a shrill, piping note of three syllables, supposed to resemble the words *wet my lips,* or *wet my feet,* according to the hearer's fancy. This call is repeated again and again, with some slight variation in the sound. The nest is a slight hollow scratched in a corn-field, among grass or clover, and the eggs number seven or eight to twelve, and even a larger number is sometimes found. They are speckled and blotched with umber-brown on a yellowish white ground. Two broods are reared in the season. The quail prefers open, rough grass country to cultivated land. Its food consists of seeds, grain, and insects.

The quail is in appearance a very small partridge, being little more than half the size of that bird. It is singular that in the very limited number of gallinaceous birds that exist wild in this country there should be included the capercaillie, the largest of the order, with, perhaps, the exception of one American species, and the diminutive quail—a giant and a pigmy.

Historically, the small species is the more important of the two. He is a Bible bird, and was as familiar as the eagle and the crane to the civilised nations of antiquity in Asia and Africa, where letters and arts had their origin, when the great wood-grouse was known only to the barbarians of Europe.

When we consider how bound to earth (like our unfortunate selves) the gallinaceous birds are, seldom using their wings, unless to escape from some sudden, pressing danger into the nearest cover, it strikes us as very wonderful that the plump little quail should be as great a migrant as the most aërial kinds—the swallows and the warblers. When with us in the summer he is a dweller on the ground, an earth-lover, like his stay-at-home relation, the partridge; yet in his wide wanderings he crosses seas, vast deserts, and the loftiest mountain chains; and by means of this migratory instinct he has diffused himself over the three great continents of Europe, Asia, and Africa.

Ptarmigan.

Lagopus mutus.

Winter: pure white; a black line from the angle of the beak through the eye; outer tail-feathers black; above the eye a scarlet fringed membrane; beak black; tarsi and toes thickly clothed with woolly feathers. *Female :* without the black line through the eyes. Summer: wings, under tail-coverts, two middle tail-feathers, and legs white; outer tail-feathers black, some of them tipped with white; all the rest of the plumage ash-brown marked with black lines and dusky spots. Length, fifteen inches.

In the British Islands the ptarmigan is at present confined to the Highlands of Scotland, the 'region of stones,' and to some of its islands, where, however, it is decreasing in numbers.

PLATE XIII. PTARMIGAN (WINTER AND AUTUMN PLUMAGE). $\frac{3}{4}$ NAT. SIZE.

A peculiar interest attaches to this bird on account of its change of plumage from brown in summer to snow-white in winter, and of the fact that it inhabits only the summits and slopes of high mountains. These two things—the white winter plumage and the mountain habit —have a close connection. The periodical change to white is a common phenomenon in arctic animals, both birds and mammals, and all the species of grouse of the genus to which the ptarmigan belongs assume the white dress in winter, with one exception—the red grouse of the British Islands. Thus, in Britain we have two grouse of this group (Lagopus), one of which turns white like the continental grouse, while the other keeps its brown dress throughout the year. To explain this difference it must be assumed that both species inhabited Britain at a period when its climate was an intensely cold one, and that both species changed their colour to protective white in the season of snow. When the British climate changed, and became so mild that the snow no longer remained unmelted for months at a time on the lower levels, all such creatures as had the arctic habit of becoming white in winter would be in danger of extermination, since their intense whiteness on the brown or green earth would make them fatally conspicuous to their enemies. A white grouse on a brown moor would be visible for miles to high-soaring birds of prey. The red grouse escaped destruction by losing its white winter dress : the change in it from two distinct liveries to one colour for all seasons was doubtless gradual, extending over a period of very many centuries, keeping pace with the slowly improving climate. He ended by becoming a bird that was wholly brown in winter, while the willow-grouse of northern Europe and Asia—the continental form, and, it may be added, the parent, form of our bird of the moors—continued to change to white periodically. Meanwhile no such change took place in the ptarmigan's plumage : he alone continued to assume the pure white winter dress, as if to keep alive the tradition of an ancient arctic Britain ; and yet he survived. He escaped destruction because he was a hardier bird, and preferred the higher grounds, where the snows never melted in winter. At the northern limit of its range, north of the arctic circle, the ptarmigan inhabits the fells and level country ; in Europe it is everywhere confined to the higher slopes of lofty mountains; in other words, wherever found—and it ranges as far south as the mountains of Spain—it still has an arctic climate. The bird exists ' islanded ' on high mountains, separated from the rest of its kind by wide spaces of low-lying country as impassable to it as the sea.

The ptarmigan breeds in May. Its nest is well concealed, and is merely a slight hollow in the ground, lined with a little dry grass. Eight to ten eggs are laid, of a yellowish white blotched with dark brown. In autumn or early in winter the birds pack, and sometimes as many as fifty are seen in one flock. Macgillivray has the following interesting account of the bird in its mountain haunts: 'These beautiful birds, while feeding, run and walk among the weather-beaten and lichen-crested fragments of rock, from which it is very difficult to distinguish them when they remain motionless, as they invariably do should a person be in sight. Indeed, unless you are directed to a particular spot by their strange low, croaking cry, you may pass through a flock of ptarmigans without observing a single individual, although some of them may not be ten yards distant. When squatted, however, they utter no sound, their object being to conceal themselves; and if you discover the one from which the cry has proceeded, you generally find him on the top of a stone, ready to spring off the moment you show an indication of hostility. If you throw a stone at him, he rises, utters his call, and is immediately joined by all the individuals around, which, to your surprise, if it be your first *rencontre*, you see spring up one by one from the bare ground.'

Red Grouse.

Lagopus scoticus.

Plumage reddish brown on the head and neck, and chestnut brown, barred and speckled with black, on the upper parts; the feathers of the breast almost black, with white tips. In summer the general colour is lighter; in winter the under parts are frequently mottled with white. Length, sixteen inches. *Female*: more reddish yellow in colour.

One sunny morning a few months ago, as I stood on a mountain slope among bracken, ling, and furze, and scattered masses of grey rock, watching a small party of grouse near me, it struck me that I had never looked on a more beautiful creature than this bird:—so finely shaped and richly coloured, and proud and free in carriage, and in such perfect harmony with the rough vegetation and that wild and solitary nature amid which it exists. It is not strange that this species should have a fascination above all others for the sportsman that he is willing to go farther and spend more in its pursuit ; for it is not the bird only that draws him : the fascination is of that un-adulterated nature of which the bird is a part, and the sense of liberty and savage life that returns to man in the midst of mountain and moorland scenery.

To the ornithologist the grouse has another great distinction : it is the only species of bird exclusively British. It is generally distributed in Scotland and its islands, the Shetlands excepted. It also inhabits the moors in the northern counties of England, and of Wales as far south as Glamorgan ; and of Ireland, where, un-happily, it is decreasing in numbers.

The grouse feeds principally on the tender shoots of the heather ; and also eats leaves and buds of other plants, and such wild fruits as grow on or near the moors. In autumn and winter it is gregarious, and in some localities the males and females pack separately. Pair-ing takes place very early in the spring, and the male, as is usual in the grouse family, courts the female with curious sounds and a fan-tastic dancing performance. The wooing takes place very early in the morning, before there is light enough to feed. Flying up to a height of fifteen or twenty feet into the air, he drops down uttering a succession of powerful ringing notes, which end as the bird reaches the ground. This is repeated again and again until daylight and feeding-time suspend the performance. The red grouse is strictly monogamous, and each pair retires to its own chosen nesting-place, where a slight hollow is scratched under a tuft of ling, and five or six to twelve eggs are laid. They are pale olive in ground-colour, blotched with dark red. The female alone incubates, but the male assists in rearing and protecting the young. The chicks when small feed chiefly on small caterpillars.

Black Grouse.

Tetrao tetrix.

Black with violet reflections ; a broad white band on the wings ; secondaries tipped with white ; lower tail-coverts white ; eyebrows naked, vermilion ; a white spot beneath the eye. Length, twenty-three inches. *Female* : head and neck rust-red barred with black ; rump and tail-feathers black barred with red ; belly dusky brown with red and whitish bars.

U

The black grouse is most abundant and generally distributed in Scotland and the northern counties of England, but is everywhere decreasing in numbers. In England its decline has been most marked, and in the southern counties, where it was formerly common, it ceased to exist, except in the New Forest, where a few birds survive. It has been reintroduced in some localities, but so far has not thriven well. In Ireland it is not indigenous.

Fig. 93.—Blackcock.　$\frac{1}{10}$ natural size.

Its large size, rich blue-black plumage, white wing-bar, scarlet wattles, and strange lyre-shaped ornament, formed by the outward-curving feathers of the tail, give the black cock an exceedingly fine appearance, and he is, perhaps, the handsomest of our game-birds. He inhabits both woods and moors, but is most partial to grounds of a mixed character, such as are found on the fringe of a moor, where woods and thickets are broken and varied with patches of heath.

The black cock is polygamous; and at the end of winter many birds meet together at an early hour of the morning, when the males utter their powerful call-notes, and strut to and fro, with tail expanded and trailing wings, in the presence of the hens. These 'matrimonial markets' are scenes of desperate combats between rival cocks. In the end each male retires with the females he has secured for his harem. The hen makes a slight nest under the shelter of a bush, and lays six to ten eggs, yellowish white, with orange-brown spots. The young feed principally on larvæ of ants and other insects. Grain, seeds, berries and buds, and shoots of many kinds, are eaten by the old birds.

Capercaillie.

Tetrao urogallus.

Fig. 94.—Capercaillie. $\frac{1}{12}$ natural size.

Feathers of the throat elongated, black; head and neck dusky; eyes with a bare red skin above and a white spot below; wings brown speckled with black; breast lustrous green; belly black with white spots; rump and flanks marked with undulating lines of black and ash colour; tail black with white spots; beak horn-white. Length, two feet ten inches. *Female*: a third smaller, barred and spotted with tawny red, black, and white; throat tawny red; breast deep red; tail dark red with black bars, white at the tip.

North Britain, with its islands, although poor in species comparatively, has one glory which her larger, richer neighbour is without: her wilder districts still afford breeding-places to several of the larger species which have long ceased to exist in England. Of these are the osprey, sea-eagle, golden eagle, ptarmigan, and capercaillie, the last the finest game-bird of Europe, with the sole exception of the great bustard. The story of the capercaillie in Great Britain is singularly interesting. It became extinct about the middle of the last century, and was recovered some eighty or ninety years later, when it was reintroduced from Sweden in 1837–8, and has since spread over a large portion of Scotland, and continues to extend its range.

The difference in size between the cock and hen capercaillie is greater than in any other game-bird. In Scotland, the weight of the male is from ten to eleven pounds, that of the female about four pounds and a half. In northern Europe the cock weighs as much as seventeen pounds. It is curious to find that in a large number of gallinaceous birds, the pheasants and grouse more especially, the females have a near resemblance in size, form, and colouring. The divergence is mostly in the males, and is greatest in the polygamous species. Thus, it would be difficult to find two birds in the same order more utterly unlike in appearance than the cock pheasant and capercaillie; yet the females of the two species preserve a strong family likeness.

The capercaillie feeds on the tender shoots of the Scotch fir, and on buds and shoots of other trees and plants, and berries of various kinds. He is an early breeder, and in spring the cock is heard uttering his powerful double cry, several times repeated in succession, from a lofty perch in a pine-tree. While calling he puffs out his plumage and expands his tail like an angry turkey-cock. The call, which is uttered early in the morning, is a summons to the hens, who are not slow to obey it, and is also a challenge to other males. The same spot is used morning after morning for meetings, displays, and combats, until each male has secured his tale of hens, whereupon breeding begins. The nest is a slight hollow scratched in the ground under a bush, and the eggs are six to twelve in number. They are pale reddish yellow in ground-colour, spotted and blotched with brown.

The male does not assume the mature plumage until the third year.

Water-Rail.

Rallus aquaticus.

Bill red; crown, hind neck, and upper parts olive-brown, a black streak in the centre of each feather; cheeks, neck, and breast grey; flanks blackish, barred with white; legs and feet brownish flesh-colour. Length, eleven inches and a half. *Female*: duller in colour, the wing-coverts sometimes barred with white.

The water-rail inhabits fens, marshes, and watercourses, moving rapidly in the rank vegetation, swimming and diving with ease, flying only when compelled, and rising heavily, with fluttering wings and dangling legs, and after a short flight dropping again into cover. Its shy, skulking habits make it appear a very rare bird, but it is found, although in small numbers, in most suitable localities in Great Britain and Ireland. Although it is met with throughout the year in this country, it is believed to be migratory, the birds that breed with us moving southwards in winter, when their places are taken by migrants arriving from more northern regions.

The nest is made of reed-leaves, and is placed among coarse herbage or in a tussock of sedge. Seven to eleven eggs are laid, in colour pale creamy white, thinly flecked with reddish brown and grey. The nestlings are covered with black down. During the pairing and breeding time the rails are loquacious, frequently uttering their loud peculiar cry.

Three other rails (genus Porzana) occur in the British Islands, one a regular visitant. They inhabit marshes, but in form are more like the corncrake than the water-rail.

Spotted crake (*Porzana maruetta*).—A summer visitor, breeding sparingly in different parts of Great Britain. On account of its skulking habits and small size it is rarely seen. It lays eight to ten eggs, olive-buff in ground-colour, spotted with dark reddish brown. In size it is about a fourth less than the water-rail; the upper parts are olive-brown spotted with white; crown dark brown; face and neck dull grey; breast brown spotted with white.

Baillon's crake (*Porzana bailloni*).—A somewhat rare visitor to Great Britain, but known to have bred in Norfolk. General colour warm brown flecked with black and white. Length, seven inches.

Little crake (*Porzana parva*).—A rare visitor to the British Islands, chiefly to the east coast. Upper parts olive-brown; under parts slate-grey. Length, eight inches.

Corncrake.

Crex pratensis.

FIG. 95.—LANDRAIL. ⅐ natural size.

Ash-grey patches above the eyes and on the cheeks; feathers of the upper parts yellowish brown with dark centres; wing-coverts and quills chestnut; throat white; breast greyish buff; belly white in the centre, and flanks broadly barred with brown and buff; bill and feet pale brown. Length, eleven inches.

The corncrake is one of the commonest British birds. It is as large as a partridge and more brightly coloured; it lives on the ground, and, like the partridge, is to some extent a bird of the homestead. Yet it is rarely seen, for, of all skulking creatures, it is the shyest, swiftest of foot, and most elusive. Its narrow, wedge-like shape fits it to pass through the close, upright stems of the grass with perfect ease, and, with head and neck extended as if flying, it runs in the grass as rapidly as a plover or partridge over the smoothest ground. But though not seen it is heard, its low creaking cry sounding incessantly from morning till night in spring from the meadows and fields. This curious sound may be imitated by rapidly passing the thumb-nail along the teeth of a fine comb. The note is said to be uttered by the male, and is not often heard after breeding begins. The nest is made at the end of May, or in June, and is placed among growing corn or meadow grass, and is formed of dry grass and leaves. Seven to ten eggs are laid, reddish white in ground-colour, spotted with bright brown and grey.

The corncrake, or landrail, is found throughout the British Islands, and is most abundant in rich pastures; in southern England and in Ireland it appears to be most numerous. At the beginning of October it migrates, but birds are not unfrequently met with in winter, particularly in Ireland.

Moorhen.

Gallinula chloropus.

Fore part of the bill yellow; base and frontal plate red; irides red; upper parts dark olive-brown; head, neck, and under parts slate-grey, with some white streaks on the flanks; under tail-coverts pure white; legs greenish yellow, red above the tarsal joint. Length, thirteen inches. In this species the female is larger and more brightly coloured than the male.

The moorhen is one of our most familiar wild birds; for not only is it common and generally distributed in the British Islands, but where it is not molested, and the stream, or pond, or ditch it inhabits is close to the homestead, it becomes almost domestic in its habits, and will freely mix with the poultry and share their food. Furthermore, it attracts a good deal of attention, and is something of a favourite with most people, on account of its pretty appearance and quaint, graceful carriage, as it moves over the turf with measured steps, nodding its head and jerking its tail in order to display the conspicuous snow-white under-coverts.

The name of moorhen, which some writers dislike, is old English for marsh-hen, from *moorish*, which had the same meaning as marshy. Water-hen, another time-honoured name for this bird, is still in common use; but mot-hen, or moat-hen, from the bird's habit of frequenting moats when moated houses were common in England, is now obsolete.

The moorhen swims and dives with ease, and feeds a good deal in the water, usually keeping near the fringe of weeds, in which it takes refuge on the slightest alarm. When hunted it dives, and is able to remain submerged for an indefinite time by grasping the weeds at the bottom with its claws and keeping its nostrils above the surface.

The nest is generally placed on the ground among the reeds or rushes, but many other sites are used; and sometimes it is built in a tree several feet above the ground. Seven or eight eggs are laid, reddish white in ground-colour, thinly speckled and spotted with orange-brown. The young when hatched are covered with a black hairy down. Two or three broods are reared in the season, and it has been observed that the young of the first brood sometimes assist the parents in making a new nest and in rearing the young of the second brood.

The moorhen feeds on worms, slugs, insects of all kinds, and vegetable substances.

Coot.

Fulica atra.

Beak pale flesh-colour; bald patch on the forehead white; irides crimson; under parts sooty black; above, slate-grey with a narrow white bar across the wing; legs and feet dark green. Length, eighteen inches.

In its appearance the coot is a large plain-coloured moorhen. It is more aquatic in its habits than that bird, keeping almost as constantly on the water as a diving duck. Like its smaller relation, it prefers stagnant meres or ponds, or sluggish streams with marshy borders and a deep fringe of reeds for cover; and it is to be met with in all suitable localities throughout the British Islands. It is resident all the year, but in the north, when the watercourses are frozen over in winter, it migrates to the tidal estuaries and the sea-coast, where it feeds on the mud-flats. The nest is a large structure, placed among the reeds or rushes, and built up to a height of several inches above the water. Seven to ten eggs are laid, of a light stone-colour, speckled with dark brown. The coot was formerly much more abundant than it is now in England, and was, perhaps, most numerous in the district of the Broads in Norfolk. Sir Thomas Browne, writing of the birds of Norfolk two centuries and a half ago, gives the following account of a singular habit of this bird : ' Coots are in very great flocks on the broad waters. Upon the appearance of a kite or buzzard I have seen them unite from all parts of the shore in strange numbers ; when, if the kite stoop near them, they will fling up and spread such a flash of water with their wings that they will endanger the kite, and so keep him off again and again in open opposition.' This story, which reads like a fable, was found to be plain truth by Lord Lilford, who observed the coots on the lakes of Epirus, a district where birds of prey are abundant. He writes : ' I have several times observed the singular manner in which a flock of these birds defend themselves against the white-tailed eagle. On the appearance over them of one of these birds they collect in a dense body, and when the eagle stoops at them they throw up a sheet of water with their feet, and completely baffle their enemy ; in one instance . . . they so drenched the eagle that it was with difficulty that he reached a tree on the shore not more than a hundred yards from the spot where he attacked them.'

The order Alectorides, which follows, includes two noble forms once common, but now extinct in this country. One is the crane (*Grus communis*), which was abundant in the fen country down to the latter end of the seventeenth century. The other, finest of British birds, is the great bustard (*Otis tarda*), which lived in all suitable localities in England, from the southern counties to Yorkshire, and was wantonly extirpated during the first half of the present century.

The little bustard (*Otis tetrax*) occurs as a rare straggler in the eastern half of England.

A single example of Macqueen's bustard (*Otis macqueeni*), an Asiatic species, was obtained in England half a century ago.

Stone-Curlew.

Œdicnemus scolopax.

Fig. 96.—Stone-Curlew. ½ natural size.

Beak black, yellowish at the base; irides, orbits, legs, and feet yellow; upper parts mottled pale brown; wing-coverts with white tips, forming two narrow bars; quill black; throat and stripe beneath the eye white; neck and breast buff streaked with dark brown. Length, seventeen inches. Sexes alike.

The stone-curlew owes its name to a superficial resemblance in its size and pale brown, mottled plumage to the common curlew, and to its preference for a sandy or stony soil. It is also called the thick-knee, from the curious conformation of its knees, which are very massive, and have a somewhat bulbous appearance. Its other common names are big plover and Norfolk plover, Norfolk and Suffolk being now the headquarters of this species in England, although it is still found in small and, sad to say, diminishing numbers in suitable localities from Hampshire and Dorsetshire in the south to the wolds of Lincolnshire and the East Riding of Yorkshire in the north. It does not occur in Ireland. It is a bird of a somewhat singular appearance, and is the sole representative of its family in Europe. It is a summer visitor to England, a few birds remaining to winter in the southern counties, and inhabits extensive heaths where there are patches of stony or pebbly ground; and it also frequents fallows and downs. In its habits it is semi-nocturnal, feeding principally by night; it is by night that its wild, clear, ringing cry is usually heard. Its breeding-time is about the middle of April, when it deposits its two eggs in a slight hollow in the ground, among the flint pebbles and scanty vegetation. The eggs are buff-coloured, spotted and streaked with grey and brown, and are very hard to discover, so well do they harmonise in hue and markings with the sandy and pebbly ground on which they are placed.

Mr. Trevor-Battye thus describes the nesting habits of the stone curlew in his 'Pictures in Prose':—'This bird, quite apart from its own very quaint appearance and habits, must always have a great interest for British ornithologists, as it is the nearest surviving link we have with the great bustard, now, alas! extinct in this country. It is nocturnal in its habits, and is extremely wary and shy. Although on its arrival in spring it keeps well away in the open, it generally lays its eggs not far from a belt or covert of trees. The pair of which I speak had chosen the middle of a gravelly space among the pines. By creeping upon hands and knees under cover of a bank one could gain a position, just fifteen paces away from the nest, without being observed, so close that with my glass I could see the light shine through the crystal prominence of the sitting-bird's great yellow eyes. At intervals one bird would relieve the other on the nest. When disturbed the birds ran away for shelter to a bank beneath the pines. And here the bird that was not sitting always stood sentry. When its turn came to relieve its mate it would walk pretty deliberately across the first part of the open, where it was more or less screened by a fringe of trees; and then, having reached a point that was commanded from a long way off, it would suddenly lower its head, and run as fast as a red-leg to the nest. When it was about a yard away the sitting-bird would slip off, and, staying for no greetings, run past, and away to the pine-bank. . . . It was interesting to notice that the bird always rose backwards from the nest, so that its long legs should not disturb the eggs; and that the new-comer did not turn the eggs immediately, but squatted perfectly still for perhaps a minute, as if to make sure it was not disturbed. And after the eggs were satisfactorily disposed, and all the coast seemed clear, the bird would close its eyes in the hot sunshine, and appear to go to sleep. But even then I could scarcely so much as move a finger above the ground but instantly it was off its nest and away.'

It is very delightful to be thus let into the domestic secrets of so shy and wary a bird by so close and sympathetic an observer as Mr. Trevor-Battye.

When anxious to avoid being seen the stone-curlew practises the device of squatting close on the ground with its neck extended. The South American rheas have a similar habit, and it is, perhaps, possessed by other large birds that have a more or less protective colouring and inhabit the open country.

The stone-curlew feeds on slugs, worms, and insects, and also devours mice and small reptiles.

The family Glareolidæ is represented in works on British birds by one species, the collared pratincole (*Glareola pratincola*), a rare straggler to Great Britain from Southern Europe. This bird comes between the stone-curlew and the true plovers (family Charadriidæ), which follow.

The cream-coloured courser (*Cursorius gallicus*) is another rare straggler to England from Western Asia and North Africa.

Golden Plover.

Charadrius pluvialis.

Upper parts greyish black spotted with gamboge-yellow; above the eye a white line, which continues down the neck to the flanks; under parts black. After the autumnal moult the under parts are white, and the upper parts more yellow than in spring. The female, in summer, has less black on the breast. Length, eleven inches.

The golden plover has for several centuries been in great esteem for the table, its fame in this respect being equal to that of the dotterel, woodcock, ruff, and black-tailed godwit. The two last named have now ceased to exist in this country as breeding species.

The golden plover, although incessantly persecuted by fowlers and sportsmen, is still not uncommon ; probably because the great majority of the birds that visit the British islands on migration in autumn and winter have their breeding-grounds in remote regions north of the arctic circle, where there are no human beings to molest them. The birds that breed with us are also migratory, and escape destruction by going south in autumn.

FIG. 97.—GOLDEN PLOVER (summer plumage). $\frac{1}{6}$ natural size.

The golden plover gets its common name from the rich yellow spots that decorate its upper parts. All the species of the genus to which it belongs undergo a very remarkable change of plumage every year : in winter the whole under parts are pure white ; in spring the white changes to intense black, and this nuptial, or summer dress, lasts until the autumn moult, when the winter white is resumed. With us this species breeds in suitable localities throughout the British Islands, but very sparingly in the southern half of England. The nest is a slight hollow among heather or short grass, sometimes on the bare ground, and is scantily lined with dry grass. The eggs, of a yellowish stone-colour, spotted and blotched with blackish brown, are four in number, and are handsome, and large for the bird. The young when hatched are pretty little creatures, orange-yellow and brown in colour.

The call-note of the golden plover, clear and wild and far-reaching, is one of the bird-sounds that have a great charm. In the pairing season the male emits a different sound, by way of love-song, as he rises and flutters in the air above his mate, and reiterates a double note so rapidly that it runs into a trill.

After the breeding season the birds unite in flocks, and leave the moors for the lowlands and seashore.

The Eastern, or lesser golden plover (*Charadrius fulvus*), a form of the British golden plover differing only in its slightly smaller size, has been obtained on two or three occasions in this country.

Grey Plover.

Squatarola helvetica.

Fore-crown white, and upper parts mottled blackish brown and white; lores, cheeks, throat and neck, and under parts, black. Length, twelve inches. After the autumn moult the upper parts are more greyish, and all the rest white.

This species so closely resembles the golden plover in size and appearance, both in summer and winter, changing, like it, from black to white, and from white to black, that it seems strange to find it classed in a separate genus. But there is a slight anatomical difference in the two birds: the grey plover is provided with a rudimentary hind toe, while the golden plover has only three toes on its foot. The present species does not breed in the British Islands. Its summer home is in arctic Siberia. From August, when it begins to arrive, until the following spring it is found on our coasts every year in small flocks. It is much less common than the golden plover, and while with us is almost exclusively a bird of the seashore.

The grey plover is considered a poor bird for the table; but in Yarrell's work it is stated that Englishmen have not always been of that opinion, that it was formerly esteemed above most birds, and that the saying, ' a grey plover cannot please him,' was used of a person with an excessively fastidious palate. The bird proverbial for its delicacy was probably our golden plover, which to this day is called grey plover in Ireland.

Kentish Plover.

Ægialitis cantiana.

Forehead, stripe above the eye, chin, cheeks, and under parts white; upper part of forehead, a band from the base of the bill extending through the eye, and a large spot on each side of the breast, black; head and nape light brownish red; upper plumage ash-brown; two outer tail-feathers white. Length, six inches and three-quarters. The female is without the black on the fore-crown, her neck patches are brown instead of black, and her colours duller than in the male.

This species, in appearance a small and pale-coloured ringed plover, is a summer visitor to the south-east and east coasts of England from Sussex to Yorkshire, and received its name of Kentish plover when first described, nearly a century ago, by Latham, from specimens obtained at Sandwich. Its sojourn in this country is a short one, excepting on the Sussex and Kentish coasts, where a few pairs remain to breed; but as a breeding species the bird has now been almost extirpated by the egg-collector—the soulless Philistine who is without any feeling for wild nature, and whose vulgar ambition it is to fill a cabinet with the faded shells of eggs which he can label ' British-taken.'

The Kentish plover has a very extensive distribution in Europe, Africa, and Asia. In its habits it resembles the ringed plover, and lays its three, and sometimes four, eggs in a slight depression among the fine shingle or broken shells. The eggs are of a yellowish stone-colour, spotted and scratched with black.

Ringed Plover.

Ægialitis hiaticula.

Forehead, lores, and gorget reaching round the neck black; a band across the forehead, a stripe over each eye, broad collar, and lower parts, white; nape and upper parts hair brown; outer tail-feathers white; bill, orbits, and feet orange. Length, seven inches and three-quarters. In the female the black collar is less well defined.

The small ringed plover is a sprightly, prettily marked bird, with conspicuous white and black collar, and a melodious voice. His modulated alarm-note, somewhat plaintive in character, is familiar to most persons who walk by the seashore, for he is a common species on our coasts, and has the habit of betraying his presence by sounding an alarm when approached; and if the intruder moves quietly, and occasionally pauses in his walk, the little plover will not take to flight, but continue running on before him, all the while playing on his wild and sorrowful little pipe. In spring the male has a fuller, sweeter note, by way of love-call or song, uttered occasionally on the wing. He is an extremely active and lively bird, running rapidly on the sands, and, when the tide is going out, often keeping close to the water to pick up the small marine insects and crustaceans on which he feeds. He is not, however, exclusively a bird of the seashore, but is also found on the margins of rivers and lakes, and sometimes breeds at a distance from the sea. As a rule the nest is placed on the sandy beach, or fine shingle, above high-water mark. The nest is merely a slight depression in the sand, in which four pear-shaped eggs are laid, of a pale stone or cream colour, marked with small round, blackish brown and grey spots. The breeding season begins in May, and as eggs continue to be found to the end of July, it is probable that two broods are reared in the season. When the young are hatched the parent birds manifest the utmost anxiety, and will attempt to lead a man or dog from the spot by fluttering as if wounded along the ground.

The ringed plovers are social in disposition, and even during the breeding season it is common to find them in small parties. In the autumn they unite in flocks.

This species is to be met with in this country throughout the year; but in spring our coasts are visited on migration by a ringed plover of a different race, smaller in size. It is with this smaller bird that the lesser ringed plover (*Ægialitis curonica*), a rare straggler to England from continental Europe, is sometimes confounded.

Another member of this genus, the North American killdeer plover (*Ægialitis vocifera*), has been once or twice obtained in this country.

PLATE II.　　DOTTEREL. $\frac{1}{2}$ NAT. SIZE.

Dotterel.

Endromias morinellus.

Crown · dusky black, bordered by a white band extending backwards from the eye round the nape; upper parts ash-brown, the inner secondaries margined with rufous; tail-feathers broadly tipped with white, except the middle pair; throat dull white; upper breast ash-brown; white gorget or band lower breast, and flanks bright chestnut; belly black; tail-coverts white. The female is larger and brighter than the male. Length, nine inches.

This is a richly coloured, handsome little plover; it was familiar to our forbears, and is often mentioned by old British and Continental writers as a very delicate bird to eat—a ' very daintie dish,' as Drayton wrote. Much was also said, both in verse and prose, about its supposed foolishness, which was proverbial, so that dull and weak-minded persons were compared to the dotterel. It was believed that when the fowler, on approaching the bird, stretched forth an arm, the dotterel responded by stretching out a wing; that when a leg was put forth, the action was immediately copied; and that the bird, being intent on watching and imitating the motions of the man, neglected its own safety, and was taken in the net. The origin of this notion, which was credited by everyone, ornithologists included, for the space of two or three centuries, is no doubt to be found in the fact that the dotterel is less shy and active than most plovers, and, like very many other birds, when approached and disturbed during repose has the habit of stretching out a wing and leg before moving away.

The dotterels arrive in this country in small flocks, called ' trips,' about the beginning of May. From the south-east coast, where they first appear, they travel from place to place on their way north. Arrived at their breeding-haunts in Westmorland and Scotland, they are seen at first frequenting heaths, dry pasture-lands, and fallows, but soon retire to the mountains to breed. The nest is a slight depression in the short, dense grass on or a little below the mountain summit. and several pairs are usually found breeding near each other. The eggs are three in number, in colour yellowish olive, spotted and blotched with brownish black.

In August or early in September the dotterels take their departure for the south. It is known that this bird, which was once common in this country, has been diminishing in numbers for many years, and that very few pairs, if any, survive in the Lake District.

Lapwing.

Vanellus vulgaris.

Fig. 98.—Lapwing. ⅛ natural size.

Crown and crest greenish black ; sides of neck whitish ; upper parts metallic green with purple reflections ; quills black ; tail-feathers white with a broad black band ; face, throat, and upper breast bluish black ; belly and axillaries white ; tail-coverts fawn-colour. Length, twelve inches.

The lapwing, pewit, or green plover, as he is variously named from his manner of flight, note, and colour, is a familiar bird to most persons, and undoubtedly the best and most generally known member of the order which includes plover, snipe, and their allies. He is widely distributed in the British Islands, and fairly abundant, and, furthermore, is a bird it is impossible to overlook, on account of his conspicuous colouring, his singular manner of flight and appearance on the wing, and his unique voice. A first meeting with the lapwing invariably excites surprise in the beholder. Seen on the ground he is a handsome bird ; in plumage and long, curling crest unlike any other British species, elegant in form, and graceful and somewhat stately in his movements. The moment he takes flight, displaying his curiously shaped, rounded wings, that have a heavy, flopping, heron-like motion, he appears like a different creature : he looks awkward and strange, like an owl or a goatsucker driven out of its hiding-place in the daylight. But no sooner does he begin to practise his favourite evolutions in the air than a fresh surprise is experienced. Rising to a height of forty or fifty yards, he suddenly dashes in a zigzag, downward flight, with a violence and rapidity unsurpassed by even the most aërial species in their maddest moments, and, turning like lightning when almost touching the surface, he rises, to repeat the action again and again. The heavy appearance and slow, flopping movement, and the marvellous wing-feats, are in strange contrast.

He is a vociferous bird, and when his breeding-ground is invaded he circles high above the intruder, dashing down at intervals, as if to intimidate him, and uttering all the while a wailing cry, somewhat cat-like in character. His call, heard both by day and night, most frequently in the breeding season, is a hollow, bubbling sound, followed by a prolonged and modulated clear note of a peculiar quality, not readily describable, except by the epithet ' eerie,' which is somewhat vague. It is a quality heard chiefly in the voices of nocturnal species—owls and others.

The lapwings begin to nest at the end of March on heaths and waste lands, and in meadows, pastures, and fallows. As a rule, more than one pair, and often several pairs, have their nests near each other ; and so gregarious are the birds at all times, that even during incubation, and when the young are out, they are to be seen associating together when feeding, and when indulging in their sportive exercises in the air. A slight depression in the soil, with a few dried grass-stems for lining, serves for nest, and the eggs are four in number, olive-green, thickly mottled with black and blackish brown spots. False nests are often found near the nest containing eggs, and these are said to be formed by the male in turning round and round when showing off to his mate.

The lapwing is common throughout the year, but in autumn, when they congregate, often in flocks of many hundreds, and even thousands, there is a very general movement ; and no doubt at this season a large proportion of the birds that breed with us leave the country, their places being taken by others from more northern regions. Throughout the British Islands it is a fairly common species, but it is believed that for many years past the lapwing has been decreasing in numbers, chiefly on account of the demand for plovers' eggs, and of unrestricted egging.

Turnstone.

Strepsilus interpres.

Fig. 99.—Turnstone. ⅕ natural size.

Head, neck, breast, and shoulders variegated with black and white; upper surface black and chestnut-red; rump white; tail-feathers and a patch on the coverts dark brown; under parts white; legs and feet orange. *Female*: not so bright. Length, nine inches.

The turnstone is very nearly of a size with the song-thrush, although its conspicuous black-and-white and curiously marked plumage causes it to appear much bigger to the eye. The plumage is very handsome, the upper parts being mottled with black and red—a tortoiseshell colouring which is rare in birds. It is a visitor to our coasts after the breeding season, the young birds arriving towards the end of July, the adults following in August, after the moult. From the east coast of England most of the birds depart in autumn ; on the south and west coasts many remain all winter. The return migration to the breeding-grounds in the arctic regions takes place about the middle of May ; but it is believed that a few pairs breed annually within the limits of the British Islands, as birds have been observed in summer in full nuptial dress. There are few birds with so wide a distribution as the turnstone, its range extending along the coasts of Europe, Asia, Africa, North and South America, Australia, and the Atlantic and Pacific islands.

The turnstone is a bird of the seashore exclusively, with a partiality for rocky coasts, and feeds on marine insects and small crustaceans, which it picks from the stranded seaweed, and on this account it is called ' tangle-picker ' on the Norfolk coast. It also turns over the small stones and shells on the sand, to search for insects concealed beneath them ; and when the stone is too large to be moved by the bill, the breast is used in pushing. Two or three birds have been observed to unite in pushing over an object too large to be moved by one.

Oyster-catcher.

Hæmatopus ostralegus.

Plumage intense black and pure white ; bill orange-yellow : irides crimson ; legs and feet purplish pink. Length, sixteen inches.

The oyster-catcher, or sea-magpie, is regarded by many persons as the most beautiful of our shore-birds. When seen running on the sands with a rapid, trotting gait, or standing motionless—a pied bird with thick, orange-red bill and pink legs, the large head drawn in—his appearance strikes one as singular rather than beautiful. No sooner does he take to flight, exhibiting the sharp-pointed, wonderfully conspicuous, black and white wings, than the beauty is revealed. The flight is rapid, and as he wheels round the intruder in a wide circle he utters a succession of cries, somewhat like those of the golden plover and curlew in character, but shriller and more vehement. The oyster-catcher is a resident species, to be met with throughout the year in all suitable localities on the coasts of Great Britain and Ireland. He is most partial to rocky coasts with patches of sand and shingle, his food consisting chiefly of small shellfish left exposed on and among the rocks at low water. With his strong, wedge-shaped bill he strikes the limpets from the rocks and scoops out their contents; and he opens the mussel-shells by driving his beak between the closed valves and prising them apart. He also devours sea-worms, shrimps, and other crustaceans.

The nest is placed on the rocks or on rough shingle, a little above high-water mark. It is very simple, being nothing more than a slight depression in the shingle, with small pebbles and fragments of shells for lining. Several false nests are sometimes made by the birds near the one containing the eggs.

Three, or very rarely four, eggs are laid, of a pale stone-colour with a yellowish tinge, spotted and streaked with black, blackish brown, and dark grey. During incubation the male keeps watch, and gives warning of danger to his mate, who quietly leaves the nest; when the spot is approached both birds fly round the intruder, frequently alighting on the ground within a few yards of him, uttering their shrill, distressed cries the whole time. At all other times the oyster-catcher is an excessively shy and wary bird, owing to much persecution.

In autumn and winter oyster-catchers gather in small flocks, and the birds that breed on the northern coasts go south to winter, their place being taken by migrants from the Continent.

Red-necked Phalarope.

Phalaropus hyperboreus.

Female: head, hind neck, and shoulders ash-grey; upper parts dark grey mixed with rufous; a white bar on the wing; neck chestnut; upper breast ash-grey; under parts white; bill black; legs and feet greenish. Length, seven inches and three-quarters. *Male*: smaller, and less brightly coloured.

The phalaropes are small, handsome birds that, like the plovers they are related to, perform long annual migrations, breed in very high latitudes north of the arctic circle, and have a distinctly different summer and winter plumage. But in the form of their curiously lobed feet they are like coots, while in their habits they are, perhaps, nearest to the moorhen. There are two British species, both irregular visitors on migration to this country; but of the red-necked phalarope a few pairs remain to breed annually in the Hebrides and Shetlands, consequently this species may be regarded as indigenous. Unfortunately, the British race of this bird is now nearly extinct, victims to the 'cupidity of the cabinet,' specimens of the bird and its eggs being in great request among collectors.

The red-necked phalarope is equally at home on land or water, and picks up its food on the sandy or muddy margins of the marshy pools it frequents in summer, and from the surface of the water, as it swims rapidly about, sitting high, and with head set back like a gull.

The nest is placed on the ground, among heather or herbage and grass, at some distance from the water. The four eggs are pale brown in ground-colour, spotted with blackish brown and grey.

Fig. 100.—Grey Phalarope. ¼ natural size.

The grey phalarope (*Phalaropus fulicarius*), irregular in its visits like the last species, appears in larger numbers when it does come. Its visits to the south and south-east coasts of England occur in autumn and winter. Its range in summer is circumpolar, and it has been found breeding as far north as latitude 82° 30'. The breeding plumage is reddish chestnut, the female being brightest in colour. In winter, when it arrives in this country, its under parts are pure white, and the whole upper parts a delicate pale grey.

Woodcock.

Scolopax rusticula.

FIG. 101.—WOODCOCK.   ⅙ natural size.

Upper plumage reddish brown barred and vermiculated with black; under parts wood-brown with darker brown bars. Length, fourteen inches. Sexes alike.

The woodcock is a large species compared with other snipes, and a very handsome bird in its russet-red plumage, prettily pencilled and barred with various shades of black and brown and grey; furthermore, it is in great esteem for the table, and it is therefore not strange that, like the red grouse, it should be a favourite alike with the ornithologist, the sportsman, and the lover of delicate fare.

Nocturnal in its habits, the woodcock spends the daylight hours in close concealment in woods and brakes, often under the shelter of a thick evergreen bush, and, it is said, sometimes partially covering itself with dead leaves. Its red and mottled plumage, which so closely assimilates in colour to the fallen leaves among which it sits, is its best protection—a similar case to that of the nightjar crouching on the dry, open common. Visible it may be, but not distinguishable as a bird amid such surroundings unless the large, lustrous black eyes are caught sight of. When flushed during daylight its flight is owl-like, and its appearance somewhat singular. In the dusk of evening, when seeking its feeding-ground, it flies in a curious manner, darting rapidly this way and that through the glades and open spaces. It obtains its food by probing deep in the soft, damp soil, or in bogs, with its long bill, but how it finds the earthworms and grubs on which it feeds would be hard to say. There is no doubt that the end of the beak is an exquisitely delicate organ of touch, but it is hard to believe that it is thrust deep into the soil merely on the chance of finding something edible.

The woodcock breeds in suitable localities throughout Great Britain and Ireland, but in limited numbers, and not very regularly; but whether the birds that breed with us remain all the year, or migrate to more southern latitudes in autumn, is not known. Most, if not all, of the birds that winter in our islands are visitors from northern Europe. They begin to arrive, chiefly on the east and south east coasts, about the middle of October, travelling by night, usually in calm, hazy, or foggy weather, and sometimes arriving in immense numbers. As a rule the females arrive first, the later flights being composed of males. It is only when migrating that woodcock are seen in any number together, and at such times their gatherings are probably accidental. On their arrival they quickly scatter over the country, and for the rest of the time are solitary in their habits. The migrants from the north take their departure in March. In this country nesting begins at the end of that month, and in the pairing season the male woos his mate with a curious and pretty performance, not at all like the wild celestial love-antics of his relation, the common snipe. For a time he abandons his shy, skulking habits—a hermit in love, he comes out morning and evening, and for the space of half an hour continues flying to and fro, with a singularly slow flight, and with plumage puffed out, so that he looks twice his ordinary size. Flying, he emits two peculiar notes, one deep and hollow, the other sharp and whistling. This performance of the woodcock is called 'roding' in East Anglia. The nest is a slight hollow, placed among dead ferns and fallen leaves in a sheltered situation in a wood. The eggs are four, pale yellowish white, the larger end spotted and blotched with ash-grey and brown of a reddish yellow tint.

A little over a century ago it was discovered that the female woodcock had the habit of removing its young, one at a time, when in danger by flying away with them. But it was said that the young bird was carried in the bill of its parent, and ornithologists declined to believe it, because, as Gilbert White remarked, the long, unwieldy beak of the woodcock was unfitted for such a task. The matter remained in doubt until about twenty years ago; and it is now known that the bird carries her young with her feet, either grasping them in her claws or holding them pressed between her thighs. According to some observers, the bird uses her bill to keep her young one pressed firmly against her thighs when flying with it.

Great Snipe.

Gallinago major.

Crown black, divided lengthways by a yellowish white band; a streak of the same colour over the eye; upper parts mottled with black and chestnut-brown; greater wing-coverts tipped with white; under parts whitish, spotted and barred with black. Length, twelve inches.

The great, or solitary snipe, sometimes called the double snipe, resembles the common snipe in form and colouring, and in size is intermediate between that species and the woodcock. This species, described in the B.O.U. official list as a ' straggler,' hardly comes within the scope of the present work. But although a straggler, it comes regularly, appearing in the eastern and southern counties from the middle of August to the middle of October. These visitors are young birds, and few in number, and as they do not revisit us in spring, it may be assumed that they perish in their winter wanderings—the usual fate of stragglers from the migrating route of the species, or race. The fact that young birds in very many cases migrate in advance of the adults, that they keep to the same lines, and often journey vast distances, clearly shows that migration is performed instinctively. We may call the principle of action in this case crystallised experience, or inherited or historical knowledge, or lapsed intelligence, or by any other pretty name; but it is not ordinary intelligence—the guiding faculty that observes, considers, and profits by experience. And it is possible to believe that the young of the great snipe, when visiting Great Britain in the autumn, are going back to an ancient route abandoned by the species, perhaps thousands of years ago, on account of physical changes in the earth's surface, or of a change in the system of the bird itself.

Common Snipe.

Gallinago cælestis.

Upper plumage mottled black and chestnut-brown ; flanks barred with white and dusky; under parts white. Length, ten inches and a half.

The common snipe, like the woodcock, breeds in limited numbers throughout the British Islands. But the woodcock nests in woods, and, owing to the increase of plantations, the bird as a breeding species has increased with us. Just the contrary has happened with the snipe. He is a breeder in marshes, fens, and low, wet grounds, and as drainage and cultivation deprive him of suitable localities to nest in, he diminishes in numbers. Most of the birds that winter in our islands are migrants from Scandinavia; they come in October and November, and remain until March. During the winter months they are often compelled by changes in the weather to shift their feeding-grounds, and intense cold is very fatal to them. Their soft, sensitive bills must have a soft soil to probe in, and frost cuts off their food-supply. When approached, the snipe seeks to avoid observation by crouching close to the earth, where its mottled upper plumage fits in well with the colour of the boggy or wet ground ; on taking wing it rushes upwards with a violent zigzag flight, uttering at the same time a sharp, scraping cry, two or three times repeated. Late in March or early in April the snipes pair, and it is then that the males begin to practise their curious aërial exercises, familiar to anyone who observes wild bird life, and about which so much has been said by ornithologists. The performance takes place at all hours of the day, but chiefly towards evening, the bird rising to an immense height in the air, and precipitating himself downwards with astonishing violence, producing in his descent the peculiar sound variously described as drumming, bleating, scythe-whetting, and neighing. From this sound the snipe has been named in some districts 'moor-lamb' and 'heather-bleater.' As to how the sound is produced opinions differ still, although the question has been discussed for over a century. Probably it is in part vocal and partly produced by the wing-feathers.

The snipe makes a very slight nest of a few dried grass leaves and stalks, placed among rushes or by the side of a tussock of coarse grass. Four eggs are laid, yellowish or greenish white, the larger end spotted with various shades of brown. The female hatches the eggs without assistance from her mate, who continues his play in the air at intervals every day until the young are out. Two broods are sometimes reared in the season.

Jack-Snipe.

Limnocryptes gallinula.

Upper parts mottled with buff, reddish brown, and black, the latter exhibiting green and purple reflections; neck and breast spotted; belly white. Length, eight inches.

The small jack-snipe is exclusively a winter visitor to this country, never remaining to breed. It comes at the end of September and in October, and is found generally distributed in Great Britain and Ireland, but in less numbers than the common snipe. In its habits it is more solitary than that species, and sits closer, often refusing to rise until almost trodden upon; and when it flies it utters no alarm-note. In April it leaves us, after assuming its summer plumage, glossed with beautiful colours. In its breeding-haunts in northern Europe and beyond the arctic circle the male has an aërial performance similar to that of the common snipe, but the sound produced by the bird in descending is different, and has been compared by Wolley to 'the cantering of a horse over a hard, hollow road; it comes in fours, with a similar cadence and a like clear yet hollow sound.' It makes its slight nest on the low ground, and lays four eggs, very large for the bird, of a yellowish olive colour, spotted and streaked with brown.

Dunlin.

Tringa alpina.

Crown rufous streaked with black; mantle chestnut variegated with black; rest of upper parts grey; throat and upper breast greyish white and striped; lower breast black; belly white. The female is the largest, and measures eight inches. The winter plum-

age is chiefly grey on the upper parts; the under parts white
with a greyish band on the lower breast.

The dunlin is by far the most abundant sandpiper on our coasts
during the autumnal and vernal migrations; a considerable number

Fig. 102.—DUNLIN (summer plumage). ¼ natural size.

of birds remain throughout the winter, and non-breeders or immature birds are to be met with in summer on the sandbanks and mud-
flats.   The dunlin also breeds in this country, on moors and fells,
in the wilder portions of England, Wales, and Scotland, and, in
smaller numbers, in Ireland.   In autumn they often congregate in
such large numbers that a cloud of dunlins is on many parts of
the coast as familiar a sight as is a cloud of starlings in more
inland districts.   The well-known and esteemed writer known as
'A Son of the Marshes' thus vividly describes the variable appearance of a vast flock of these birds on the wing: 'In the distance
something is coming up . . . that looks like the smoke from the
funnel of a steamer; it waves and streams as smoke will do in a
rush of wind.   Now the smoke has vanished.   Again it shows
thick, as at first, and then it breaks up in patches.   Presently the
dark cloud becomes a light one—a great flash of silver.   It consists
of dunlins coming up the wind at full speed.   We can hear the rush
of the thousands of wings, and their soft chatter, some time before

they reach us. Now they are here; with a humming roar they pass below us up the creek; shoot up, showing black and white as they turn; dive down into the creek again; pass us, and take a sweep over the snow, where they are invisible, for their white under plumage, caused by the turn, is in the light. Another turn, and the dark cloud is passing over the snow and into the creek. One turn more, and we see the cloud of dunlins drop below us on the slub—a vast host of living silver dots moving rapidly over the dark brown mud and grey ooze. As they throw their wings up, as they flirt up from one spot to another, all busy chattering, and dibbling, now here, now there—for we can see all their actions, so close are they to us—I thought that it was one of the most interesting sights I had been privileged to witness.'

At the end of April the great body of dunlins forsake our coasts, going north to breed; those that remain to breed in the British Islands withdraw to the loneliest moors and fells, the summer haunts of the curlew and golden plover. On this account the dunlins are called 'plovers' pages' in some districts.

The language of the dunlin differs from that of most of the sandpipers, being hoarse and somewhat grating; but in spring, on the moors, the male has an agreeable trilling love-call, uttered in the air, or as the bird descends to earth with set, motionless wings and expanded tail.

A slight nest is made on the ground among the heather, and four eggs are laid, greenish white, spotted and blotched with reddish brown.

The great difference in the summer and winter plumage of the dunlin caused it to be regarded formerly, by most persons, as two distinct species: in the chestnut-and-black plumage it was the dunlin; in white-and-grey, the purre. Other local names for this species are stint, ox-bird, and sea-snipe.

Little Stint.

Tringa minuta.

Upper parts variegated with rufous and black; throat and upper breast tinged with rufous and speckled with dark brown; under parts white; bill and feet black. Length, six inches. In winter the upper parts are ashy brown, and there is no rufous on the throat.

This diminutive sandpiper, no larger than a house-sparrow, and in appearance a miniature dunlin, is the least of its order in the British Islands. It comes to us only during the autumn and spring migrations, but in small numbers, as the British coasts lie a little outside of its main lines of travel. It makes its appearance in August, chiefly on the east side of Great Britain, and is gone by October; in May it reappears, to stay till June, when it resumes its journey northwards. Its known breeding-places are in Northern Norway and Siberia, north of the arctic circle. The eggs are four in number, of the same length as those of the song-thrush, in colour and markings like dunlins' eggs. The note of this species is described in Yarrell as a 'whispering, warbling trill, very different from the louder call of the dunlin; . . . and the call of a flock is something like the confused chirping of grasshoppers or crickets.'

Temminck's stint (*Tringa temmincki*) is a visitor on migration to the coasts of Great Britain, but is less regular, and appears in smaller numbers than the little stint, which it resembles in size and colour.

Curlew-Sandpiper.

Tringa subarquata.

Head, neck, and mantle chestnut, streaked and barred with black and grey; upper tail-coverts white tinged with buff and barred with black; quills and tail-feathers ash-grey; under parts chestnut-red, slightly barred with brown and grey on the belly and flanks. Length, eight inches. In winter the upper parts are ash-brown, mottled with darker and paler brown; breast paler; under parts and upper tail-coverts white.

This species derives its name from the form of the bill, which is curved downwards, as in the curlew; pigmy curlew is one of its common names. It is an annual visitor on migration to this country, on the east side chiefly, and occasionally penetrates to inland waters. It associates with dunlins on the sand and mud flats, and resembles that species in its feeding habits, but when flying may be easily distinguished by its conspicuous white tail-coverts. On its return from its breeding-grounds it remains on our coasts from August to October. From its winter haunts in the south it begins to arrive at the end of March, the migration continuing until June.

At this season the birds are in their full summer dress, which resembles that of the knot. The bird is, Seebohm writes, ' a miniature knot with a long, decurved bill.' Its breeding-grounds have not yet been discovered.

Purple Sandpiper.

Tringa striata.

Head and neck dusky brown tinged with grey; upper parts nearly black, with purple reflections; the feathers edged with ash; throat, neck, and breast greyish; below, white; legs and feet ochre-yellow. Length, eight and a quarter inches. In winter the upper parts are sooty and the breast dark ash-brown, with faint lines and mottlings.

The purple sandpiper is an inhabitant of the British coasts in autumn and winter, and is occasionally seen associating with dunlins on the sand and mud flats, and may readily be distinguished by its darker colour and its lumpier figure, caused by the thickness of its winter plumage. But its favourite haunts are rocky shores, where it feeds among the stranded seaweed on marine insects, small shrimps, and other crustaceans. It is, in fact, a sandpiper with the feeding habits of the turnstone. It is known to breed on the Faröes, where it nests on the fells and mountains and lays four eggs, pale green or olive, blotched with reddish brown, with purplish under-markings. Its eggs have never been found within the British Islands, but it is probable that a few pairs breed annually on some of the islands and on the mainland of Scotland. In its summer haunts in the arctic regions it is said to be the most abundant sandpiper. With us it is not a common species, and is seen in small flocks of half a dozen to a dozen birds.

Knot.

Tringa canutus.

Crown and neck reddish brown with darker streaks; mantle blackish; the feathers spotted with chestnut and margined with white; tail-coverts white barred with black; cheeks, throat, and breast chestnut. Length, ten inches. In winter the upper parts are ash-grey and the under parts white flecked with grey.

This richly coloured and pretty sandpiper with a strange name is one of two species in this order of birds of which the eggs are not known to ornithologists, or do not exist in collections.   It is a regular visitor to the British coasts on migration in August, but many birds remain in this country until the following May.   In some seasons they are very abundant, especially on the north-east coast of England; and in former times they were esteemed a

FIG. 103.—KNOT. ¼ natural size.

great delicacy, and were netted in large numbers, to be fattened, like dotterels and ruffs and reeves, on bread-and-milk for the table.   According to Camden ('Britannia,' 1607), the bird was named after King Canute on account of his excessive fondness for its flesh.   Drayton, adopting this explanation of the name, wrote in his ' Polyolbion ':

> The *Knot* that called was *Canutus* Bird of old,
> Of that great King of *Danes*, his name that still doth hold,
> His apetite to please, that farre and neare was sought,
> For him (as some have sayd) from Denmark, hither brought.

It is possible that the Danish king introduced the taste for the knot, which lasted down to the end of the seventeenth century.

Y

As long ago as 1820 the knot was found breeding in the Melville Islands (lat. 80°), and later, at various times, in other arctic localities, but in no case were the eggs preserved. During the pairing-time the birds toy with each other in the air, the male uttering a sweet, fluting whistle. On our coasts they are very gregarious, feeding on the extensive mud-flats in large flocks. It has been observed that the young birds that come in advance of the adults in August are strangely tame in disposition. In May, when the return migration to their arctic breeding-grounds takes place, the birds that arrive on our shores from the south have their rich nuptial colours fully developed.

Ruff and Reeve.

Machetes pugnax.

FIG. 104.—RUFF AND REEVE. ⅓ natural size.

The male in spring dress has the face covered with yellowish caruncles; a tuft of long feathers on each side of the head; throat furnished with a shield-like ruff of feathers; general plumage mottled with ash, black, brown, yellowish, and white, the ornamental feathers being differently coloured in almost every individual. In his winter plumage the male has the face feathered, and is without the ruff and ear-like tufts; under parts pale buff. Length, twelve inches. The female, or reeve, is a third smaller

than the male, and in colour resembles the male in his winter
dress.

If by chance the reader has seen in some museum or collection
a group of ruffs in full breeding-plumage, displaying their immense,
shield-like ruffs of many colours, their beauty, singularity, and
wonderful variety must have astonished him. The curious feather
ornament is similar in form in all the birds, but the colour varies
infinitely, and it is hard to find two birds exactly alike. In some
individuals it is entirely white, in others intense purple-black, and
between these two extremes numberless varieties are found—buffs,
reds, chestnuts, browns of many shades, and mottled black or
brown and white, often beautifully streaked, or barred, or spotted,
or delicately vermiculated. But, alas! these dead, stuffed birds,
standing immovable by means of wire frames—a burlesque on the
wonderful living creatures—are the only ruffs he is ever likely to
see, since this bird, as a breeding species, has now been extirpated
in England. On migration in autumn and spring it still visits
our coasts, but in small numbers, and probably not very regularly.
These visitors, or stragglers, are without the wonderful feather
ornaments, which are nuptial, and assumed about the middle of
May, to be worn only for about six weeks.

The ruff is polygamous; and in spring the birds have the habit
of meeting on some small dry spot, or hillock, in a marsh to show
off and fight for the possession of the females, or reeves. When
engaging in combat the birds stand face to face, like fighting-cocks,
their great feather shields erected, and thrust at each other with
their long beaks. These combats usually take place early in the
morning; and formerly, when the birds were abundant, the marsh-
men made it their business to find the hillocks used by the birds,
and set horsehair nooses on them. The birds taken were fattened
for the market, and it was owing to this system of persecution
during the breeding season that the ruffs were reduced to a mere
remnant; and the remnant has since been destroyed by collectors.
In Lincolnshire the ruffs and reeves finally ceased to breed in
1882; in Norfolk the last few pairs of the once numerous British
race lingered on until within the last three or four years.

Sanderling.

Calidris arenaria.

Fig. 105.—Sanderling (winter plumage). ¼ natural size.

Feathers of the upper parts with dark brown centres, edged or spotted with rufous and tipped with grey ; base of inner primaries and edge of greater wing-coverts white, and outer feathers of tail-coverts also white ; face, neck, and upper breast pale chestnut spotted with dark brown ; under parts white; bill black ; legs and feet dark olive. Length, eight inches. In winter the upper plumage is ash-grey and the whole under parts white.

The sanderling is the sole member of its genus, and differs from other sandpipers in having no hind toe. It arrives on our coasts in August, young and old birds coming together. During the autumn months it is found in small flocks, associating with dunlins and other species on the seashore, and it is also a visitor to the margins of inland waters. A few birds remain through the winter. In April the migrants reappear, and remain until May or June before going north to their breeding-grounds. The sanderling is circumpolar in its distribution, and breeds farther north than most of the arctic species. The eggs are greenish buff in ground-colour, spotted with various shades of brown, and have been described as 'miniature curlews' eggs of a pale colour.' After the young have been reared the birds travel south along the shores of Europe, Asia, Africa, and America. On the Pacific coast of America their migration extends from the arctic regions to Patagonia, a journey of nearly eight thousand miles.

Common Sandpiper.

Tringoïdes hypoleucus.

Upper parts ash-brown glossed with olive; chin white; sides of the neck and breast pale ash with dusky streaks; under parts and tips of outer tail-feathers white. Length, eight inches.

The common sandpiper, known also as the summer snipe, is a summer visitor, to be met with from April until the end of September in suitable places throughout the British Islands. He is an exceeding lively and restless little bird, running nimbly or flitting along the margin of the water; when standing, perpetually bobbing his head and jerking his tail, on which account he is named ' fidler ' in some districts ; solitary in habit, or living with his mate only, choosing for a home the most secluded spots by streams and meres. In the southern half of England, where the localities that best suit him are fewest, he is very thinly diffused ; in Scotland, on the other hand, he is most abundant. Seebohm writes of this sandpiper : ' It is found in the same localities as those frequented by the dipper. High up among the mountains its melodious cry may be heard from the shingly margin of the stream, or the bird may not unfrequently be seen perched on a rock surrounded by water. Even here the sandpiper shows a partiality for certain haunts. The dipper loves their wildest mood, and the more they roll and toss over the rocky boulders, the more he seems at home ; but the sandpiper prefers their slow-running reaches and sandy, driftwood-covered islets, where the shingly and oozy rush-grown banks afford it the haunt it needs.'

The slight nest of moss and dried leaves is placed among coarse grass or rushes, or in a hole or sheltered hollow in a bank near a stream. Four pear-shaped eggs are laid, very large for the bird, reddish white in ground-colour, spotted and speckled with dusky brown.

The sandpiper utters on the wing a clear musical note, thrice repeated; and in the pairing season the male has a trilling note, or song, emitted while hovering in the air. Both old and young birds are able to swim with ease, and, to escape danger, dive as readily as a moorhen or water-rail.

Green Sandpiper.

Helodromus ochropus.

Upper parts olive-brown glossed with green and spotted with white and dusky; under parts white; tail white, the central feathers barred with black. Length, nine and a quarter inches.

The green sandpiper, like many other members of its family, is a visitor to the British Islands after the breeding season. This species differs from others in coming earlier and departing later. Half a century ago it was observed in Norfolk that the green sandpiper was to be met with during nearly every month in the year. The discovery was made later that it differs from other sandpipers in breeding in trees, in old nests of other birds, in squirrels' dreys, and on mossy trunks and branches. On account of this singular habit its nest is rarely found; but that it has bred, and does breed, in this country scarcely admits of a doubt.

In continental Europe it is known to breed in Scandinavia, North and Central Russia, and North Germany. The eggs are four in number, pale greyish green in ground-colour, with small purple-brown spots and markings.

The green sandpiper frequents inland watercourses and swamps in wooded districts, and is excessively shy and wary in its habits; it flies rapidly, and utters when on the wing its shrill, piping note, thrice repeated.

Redshank.

Totanus calidris.

Summer plumage: upper parts pale brown closely streaked and barred with umber; secondaries nearly white; rump white, with a few dusky flecks; tail-feathers white barred with blackish; under parts white, streaked on the neck and breast with umber; legs and feet orange-red. Winter plumage: upper parts ash-colour; rump and under parts white, sparsely streaked and spotted with grey on the neck and breast. The female is slightly larger than the male. Length, eleven inches.

The redshank, although not so numerous as formerly, is still a fairly common bird of the tidal flats and saltings on the east coast of England, and, in smaller numbers, in all suitable localities in Great Britain and Ireland. It is resident throughout the year, but is most plentiful in autumn and winter, at which time its numbers are increased by the arrival of migrants from northern Europe. Its food consists of marine worms, insects, and small crustaceans, and when its feeding-grounds are covered at flood-tide, it may be seen in close flocks on the small, dry areas, waiting for the water to subside. When thus congregated the birds are very loquacious, keeping up a perpetual confused sound of many voices, which has been compared to the chirruping concert of a flock of house-sparrows before settling down to roost of an evening. When the tide goes out the flocks break up, and the birds scatter in all directions to feed. The red-shank begins to breed about the end of May, in fens and inland marshes, and on the saltings, out of reach of the tide.

The nest is a slight depression in the ground, with a few dried bents and grass-blades for lining, or with no lining at all, and is in some cases quite exposed; but it is more often placed among coarse grass, or in the centre of a tussock, which conceals it from view. Four eggs are laid, of a yellowish grey ground-colour, blotched and spotted with purplish brown. When its breeding-haunts are approached the bird displays the greatest excitement, and flies circling about high above the intruder's head; and at such times a peculiar manner of flight, common to all the species of the genus Totanus, becomes very marked. The flight is slow and somewhat wavering, with an occasional downward stroke of the wings, which are much depressed, as of a duck about to drop on to the water. While flying in this way it clamours loudly, making the marsh ring with its shrill, piercing pipe, and at times dashes down close to the intruder's head, as if to intimidate him; and if there should be young, or eggs about to hatch, it drops on to the ground, and flutters along the surface like a wounded bird, in order to draw the danger away. Most birds in the order which includes the sandpipers, snipes, and plovers, make use of this device when their young are in danger.

At all times the redshank is a vigilant and clamorous bird, and as the meaning of its ringing alarm-note is understood by all waders and waterfowl, it is heartily detested by the gunners on the sea-coast.

Greenshank.

Totanus canescens.

FIG. 106.—GREENSHANK. ⅛ natural size.

Head and neck greyish white streaked with blackish brown; mantle and secondaries nearly black; rump and tail-feathers white, the latter mottled and barred with dusky brown; under parts white, streaked and spotted with ash-brown; legs and feet olive-green. Length, fourteen inches. In the winter plumage the upper parts are greyer and the under parts pure white.

The greenshank is an annual visitor during the spring and autumn migrations to the coasts and inland waters of Great Britain and Ireland; but it comes in small numbers. It has long been known that a number of pairs remain annually to breed in Scotland, and, according to Mr. Harvie-Brown, its breeding-range is extending in that country. Macgillivray wrote of this species: ' Its habits are very similar to those of the redshank, with which it associates in autumn. It is extremely shy and vigilant. . . . Many individuals remain during the summer, when they are to be found by the lakes in the interior. . . . At that season it is easily discovered, for when you are, perhaps, more than a quarter of a mile distant, it rises into the air with clamorous cries, alarming all the birds in its neighbourhood, flies round the place of its nest, now wheeling off to a distance, again advancing towards you, and at intervals alighting by the edge of the lake, where it continues its cries, vibrating its body all the while.'

The nest is often placed at some distance from the water. The four eggs are of a warm stone-colour, spotted with brown and blotched with purplish grey.

Whimbrel.

Numenius phæopus.

Crown dark brown, with broad pale streak down the middle; upper parts like the curlew, but darker; axillaries white barred with brown. Length of female, eighteen inches.

If it were our belief that the happiness of birds consisted in the degree of interest they, as species, excite in us, it could be said that the whimbrel suffers from his resemblance to the curlew. He is in form and colouring a lesser curlew with a less strongly marked individuality; 'half-curlew' and 'jack-curlew,' his two vernacular names, really imply that he is only half as attractive as the bigger bird. With us he is best known as an autumn and spring visitor, breeding only in the Orkney and Shetland Islands. The migration eastwards begins at the end of July, and the birds continue to pass until September, flying rapidly and at a great height. Of the flocks that alight to rest and feed on our coasts, a few birds remain through the winter. The return migration begins in April, but the greatest number of the migrants appear on our coasts about the beginning of May. On account of their punctuality, the whimbrel is known in some districts as the 'May bird.' In language and habits they resemble curlews, but have shriller voices, a more rapid flight, are not so excessively shy, and do not confine themselves so exclusively to the sand-flats when feeding. Grass-grown saltings, low meadows, and pasture-lands in the neighbourhood of the sea are visited by them. The nest is placed on moors and heaths not far removed from the shore. A slight hollow among the heather or coarse grass is lined with dead stems and leaves, and four eggs are laid, in colour like those of the curlew, but differing in size. During the breeding season the whimbrels are extremely pugnacious, and attack the skuas, lesser black-backed gulls, and other egg-stealing species, and chase them from their nesting-ground with shrill, angry cries.

Common Curlew.

Numenius arquata.

General plumage reddish ash mottled with dusky spots; belly nearly white, with dusky streaks; rump and tail-coverts white; tail-feathers barred with dark brown. Length of the female, which is the larger, twenty-one to twenty-six inches.

The curlew is the largest of its order in the British Islands; even the large woodcock looks small besides him, and among diminutive stints and sandpipers he is a veritable giant. An imperfect ibis in figure, in a pale sandy brown dress with dusky mottlings, he is, perhaps, the least handsome of the Limicolæ; in character he is one of the most interesting. What marvellously keen senses, what unfailing wariness and alertness must this large, inland-breeding species possess to keep its hold on existence in so many localities in this populous country in spite of incessant persecution! Most vigilant of birds, he is not vigilant on his own account only. He is the unsleeping sentinel of all the wild creatures that are pursued by man, warning them of danger with piercing cries that none fail to understand. The redshank, greenshank, and many other species, in this and other orders, are equally vociferous in the presence of danger, and their warnings are as promptly obeyed by all wild creatures that live with or near them; but a curious feature about the curlew is that he appears to take an intelligent interest in the welfare of beings not of his own species, and that he is distressed if they fail to act on his signal. In Yarrell's 'British Birds' (4th edit. vol. iii.) Howard Saunders gives a striking instance of this characteristic. He describes seeing one of these birds, 'after shrieking wildly over the head of a sleeping seal, swoop down, and apparently flick with its wings the unsuspecting animal, upon which the stalker was just raising his rifle.' This, to my mind, is a far more wonderful instance of the help-giving instinct in the lower animals than that related by Edwards of Banff, in which a number of terns swooped

OYSTER-CATCHERS. RINGED PLOVER. LITTLE STINT. CURLEW.

down upon one of their number which he had wounded and was pursuing, and, taking its wings in their beaks, raised it, and bore it away out to sea beyond his reach. The case of the curlew reminds us rather of the action of the rhinoceros-bird in waking the rhinoceros on the appearance of an enemy; but between curlew and seal there is no such thing as commensalism, and no tie, excepting the common knowledge that they are living creatures, and must fly for life at the approach of man, their deadliest enemy, on account of his superior cunning and his power to slay them at long distances.

During a greater part of the year the curlew is a shore-bird, seeking its food on the sand-flats which become covered at high water. When the tide overflows the flats the birds go inland, often to a distance of several miles from the sea, and wait there until the tide turns. They appear to know just when this occurs, however far from the shore they may be, and, rising and calling to each other, set out on their return, to arrive at the exact time when feeding may begin. It is during these journeys to and fro between the sea and the moors that the curlew looks at his best when, seen at a moderate distance, he passes in small flocks, disposed in the form of a wedge, or letter V, his sharp-pointed wings and long, ibis-like beak clearly outlined against the blue sky. To most lovers of nature and wild bird life the voice of the curlew is his principal attraction. He is very loquacious, and his ordinary cry of two notes, from which he takes his name, is singularly clear, far-reaching, and wild in character. His night cries have given rise to some curious and gloomy superstitions in Scotland, where the curlew is called ' whaup.' According to Yarrell, the bird is a 'long-nebbit thing,' from which the Highlander prays to be delivered, classing it with ' witches and warlocks.' In the same work we read : ' Saxby says that the Shet-landers regard with horror the very idea of using so uncanny a bird as food; in fact, a visitor who did so was afterwards alluded to, almost in a whisper, as " the man that ate the whaup." ' Long may the ' long-nebbit things ' continue to exist, to delight and invigorate us with their wild voices !

In spring—early in April as a rule—the curlews begin to forsake their feeding-grounds on the sandbanks and go inland to breed; but some unpaired or non-breeding birds remain through the summer by the sea. Wild extensive moors are its favourite summer haunts. 'Its breeding-range,' Seebohm says, ' is similar to that of the red grouse and ring-ouzel.' Its nesting-place, as a rule, is on the flat and boggy parts of the moor, and the nest is not unfrequently placed among reeds or rushes. The three or four eggs are olive-green, blotched and spotted with dark brown and dusky green. The young birds when hatched have short, straight, plover-like bills.

The family Scolopacidæ, which comprises the phalaropes, avocet, snipes, sandpipers, godwits, the curlew, and whimbrel, numbers thirty-four (so-called) British species. Eighteen have been fully described, including the ruff, now extinct as a breeder, and fallen to the position of a mere straggler in this country. The ruff is one of three interesting and handsome species in this family of birds which have been extirpated in England during the present century. Another is the avocet (*Recurvirostra avocetta*), a singular wader, conspicuous and beautiful in black and white plumage, with a long bill, curved upwards. It bred in large numbers in fens and marshes in the eastern countries; but since about 1825, when it finally ceased to visit its old haunts in summer, it has been known only as a rare straggler. The third extirpated species is the fine black-tailed godwit (*Limosa melanura*), which bred annually in Norfolk and the neighbouring county until about 1835. It is now a visitor on migration, in very small numbers, to the east coast. The bar-tailed godwit, which has never bred in the British Islands, also appears occasionally in small numbers during migration. It breeds in northern Europe. The black-winged stilt, which resembles the avocet in its black and white dress, but has longer legs and a straight bill, is a rare straggler from southern Europe. Of several species of sandpipers that appear as stragglers on our coasts during migration, there are two that have some claim to be regarded as British species. One is the wood-sandpiper (*Totanus glareola*), which comes nearest to the green sandpiper is size, colour, and general appearance. It appears on the east and south coasts in autumn, in small flocks composed of young birds. The wood-sandpiper is known to have bred on one occasion in this country —at Prestwich Car, in Northumberland, in 1853. The second species is the spotted redshank, a rare and irregular visitor during migration, chiefly to the eastern counties. Its winter plumage is ash-grey above and white beneath; in summer it differs from all other sandpipers in its dark hue, the general colour being sooty black, the upper parts studded with triangular spots of pure white. It breeds in northern Europe in wooded situations, and is partial to burnt grounds, where its dark plumage assimilates in colour to the charred wood and blackened earth. Like the redshank, it is, when breeding, exceedingly vigilant and noisy when approached.

Eight species, all rare stragglers, remain to be mentioned : the broad-billed sandpiper, pectoral sandpiper, Bonaparte's sandpiper, American stint, buff-breasted sandpiper, Bartram's sandpiper, red-breasted snipe, and Esquimaux curlew. With the exception of the first, which breeds in northern Europe and winters in Africa, these are all American species, breeding in or near the arctic regions, and migrating in autumn to South America, in some cases as far south as Patagonia.

Roughly speaking, we may say that, of the thirty-four species of the snipe family described in most ornithological works as 'British,' seventeen or eighteen are breeders in or annual visitants to this country; six are occasional visitors—two or three of these are perhaps, annual visitors, but in very small numbers; and the remaining ten are all rare stragglers.

Arctic Tern.

Sterna macrura.

Bill blood-red; legs and feet coral-red; head and nape black; mantle pearl-grey; rump and tail white; under parts paler pearl-grey. Length, fourteen and a half inches.

The tern has been called a sea-swallow, and he is certainly swallow-like in his slender figure, sharply forked tail, and aërial habits; but he is built on more graceful lines, with proportionately longer wings, and in his white and pearl-grey plumage is the more beautiful bird. The blood-red hue of the beak in the arctic tern gives that touch of bright colour which adds so much to the beauty of a species otherwise wholly black or white; it intensifies a black plumage, as we see in the blackbird and chough, and makes the white plumage seem more immaculate in its whiteness. The flight of the tern is unlike that of any other bird, whether of the sea or land : it is more airy, and suited to the pale, slender, aërial figure; buoyant and slightly wavering, it reminds one a little of the high, apparently uncertain, flight of some large-winged butterfly; and it is in perfect harmony, not only with the slimmer form, but with the idea of a being whose life is passed amid wind and mist and fluctuating wave. It is a rare pleasure to watch a number of these terns feeding in an inlet or bay, where the spectator can sit or lie on a cliff or jutting rock near to and on a level with the birds. They are not concerned at his presence, but, intent on their prey, pass and re-pass before him so near that their round, brilliant eyes may be distinctly seen. The blood-red, dagger-like beak is pointed downwards almost constantly as the bird gazes on the water thirty or forty yards below. All at once the buoyant flight is arrested, the bird hangs motionless in mid-air, the snow-white, forked tail expanded and depressed, the slow-moving, wavering wings rapidly vibrated. In such an attitude he reminds you less of a windhover than of the humming-bird, when that little feathered fairy is seen hovering motionless *above* the flowers on which its eyes are fixed. Suddenly the wings partly close, and the white figure drops plumb down, with such force as to send up a shower of foam and spray as it strikes on and disappears into the water, to emerge in a moment or two with a small fish in its bill.

The terns, of which there are five breeding-species in the British Islands, are all migrants, and come to us in spring. The arctic tern ranges farthest north : it is the most common species on the coasts of Scotland and its islands ; its most southern breeding-station is at the Farnes, off the coast of Northumberland. It breeds in communities sometimes numbering thousands of birds. The nests are placed very near each other, often within half a yard, among scanty grass and herbage, or on the shingle and sand of the beach, and sometimes on the bare rock. Two or three eggs are laid, greatly varying in their ground-colour, olive, buff, greyish brown, stone, and other tints being found ; and the spots and blotches of blackish brown and grey may be few or many. The young birds are at first covered with a yellowish down with dark brown spots, and are very active. When the nesting-ground is entered the birds rise up, and hover in a dense cloud above the intruder's head, their united powerful screams producing an extraordinary noise, like that of the sea on a shingled beach when the withdrawing wave drags back the pebbles with shrill and grating sounds.

In September and October the arctic tern migrates to warmer regions.

Common Tern.

Sterna fluviatilis.

Fig. 107 —Common Tern. ½ natural size.

Bill, legs, and feet orange-red ; entire plumage as in the arctic tern, except the lower parts, which are more nearly pure white. Length, fourteen and a quarter inches.

So nearly alike are the arctic and common terns that it is hard, well-nigh impossible, in fact, to distinguish them when they are observed flying about in company. In size, manner of flight, language, and general appearance, they are identical. On a close examination the common tern is found to be slightly less slender in build, its under parts dull white instead of pale grey, its beak tipped with black and coral-red, instead of blood-red. It is doubtless owing to their similarity that the two species associate freely together at all times, and are often to be found breeding side by side. But while the arctic tern is most common in the north, from the Shetlands, Orkneys, and Hebrides, to the coast of Northumberland on the one side of the country, and of Lancashire on the other, the common tern is common only on the coasts south of these two points. The nest is a slight depression, sometimes with a little dry grass for lining, placed on the shingle of the beach ; the three eggs are yellowish stone, grey, or olive colour, spotted and blotched with dark brown and grey.

z

Roseate Tern.

Sterna dougalli.

Bill black, orange-red at the base in the breeding season; legs and feet red; head and upper parts the same as in the arctic and common terns, except that the mantle is a paler pearl-grey; lower parts white suffused with rose. Length, fifteen inches and a quarter.

This species differs from the two already described in its slimmer body and greater length of tail, and in its shorter and narrower wings. It also differs in the delicate rose-colour suffusing or tinging the white under-plumage; but this faint exquisite hue is seen only when the bird is in the hand. On the wing, unless very near, it appears white and pale grey like the common tern, and only an accustomed eye can distinguish it among the others by its slightly different shape. It may be more easily recognised by its short, con-stantly repeated note, which is more musical than that of the other species. Besides this short, excited note, it has the long, somewhat guttural, and gull-like cry common to all the terns. It breeds only on islands, and Howard Saunders, our best authority on the birds of this order, says that it is more 'intolerant of interference' than other terns: hence many of its old breeding-stations on the British coasts have been successively abandoned during the last half-century owing to egg-collecting, and the bird is now becoming so rare that its extinction as a British species at no distant date is feared by ornithologists. In the north of England, and at various places on the coasts of Scotland, a few pairs still breed in company with the common and arctic terns. The nest is a slight depression in the sand and gravel, and two or three eggs are laid, creamy white or buff-colour, blotched and clouded with bluish grey and rich brown. As soon as the young have been reared the breeding-ground is aban-doned, and the migration southwards begins.

Little Tern.

Sterna minuta.

Bill orange-yellow tipped with black; legs and feet orange; crown and nape black; forehead and stripe over the eye white; mantle pearl-grey; tail and under parts white. Length, eight inches.

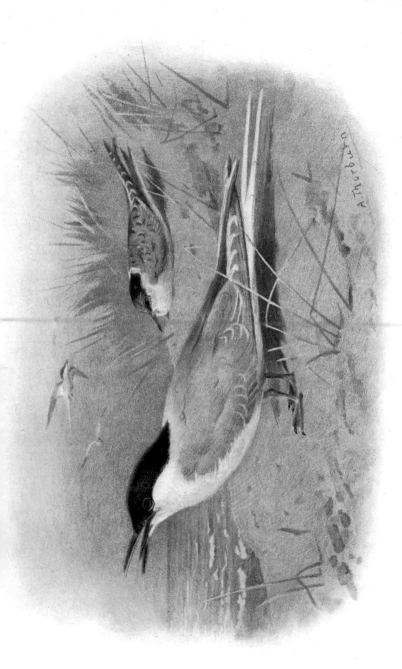

A. Thorburn

PLATE XII.   ROSEATE TERN (ADULT AND IMMATURE). $\frac{2}{3}$ NAT. SIZE.

The little, or lesser tern, is a third less than the common species in size, measuring only eight inches in length. The colour is nearly the same in both birds, except that the under parts in the little tern are pure white, and the bill orange—instead of coral-red. The voice differs somewhat, being thinner and shriller in tone ; otherwise the language is the same. The flight is more wavering. This species is much less numerous than the arctic and common terns ; in its habits it closely resembles them, breeding in communities, sometimes in company with the other kinds. When breeding alongside of the common tern its nests, as a rule, are placed a little

FIG. 108.—LESSER TERN. ¼ natural size.

apart and nearer to the water. The nest is a slight depression in the loose sand and gravel, sometimes with a few bents and fragments of dry seaweed for lining ; the eggs are two or three in number, of a light stone-colour, spotted with grey and brown. In size and colour they closely resemble the eggs of the ringed plover. This tern, like the others, hovers screaming overhead when its breeding-ground is intruded on ; but recovers from its anxiety only too quickly, for no sooner has the intruder got a little distance away than the bird drops down directly on to its nest. When the female is incubating the male brings food for her, and Mr. Trevor-Battye has described in his ' Pictures in Prose ' the pretty way in which the birds play with each other before the fish is delivered. ' Returned from his quest, the bird with a fish in his bill circles round and round, and lower and lower, over his mate, and presently drops down beside her. Then he begins a series of extraordinary evolutions. With head thrown back, wings drooping, and tail cocked straight up, he struts—no other word expresses it—he struts about in front of his mate. . . . He jumps at his mate, as if daring her to take the fish. Then he will fly round for a bit, only to settle again and repeat the play. I have seen on several occasions a female "chit," before she had settled down on her eggs, get up, fly off, settle on the shingle off and on for a considerable time, followed persistently by her fish-bearing partner, but always avoiding him, as if coquetting or really annoyed. Sooner or later the fish is always relinquished, or, as I suspect, taken by the female bird.'

In Norfolk the little terns are called chits, or chit-perles.

Sandwich Tern.

Sterna cantiaca.

Bill and feet black; upper part of the head black; mantle pearl-grey; rump, tail, throat, and under parts white; the breast suffused with rose. Length, sixteen inches.

This is the largest of the British terns, being as much superior as the little tern is inferior in size to the arctic and common species. In its manner of flight and language it differs somewhat from the others. At a distance the under parts appear to be of a snowy whiteness; in the captive or dead bird the white plumage is seen to be suffused with an evanescent delicate pink colour. On the wing the Sandwich tern does not look so graceful and beautiful as the smaller species : the flight is heavier, straighter, unwavering, the wings beating more rapidly. Its scream is shorter, less inflected, and has a harsh and even grating sound.

This tern suffers much from the persecutions of the egg-collector, as well as of that base kind of sportsman who is allowed to amuse himself in August and September by slaughtering terns. On the Farne Islands, which are protected during the breeding season, there now exists a considerable colony of Sandwich terns, numbering about one thousand pairs, and a few smaller colonies are found on the coasts of Scotland and Ireland, and on some of the lakes of those countries. On the Farnes the birds breed on one of the islands on a flat surface overgrown with sea-campion, and here their nests are placed so close together that it is difficult at times to walk over the ground without treading on the nests containing eggs or young birds. The eggs are two or three in number, and are stone-colour with a yellow tinge, thickly spotted with grey or brown.

Besides the five species described, there are eight terns set down in the books as British. Of these, the Caspian tern, gull-billed tern, and black tern, are described as 'irregular visitors,' and come in small numbers ; the whiskered tern, white-winged black tern, sooty tern, Scopoli's sooty tern, and noddy, are all rare stragglers, the last three from the tropics. The black tern (*Hydrochelidon nigra*) was in reality a British bird in former times, a summer visitor, breeding in immense

FIG. 109.—BLACK TERN. ⅟₇ natural size.

numbers in the fens and marshes in some of the eastern counties. It bred 'in myriads' in Norfolk as late as 1818, and, in diminishing numbers, down to 1835. 'Drainage and persecution' caused the destruction of this graceful species.

Kittiwake.

Rissa tridactyla.

Bill greenish yellow; legs and feet black ; mantle deep grey : head, neck, tail, and under parts white. Length, fifteen and a half inches.

The kittiwake takes its pretty name from its usual cry, composed of three notes, two quick and short, and one long. It is the smallest of the British gulls, excluding the stragglers, and is also one of the handsomest and most interesting in its habits. It is more of a sea-bird than most gulls, feeding principally on small fish, which it captures after the manner of a tern, hovering motionless for a few moments, then dashing down on to the water with great force.

It is common round the British Islands throughout the year, but probably most of the birds that breed on our coasts migrate to more southern regions in winter, their places, meanwhile, being taken by visitors from the north. Its breeding-sites, often shared with the guillemot and razorbill, are precipitous rocky cliffs fronting the sea, the nest being placed on the ledges and wherever a projecting rock affords standing-room for a bird of its size. When the colony is a numerous one the birds may be seen whitening the face of the precipice from within a few feet above high-water mark to within a few feet of the top. The nests, often placed so near together as to be almost touching, are rather bulky, built of seaweed mixed with turf, and lined with dry grass. Two or three, sometimes four, eggs are laid, varying in ground-colour from greenish blue to olive-brown, or buff, or buffish brown, spotted and blotched with reddish brown, and under-markings of pale brown and grey.

Where suitable sites exist, and the birds are not too much molested, the kittiwakes have breeding colonies on the British coasts from the Scilly Islands and the Cornish and Devon cliffs right away to St. Kilda in the north. The kittiwakes breed later than most gulls, unfortunately for them. It has been pointed out again and again that the young birds are often hardly able to feed themselves, and in many cases are not yet out of their nests, at the end of July, which is also the end of the close time for sea-birds. It then becomes lawful for the scoundrels who practise this form of sport to slaughter the kittiwakes—both the helpless young and the parent birds that are engaged in feeding and protecting them.

Herring-Gull.

Larus argentatus.

Bill yellow; legs and feet flesh-colour; mantle grey; head, tail, and lower parts white; outer primaries black. Length, twenty-four inches.

The herring-gull, which derives its name from its habit of following the shoals of herrings, is common on our coasts throughout the year. Like most gulls, it searches the shore at ebb-tide for stranded marine animals, dead and alive, and garbage of all kinds. It quarrels with ravens and crows over the carcass of a dead sheep, and, like the raven, is a plunderer of eggs and young birds from the cliffs. It is often seen at a distance from the sea, roaming over the moors in search of prey or carrion; and it also feeds on insects and, like the black-headed gull, sometimes follows the plough to pick up worms and grubs. It nests on precipitous, rocky shores, usually making choice of the summit or upper ledges. It also breeds on flat islands, sometimes in company with the lesser black-backed gull, which it resembles in size and general appearance. It usually breeds in communities, but is not so strictly gregarious as most gulls at this season. The nest, which is usually somewhat bulky, is composed of seaweed and herbage, and lined with dry grass. Three eggs are laid, stone-colour or light olive-brown, spotted and blotched with dark umber.

Lesser Black-backed Gull.

Larus fuscus.

Bill, legs, and feet yellow; summer plumage of the adult white, except on the mantle, which varies from slate grey to black. Length, twenty-three inches.

From its abundance, its large size—which is nearly the same as that of the herring-gull—and its extremely conspicuous black-and-white plumage at maturity, the lesser black-back is one of the most familiar birds on our coasts. The young differ greatly from the adults, having a slate-grey beak, flesh-coloured legs, and a general brown plumage. The mature breeding colours, including yellow on legs and bill, with a vermilion patch on the lower mandible, are not perfect until the fourth year. Judging solely from this fact of its slow growth to maturity, we may take it that the lesser black-back lives long—that its natural term, as in some accipitrine species, probably exceeds a century. It is certainly the case that this gull is able, not only to keep itself alive, but to keep up its numbers, notwithstanding its large size and the dislike with which it is regarded on account of its predacious habits. The unfeathered biped is ever anxious to keep all the killing and plundering in his own hands. The voice of this gull is very powerful and far-reaching, and, when soaring with its fellows, occasionally all the birds unite their voices in a chorus of short and long cries, laughter-like in character, yet with something solemn, and even desolate, in the sound, as of the sea. It is gregarious and social at all seasons, and breeds in gulleries, where the nests are placed close together on the level ground. The three eggs are of a light stone colour, spotted and blotched with blackish brown and grey. The largest and best-known colony on the British coasts is at the Farne Islands, and of that colony Seebohm writes: 'It is a wonderful sight on approaching an island to see the green mass sprinkled all over with large white-looking birds, every one standing head to wind, like an innumerable army of white weathercocks.' It is also fine to see and hear them, when a person walks about among the nests, stooping occasionally to examine eggs or handle the yellow, black-spotted chicks: the birds hover in a dense cloud over his head, their deep, powerful cries mingling in one mighty uproar, and, at short intervals, one or two birds dash down out of the bird-cloud as if to strike his head, and, missing it by an inch or two, reascend to repeat the action.

Common Gull.

Larus canus.

Bill greenish at the base, yellow at the tip; legs and feet greenish yellow; mantle ash-grey; first two primaries black, with a white patch near the extremity; the rest black near the end; head, neck, tail, and under parts white. Length, eighteen and a half inches.

The name of this species is somewhat misleading, as it is less numerous on most of our coasts, and in estuaries and rivers, than the black-headed species, which indeed is often called the common gull. When flying about in company, the two species are indistinguishable in the winter plumage. The common gull has no breeding-place south of the Border. In Scotland and its islands there are several colonies, and in Ireland a few. In its habits it is intermediate between the marine and inland species, and its gulleries are placed both on islands near the sea-coast and in lochs at a distance from the shore. Like the herring-gull and black-headed gull, it follows the plough to pick up worms and grubs, and roams over moors, marshes, and pasture-lands in search of insects, small vertebrates, and carrion. The nest is bulky, and composed of sea-weed, herbage, and dry grass. Three eggs are laid, olive-brown, spotted and streaked with blackish.

Great Black-backed Gull.

Larus marinus.

Bill yellow; legs and feet flesh-colour; plumage as in the lesser black-backed gull. Length, thirty inches.

Turner, who wrote on British birds three centuries ago, in describing the great black-backed gull, says that it was called 'cob' on

Fig. 110.—Great Black-backed Gull. $\frac{1}{11}$ natural size.

the Kentish and Essex coast. It is curious to find that it is still known by this name in the same localities, where it is now very rare. In colour and appearance it closely resembles the lesser black-back, but exceeds it in size, and is nearly twice as heavy—it is, in fact, the largest of the gulls. It is also the rarest species in the British Islands; for although its breeding-sites are not few in Scotland, while others exist on the coasts of England, Wales, and Ireland, its colonies are very small compared with those of other species, and in many cases the breeding-place is occupied by a single pair. Its habits are similar to those of the herring and lesser black-backed gulls; but being so much larger and more powerful, it is more injurious to other sea-birds, whose nests it plunders of their eggs or young. It is also more oceanic, straying to a great distance from land in its search for dead animal matter floating on the waves—a veritable ' vulture of the sea.' Its nest is placed, as a rule, on the summit of an inaccessible rock on the coast, or on a small rocky island, and is carelessly formed of seaweed and grass. Two or three eggs are laid, greyish brown, sometimes tinged with olive, with dark brown spots distributed sparingly over the whole surface.

Black-headed Gull.

Larus ridibundus.

Bill and feet red; head and upper part of the neck blackish brown; mantle grey; all the rest, white; the under parts tinged with pink. The black on the head is lost in winter. Length, sixteen inches.

The black-headed gull, if not the most abundant of its genus, is without doubt the most generally known, on account of its wide diffusion in the country, and of its habit of breeding in inland marshes. It remains throughout the year, most of the time frequenting the flat parts of the sea-coast, estuaries, and tidal rivers, where it is seen perpetually roaming up and down in search of the small fishes and crustaceans on which it feeds, and any dead animal matter cast up by the tide. In its winter dress it is almost impossible to tell this species from the common gull and kittiwake when they are seen together, as in size they are nearly alike, and the buoyant, leisurely flight and circling motions in the air are the same in all. But very early in spring the distinguishing mark and nuptial ornament of a black hood is assumed, after which there can be no mistake. And here I may remark that I differ from Howard Saunders when he says that, as the hood is not black, the bird should be called the brown-headed gull. Vernacular names of this kind are descriptive of the creatures as they appear to us when seen living in a state of nature; and at a distance of twenty or thirty yards, which is as close as a flying gull will come to a man, the hood certainly appears to be black.

In March the gulls withdraw to marshes and meres to breed

BLACK-HEADED GULLS. POCHARDS. SHOVELER. WATER-HENS.

The breeding-place is usually in the neighbourhood of the sea, sometimes in an inland district. Year after year the same spot is resorted to, and it is known that some of the gulleries in this country have existed for centuries. One of the largest and best known in England is at Scoulton Mere, in Norfolk. Half a century ago 20,000 birds annually bred at this spot, but the colony has now diminished to less than half that number. A favourite site for the gullery is an island in a mere or swamp, and the nests are placed both on the ground and on clumps of rushes or tussocks of grass. Three or four eggs are laid, varying in ground-colour from olive-brown to pale green, blue, or salmon, blotched with black and dark brown. During the breeding season the birds seek their food over the surrounding country in marshes, meadow-lands, and fields that are being ploughed. Seebohm says: 'So easily do they adapt themselves to changed circumstances, that they have already become used to the steam-plough. It is a very pretty sight to watch a party of these little gulls, looking snow-white in the distance against the rich brown of the newly turned-up soil, paddling amongst the clumsy clods with dainty, red-webbed feet, and continually lifting their white wings to balance themselves on the rough ground, reminding one of a group of angels by Gustave Doré.' One suspects that Doré, being, like other artists, incapable of imagining the un-imaginable, made use of gulls and such like as models for his angels.

This gull, like most of the Laridæ, is a vociferous bird, and his notes—short and rapid, like excited exclamations, or drawn out, guttural in tone, and inflected in various ways—often sound like laughter; hence the name of laughing gull, sometimes given to this species, and the specific name of *ridibundus.* To my ear it is like the guttural and extravagant laughter of the negro, rather than that of the white man.

Besides the six species described, there are six others, belonging to the sub-family Larinæ (true gulls), which figure in the books as British species. One of these (the second on the list) is perhaps a regular visitor.

Ivory gull (*Pagophila eburnea*).—A circumpolar species; occasionally straggles to the British coasts.

Glaucous gull (*Larus glaucus*).—Circumpolar in its range; a winter visitor to the northern parts of the United Kingdom.

Iceland gull (*L. leucopterus*).—A rare winter visitor (to the north) from the arctic regions.

Great black-headed gull (*L. ichthyaëtus*).—A single specimen of this southern species was obtained many years ago in this country.

Little gull (*L. minutus*).—An irregular visitor from continental Europe.

Sabine's gull (*Xema sabinii*).—A rare straggler from North America.

Common or Great Skua.

Stercorarius catarrhactes.

FIG. 111.—GREAT SKUA. $\frac{1}{12}$ natural size.

Upper parts mottled brown; shafts of the quills and tail-feathers white; under parts rufous-brown; bill, legs, and feet black. Length, twenty-five inches.

Of skuas there are but six species, two of which inhabit the southern hemisphere, and breed on the confines of the antarctic regions. The others belong to the northern half of the globe, and range in summer to the arctic regions. These four are all claimed as members of the British avifauna, but only two species need be fully described in this work. The skuas are gull-like birds, very strong on the wing, and swift flyers; and, like the gulls, they have a variety of feeding-habits, and are both the vultures and hawks of the sea.

In the skuas there is more of the hawk and not so much of the vulture. Their predatory habits, extreme violence in attack, and readiness to take and destroy their feathered fellow-creatures and toilers of the deep when the occasion offers, have won them a reputation among birds similar to that of a pirate among men—the lawless rover of the sea, who is without compunction, and whose hand is against every man. In shape and general appearance the skuas are gull-like; they differ chiefly from the gulls in the form of the beak, which is straight for two-thirds of its length, and for the rest curved into a hook, as in the raptorial birds; and in the form of the tail, which is cuneiform, with the two centre feathers projecting beyond the others. In the gulls the tail-feathers are of equal length; while the terns, at the other end of this order of birds, have sharply forked tails like the swallow.

The great skua, or bonxie, as it is called by the Shetlanders, is the largest of the family. Except during the breeding season it is a solitary bird, oceanic in its habits, roaming far and wide over the waters in quest of food, its visits to land being restricted to rocky island coasts. Like the marine gulls, it feeds on dead fish found stranded or floating on the water, and on dead animal matter of all kinds, and also catches fish by pouncing on them as they swim near the surface. But it prefers to watch the movements of the other fishing-birds, which it follows and associates with to rob them of their prey. The herring-gull and lesser black-back may be frequently seen pursuing a tern or kittiwake to take from it the fish it has just captured; but these would-be robbers are not very successful—the chased tern, or small gull, in most cases proves too quick for them. These are like the merest mock chases and playful interludes in the day's work compared with the sudden, furious onslaught of the bonxie. The swiftest gull or tern cannot escape from him; he can turn as quickly as a swallow, and keep close to his victim in all his doublings, until the chased bird in his terror disgorges the fish he has just swallowed. The skua stays his flight to pick up the falling morsel, and the chase is over. Besides robbing the birds of their prey, he is also a bird-killer, making his deadly attacks on the sickly or wounded, and on the young in the breeding season.

The great skua breeds in the Shetlands, but the birds have now been reduced to a few pairs, chiefly owing to the persecution of collectors. Every effort has been made to protect the birds in their two small colonies on Unst and Foula, but it is scarcely to be hoped that this insignificant remnant will continue to exist many years, when we consider that the childish and contemptible craze of eggshell-collecting is very common, and that many collectors do not hesitate to steal, or to bribe others to steal for them, the eggs they desire to have in their cabinets.

About April the surviving birds return to their ancestral breeding-grounds and make their simple nests, composed of a few twigs or a little dry grass, in a slight hollow in the ground. The two eggs laid vary in ground-colour from pale to dark buffish brown, and are spotted with dark brown, with greyish brown underlying spots. They resemble the eggs of the herring-gull and lesser black-back.

In the breeding season the skua is a terror to all birds in the vicinity of its nest, as it is even more savage and impetuous in the defence of its eggs than when seeking its prey. Ravens, sea-eagles, dogs, and foxes, are violently attacked and driven off by it. It is also very bold towards a human intruder, gliding to and fro close to the surface within a few feet of him, and hovering overhead, screaming, and occasionally dashing down violently at his head, and all but striking it. They do strike sometimes, it is said, and it is related by the Shetlanders that birds have impaled themselves on a knife held up to ward off an attack, and have met their death in other curious ways, when trying to defend their nests. These stories are doubtless true, although the birds are less bold now than formerly, a long and sad experience having taught them that there is one enemy they cannot frighten away. I have often been struck by birds engaged in defending their nests—hawks, waders, and perching birds—and in some cases the striker has stunned himself ; but this happened at a distance from Britain, in a region where birds have not been persecuted so long, and fear man less.

It is from its exceedingly violent down-rushing method of attack that the great skua derives its specific name of *catarrhactes*. It rushes down like a cataract. This is an ancient name for a bird of prey, and, in this case, a singularly fit one. But what shall we say of Brisson's hideous and ridiculous invention of *Stercorarius* as the generic name for all the skuas ?

Richardson's Skua.

Stercorarius crepidatus.

Crown dusky; cheek, neck, and under parts white tinged with yellow and brown; rest of the plumage dusky. Length, twenty inches.

This species breeds in the Outer Hebrides, the Orkneys, and the Shetlands; it is also said to be a regular breeder in Sutherlandshire. It is a much more numerous species than the great skua, being a regular visitor to the coasts of Scotland in the autumn and spring migrations. In its preying habit it resembles the bonxie, but, unlike that species, is gregarious. It breeds on moors, often at a considerable distance from the sea, and its nests are widely scattered on the breeding-ground. A slight hollow in the ground, with a little dry grass for lining, serves as a receptacle for the eggs. Two eggs are laid, and in some cases only one. These vary greatly in shape, some being nearly round, others long and pointed. In ground, colour they vary from russet-brown to pale olive, and are evenly and sparingly spotted with dark brown.

A curious fact about this species is that there are two forms, one light in colour, the other dark, and that these habitually interbreed; but the young, instead of being intermediate, are, according to Seebohm, light or dark, like one of the parents.

The pomatorhine skua (*S. pomatorhinus*) is an autumn and spring visitor on migration to the seas in the vicinity of the British coasts. In some seasons it occurs in large numbers, but is not very regular in its appearance. Buffon's skua (*S. parasiticus*) is a rare and irregular visitor on migration to the British coasts. It breeds in the arctic regions, and is circumpolar.

Stormy Petrel.

Procellaria pelagica.

Upper parts black, except the tail-coverts, which are white at their bases; edges of the wing-coverts slightly edged with white; under parts sooty black; bill and feet black. Length, six inches.

A A

The names of stormy petrel and Mother Carey's chicken are as familiar to everyone as that of rook, or partridge, or hedge-sparrow ;

FIG. 112.—STORMY PETREL. ½ natural size.

but the little bird they belong to is known by sight to comparatively few persons. It is pre - eminently an oceanic species, that comes to land only to breed; its breeding-places are on remote and lonely islands not easy of access; and, when breeding, the bird is nocturnal in habits, and it would be possible for anyone to spend many days in the very midst of a colony of petrels and not see them, or suspect that they were there.

The name of stormy petrel has been altered in several modern ornithological works to that of storm petrel; and on this subject Seebohm makes a delightfully characteristic observation. 'The words stormy petrel,' he writes, 'are doubtless a very ungrammatical combination, as many other familiar English words are ; but that is no reason why they should be altered, although they may have offended the ears of Yarrell and his academical friends.' The rebuke is the more deserved when we remember that these same 'academical friends' have been quick to ridicule the attempts of certain ornithologists to substitute the name of hedge-accentor for that of hedge-sparrow—the absurdest name of all, but 'consecrated,' as they say, by long use, and Shakespeare. The name of 'petrel' comes about in a very curious way. It is the diminutive of Peter, given to the bird on account of a habit it has, when gliding along just above the surface, of dropping its feet and paddling, producing the idea that it is walking on the water. I am not quite sure that this is a correct derivation ; Peter (the apostle), it will be remem-

bered, was not wholly successful in his attempt to walk on the
waves. Sailors call the petrels ' Mother Carey's chickens ' ; but not,
as might be imagined from such a name, on account of any tender
regard or feeling of affection for the birds. Mother Carey is supposed
to be a kind of ocean witch, a supernatural Mother Shipton, who
rides the blast, and who has for attendants and harbingers the little
dark-winged petrels, just as the more amiable Mother Venus had
her doves.

The stormy petrel is known to be the smallest bird with webbed
feet, consequently his smallness is to the ornithologist his chief
distinction. He is no bigger than a sparrow, and when seen flying
in the wake of a ship, gliding to and fro close to the surface, his
small size, sharp-pointed, swallow-like wings, dark plumage, and
snow-white rump, give him the appearance of the house-martin.
Like other pelagic birds, the petrel when on the wing is perpetually
seeking its food, and is seen to drop often on to the surface to pick
up some floating particle from the water; and yet to this day
ornithologists do not accurately know what it feeds on. The bird
is generally excessively fat, and when taken in the hand it ejects a
small quantity of amber-coloured oil from its mouth. When
dissected, its stomach is found to contain an oily fluid, and the
young are fed with the same substance, injected by the parent bird
into their mouths. Where this oil springs from, and how it comes to
be floating on the water, is one of the secrets of the sea which this
bird shares with other members of the petrel family ; but they have
no tongue to tell it.

The petrels do not arrive at their breeding-grounds until about
the middle of June. They have colonies on the Scilly Islands, and
at various other points on the west coast to St. Kilda, and the Orkneys and Shetlands. A few small colonies are also found on some
of the islands on the Irish coast. The birds breed in holes in stone
walls and piles of loose stones, and, in some localities, in old rabbit-
burrows and holes in banks. A single egg is laid, on a slight bed of
grass ; it is very large for the bird's size, rough in texture, pure
white, and in most cases thinly sprinkled with minute reddish brown
specks.

The young birds are fed at night, and may then be heard faintly
clamouring for food after dark.

The fork-tailed, or Leach's petrel (*Procellaria leucorrhoa*), is a
larger bird than the last, being about the same size as the swift. It

is a much rarer species than the stormy petrel, and has only two known breeding-places in the United Kingdom, one at St. Kilda, the other on the island of North Rona, off the west coast of Scotland. On all other parts of the British coast it is known only as a storm-driven straggler. The birds breed in June, in holes which they make in the soft peaty soil to a depth of two or three feet, or deeper. A slight nest of dry grass is made, and a single egg deposited, pure white in colour, with a zone of small reddish spots at the large end. During the daytime the birds remain silent in their holes; in the evening they become active and garrulous.

Wilson's petrel (*Oceanites oceanicus*), a bird about the size of a swift, with a black plumage and white rump, appears occasionally as a straggler in the British Islands. Its only known breeding-grounds are in the southern hemisphere.

Manx Shearwater.
Puffinus anglorum.

Fig. 113.—Manx Shearwater. ⅛ natural size.

Bill blackish; legs and feet yellowish flesh-colour; crown, nape, and upper parts sooty black; under parts white; sides of neck mottled with greyish brown. Length, fifteen inches.

The Manx shearwater is the most abundant and best known of the four petrels that frequent the British seas. It has several breeding-stations in the Channel and along the west coast of Great Britain, and a few on islands off the coast of Ireland; but its principal colonies are on St. Kilda, the sea-bird's paradise. Like the stormy petrel, the shearwater is nocturnal in its habits during the summer, feeding by night, and remaining concealed in its burrows during the day. In winter it seeks its food at all hours. It has the same habits as the stormy petrel of dropping its feet and paddling in the water, while sustained by its motionless, outspread wings. Its name of shearwater is derived from its custom of gliding along very close to the surface. Seebohm likens it to ' a gigantic swift ' in appearance as it careers to and fro over the waves when the gale is at its height. Except when breeding its whole time is spent on the open sea : it is as truly at home on the stormy Atlantic, a thousand miles from the nearest land, as is the blackbird in its favourite shrubbery or the sedentary owl in its hollow beech-tree. But it remains longer at its breeding-grounds than the other species. At St. Kilda it begins to arrive as early as February, and remains until the end of the summer. It forms a burrow, often of great depth, in the peaty soil, and lays a single egg, pure white, and smooth in texture. According to Dixon, the birds are very garrulous at night, uttering their peculiar notes both when flying and in their nesting-holes ; the syllables ' Kitty-coo-roo ' are given by this author in imitation of the notes.

The sooty shearwater (*Puffinus griseus*) and the greater shearwater (*P. major*) are occasionally met with in autumn and winter on the British coasts. A third species, the dusky shearwater (*P. obscurus*), has a place in the list of British birds, two specimens having been obtained in the United Kingdom.

Fulmar.

Fulmarus glacialis.

Bill yellow; legs and feet grey; mantle and tail grey; quills dusky; head, neck, and under parts white. Length, nineteen inches.

The fulmar is the largest of the petrels; it exceeds the black-headed gull and common gull in size, and is a giant by comparison with its diminutive relation, the stormy petrel. It is a circumpolar species, and in winter inhabits the Atlantic and Pacific oceans in the northern hemisphere. On the British coasts it is a rare straggler in winter, and its only breeding-station in the United Kingdom is at St. Kilda. It is said that formerly there were several colonies on the west coast of Scotland, but these no longer exist. In its manner of flight and general appearance the fulmar is gull-like, and may easily be mistaken for a gull. Like other petrels, it lives, when not engaged in breeding, on the open sea, and it often follows the deep-sea fishing-boats and whalers, to feed on the offal thrown

Fig. 114.—Fulmar. ⅑ natural size.

out and portions of blubber floating on the water. Seebohm says that 'if a piece of meat be thrown to them, they often seize it before it sinks, but instead of diving after it, as a duck or guillemot would do, they alight on the surface feet first, and in the most comical way let themselves sink down in the water with uplifted wings.'

The fulmar lays a single white egg in a shallow hole dug in the peaty soil. Dixon has the following graphic account of the breeding-haunts and habits of the fulmar: 'In many places, although the cliff is very precipitous, it is covered with grass, sorrel, and other plants, and a loose, rich soil. It is in such spots that the fulmar breeds in the greatest numbers. I shall never forget the imposing effect of this noble bird-nursery. . . . When I reached the summit the scene was grand : tens of thousands of fulmars were flying silently about in all directions, but never by any chance soaring over the land; they passed backwards and forwards along the face of the cliff, and for some considerable distance out to sea, whilst the waves, a thousand feet below, were dotted thickly with floating birds. The silence of such an animated scene impressed me: not a single fulmar uttered a cry. . . . No bird flies more gracefully than the fulmar: it seems to float in the air without any exertion, often passing to and fro for minutes together with no perceptible movement of its wings. . . . It is a remarkably tame bird, fluttering along within a few feet of you, its black eye glistening sharply against its snow-white dress. . . . In some parts of the cliffs, where the soil is loose and turf-grown, the ground is almost white with sitting fulmars. Every available spot is a fulmar's nest ; and as you explore the cliffs, large numbers of birds fly out from all directions where they had not previously been noticed. . . . It very rarely burrows deep enough in the ground to conceal itself whilst incubating, and in the majority of cases only makes a hole large enough to half-conceal itself, whilst in a great many instances it is content to lay its eggs under some projecting tuft, or even on the bare and exposed ledge of a cliff, in a similar place to that so often selected by the guillemot. . . . The nests are very slight, and in a great number of instances are dispensed with altogether.'

Of the number of fulmars, the same observer says : 'The myriads of birds were past all belief : the air was darkened with their numbers ; still the cliffs were white with birds, and I calculated that not more than one in ten had risen. The fulmars filled the air like large snowflakes, and the hordes of puffins looked like a huge swarm of bees, darkening the air as far as we could see. Myriads of birds swept round the vessel or filled the air above ; the face of the cliffs seemed crumbling away as the living masses swept seaward ; yet, singularly enough, little noise was made beyond the humming of countless wings. The mighty peaks of these solitary ocean rocks were indistinctly seen through the surging cloud of birds, that seemed almost as if it would descend and overwhelm us.' [1]

Two petrels remain to be noticed : the capped petrel (*Œstrelata hæsitata*) and Bulwer's petrel (*Bulweria columbina*), one straggler having been obtained of the first species, and two of the second, on the east coast of England.

[1] Seebohm's *British Birds.*

Great Northern Diver.

Colymbus glacialis.

Fig. 115.—Great Northern Diver. ⅑ natural size.

Bill black; irides red; head and neck black, glossed with purple on the upper throat, and with green on the lower neck; two throat-bands black barred with white; mantle black spotted with white; under parts white. Length, thirty-three inches.

The great northern diver, or loon, is called great because he exceeds the other divers in size; in this sense he is also great in relation to birds generally, since he is as big as a goose, and therefore the equal of the few species that are greatest. In form he differs widely from the geese. An oceanic bird that escapes from its enemies by diving, and is never seen on the wing except when migrating, and never on land except when breeding, his form has been modified so as to make swimming and diving as easy to him as careering through the air is to the swift, and climbing on trees to the woodpecker. The beak is straight, conical, and sharp-pointed;

the head, neck, and body, grebe-like in form ; and the legs set so far back that the bird is almost incapable of progression on land. It is very wonderful that a creature that spends so great a part of its time on and in the water, without leaving it, should yet retain wing-power sufficient to perform long bi-annual migrations. Probably it does not take very extended flights ; when found on inland waters during migration, it often appears incapable of flight, and if in a small stream is easily taken. In its flying powers it appears, with the grebes and auks, to occupy a position midway between the ever-soaring, aërial gannet and the penguins, that are incapable of flight. In their dark rich, variegated upper, and white under, plumage, the divers again resemble the grebes. The glossy black back, thickly strewn with symmetrical white spots, gives the present species a beautiful and somewhat singular appearance. Out at sea it is a silent bird—silent and shy and solitary—with the cormorant-like habit of making itself invisible by sinking its body beneath the water. In the breeding season it utters cries of a very strange character, powerful and uncanny in their effect on the mind, and compared by different listeners to screams uttered by tortured children, and to shrieks of insane laughter. It is a winter visitor to the British Islands, chiefly to the west coasts of Scotland and England: but as it has occasionally been met with in summer in full nuptial plumage, it is thought by some ornithologists that a few pairs may remain to breed in some of the secluded lakes in the west of Scotland, the Outer Hebrides, the Orkneys, and Shetlands. It has not yet been found breeding anywhere in continental Europe ; its known breeding-grounds are in Iceland, and in America, from Greenland to Alaska. It breeds in secluded lakes and tarns, at no great distance from the sea, and prefers an island to nest on ; but where no island exists the nest is placed on the shore close to the water. Two eggs are laid, varying in ground-colour from olive-brown to russet-brown, spotted somewhat thinly with black.

The family of divers (Colymbidæ) consists of four species, all contained in one genus; and of the four, three are British. In habits, as well as in structure, they are so closely related that a very brief description of the other two is all that will be necessary. The black-throated diver (*Colymbus arcticus*) is much smaller than the great northern diver, its length being twenty-six inches. Bill black; irides red; crown and hind head ash-grey ; upper parts blackish, spotted and barred with white ; throat purplish black, with a half-collar of short white streaks; sides of neck striped with black and white; under parts white.

This diver breeds in small numbers on the west coast of Scotland and in the Outer Hebrides. To other parts of the country it is an accidental visitor. It is less oceanic in its habits than the last species described, and goes to a greater distance from the sea to breed. Two eggs are laid, similar in colour to those of the great northern diver.

The red-throated diver (*Colymbus septentrionalis*) is the smallest of the three species, its length being twenty-three inches. It has the head, throat, and sides of the neck mouse-colour; crown spotted with black; neck marked with black and white lines; on the front of the neck a large orange-coloured patch; back dusky brown; under parts white.

This species breeds in the west and north of Scotland, and in the Hebrides, Orkneys, and Shetlands.

Great Crested Grebe.

Podiceps cristatus.

FIG. 116.—GREAT CRESTED GREBE. $\frac{1}{10}$ natural size.

Crown and crest and ruff dark brown and chestnut; cheeks white; upper parts dark brown; secondaries white; under parts silky white. Length, twenty-two inches.

The great crested grebe still survives as a British species, although it is a large and handsome bird, and, like all those to which such a description applies, it has been much persecuted. Among our large water-birds there are few more strikingly handsome and stately in appearance than this grebe in its full breeding-plumage, when viewed as it floats, unalarmed, on the secluded reed-fringed water it loves. The swan, in its immaculate white dress, with proudly arched neck and plume-like scapulars, when seen 'floating double,' is to many minds the most perfect type of a beautiful waterfowl; certainly it is the most familiar. The great grebe has a very different appearance, with its straight neck, long, boat-shaped body, dark upper and silvery under plumage, and its broad ruff and double, ear-like crest; but in some aspects he is not less attractive than the white, larger bird, especially when sailing peacefully in close proximity to tall, slender reeds, their beauty, and that of the bird, enhanced by the 'magic of reflection,' when both seem part of the glassy pool, and made for one another.

Although in sadly diminished numbers, the great crested grebe still breeds regularly in many localities in England, especially in the eastern counties, and in a few situations in Wales and Ireland. In the northern counties of England it is very rare, and does not breed in Scotland : it is there a winter migrant from the north of Europe.

The habits of the grebe when on the water are similar to those of the diver. It is adapted to a swimming and diving existence; feeds on fish, frogs, water-beetles, and other small aquatic creatures; when alarmed it sinks its body deeper and deeper into the water, and when pursued, or in danger, seeks to escape by diving. It makes little use of its wings, except when migrating. At most times it is a silent bird, but in the breeding season utters a harsh, grating cry.

The grebe makes a large platform nest of aquatic plants, placed on the water among the reeds. Four eggs are laid, the shell pale blue in colour, but covered with a soft, white, chalky substance. Invariably, when leaving the nest the bird covers the eggs with moss and weeds, and the usual inference is that this is done to hide them from rapacious egg-eating birds; but Seebohm is of the opinion that the eggs are covered to be kept warm, and he says that they are covered only after the full complement is laid and incubation begun.

Little Grebe, or Dabchick.

Tachybaptes fluviatilis.

Fig. 117.—Little Grebe. ⅙ natural size.

Head, neck, and upper parts dark brown; a little white on the secondaries; chin black; cheeks, throat, and sides of the neck reddish chestnut; under parts greyish white; flanks dusky brown; bill horn-colour; legs and feet dull green. Length, nine inches and a half.

The little grebe, or dabchick, is less than the teal in size, and differs from the great crested grebe in about the same degree as the partridge does from the pheasant. It is the one common and well-known species of grebe in this country, being resident in suitable localities in all parts of the United Kingdom. In summer it is generally diffused, and is to be met with even on small pools and streams; in winter it shifts its ground, resorting to the rivers and larger bodies of water, and in very severe weather to the sea-coast.

It begins to breed at the end of April or early in May, and forms a floating nest of aquatic weeds and grasses close to the bank or among the reeds, but in most cases little care is taken to conceal the nest. The eggs are three or four to six in number, and are white, and rough in texture. Before quitting the nest the incubating bird invariably covers the eggs with wet leaves and grass, drawn in from the edge of the nest. It is hard to believe, with Seebohm, that the object of this action is to keep the eggs warm. The nest is, in very many cases, conspicuous to the eye, but on the slightest alarm the sitting-bird quickly and deftly draws the dead, wet materials like a blanket over the eggs, and, slipping off, dives silently, to come up at a considerable distance, usually where it cannot be seen. The nest then presents the appearance of a mere bunch of dead and water-soaked weeds or grass floating on the surface. I have examined a good many nests, and am convinced that the eggs are covered to hide them from the sight of egg-robbing animals, and that only the egg-robber that is neither furred nor feathered, and is well acquainted with the habits of the bird, is capable of seeing through this pretty deception.

The dabchick has the curious habit of holding its young under its wings and diving from the nest, to take them out of danger. Like its neighbour, the moorhen, the little grebe sometimes begins to breed a second time, before the young of the first brood are able to take proper care of themselves ; and it has been observed in such cases that while one of the parents incubated the eggs in the new nest, the other has remained in charge of the partly grown young. The nest is used by the young birds after they are able to swim and dive, and while resting on it their parents bring them food.

The three remaining species of the grebe family (Podicipidæ) included in the avifauna of the United Kingdom are the red-necked grebe (*Podiceps griseigena*), a rare winter visitor to the British coasts ; the Sclavonian grebe (*P. auritus*), a not uncommon winter visitor to Scotland, Ireland, and the north and east coasts of England ; and the eared grebe (*P. nigrocollis*), an irregular visitor, usually in spring, to the southern and eastern districts of England.

Razorbill.

Alca torda.

Upper parts greenish black ; deep brown on the throat ; under parts white. Length, seventeen inches.

The black and white razorbill, with curiously shaped massive beak, viewed sitting on a rock, its body inclined a little forward, may give us some idea of the great auk's appearance. It is less

than half the size of the vanished bird, but is its nearest living
representative. Throughout the year the razorbill is not an uncommon species in the seas that surround the British Islands, but
is very much less abundant than the common guillemot, which it
most nearly resembles in its habits. That it will become still
less common than it is at present is greatly to be feared. For some
time past it has been decreasing in numbers on all our coasts,
from what cause is not accurately known. On this subject Howard
Saunders writes: ‘This may partly be owing to severe visitations of
mortality which have from time to time affected many sea-birds,
but especially the present species.’ Whether killed by an epidemic
to which they are liable, or starved to death, as some naturalists
think, it is certain that they perish in large numbers. On the south
coast I have seen their dead bodies, washed up by the waves during a
severe gale, lying in hundreds on the beach; and the same distressing
spectacle has been witnessed by others at various points on the
coast.

The razorbill is a handsome species, with shiny white under-
plumage, the black upper parts relieved by a stripe of pure white on
the head and a narrow white bar across the wing. The black, axe-

FIG. 118.—RAZORBILL (winter plumage). $\frac{1}{11}$ natural size.

like beak is also crossed in its deepest part with a white mark
in the form of a crescent. Its life is mostly passed in the water,
where it sits high and floats buoyantly like a duck. It feeds chiefly
on small fishes, for which it dives, and when pursuing them uses
the wings as well as feet in propulsion. On the sea the razorbills

are usually seen in small flocks; they fly like diving ducks, with rapidly-beating wings, in a line, one bird behind the other, and so close as to be almost touching. In March they resort to the bold headlands and precipitous rocky cliffs which are their breeding-places. They are then seen associating with guillemots and puffins; for, albeit these three auks differ in appearance and breeding-habits, they seem to be aware of their relationship, and mix together in a friendly way. It may, however, be noticed that on a ledge where many guillemots and a few razorbills are assembled, as a rule the latter form a little group by themselves. This species is somewhat silent, although they occasionally utter long cries, somewhat gull-like in character, but lower and more guttural. When disturbed they emit a different sound, peculiar and human-like in tone, resembling the low moans of a person in pain.

A single egg is laid by the razorbill, and is placed in a cranny, sometimes in a hole several feet deep; occasionally the egg is deposited in a hollow on a rocky ledge, and in such situations razorbills and guillemots are found breeding side by side. The egg is large and handsome, the ground colour white, spotted and blotched with different shades of blackish and deep reddish brown, and sometimes chocolate-colour. Both birds take part in incubating. An observer who has studied the habits of this bird says that in most cases the young fly down to the sea, usually early in the morning, and being once there, do not return to the rocks, as their wings are not then strong enough to enable them to mount upwards. ' Sometimes,' he writes, ' when the young one is obstinate, the mother will take it by the back of the neck, and fly down to the sea. (*Zoologist*, 1871, p. 2427.)' He adds that the parent teaches the young bird to dive by taking it by the neck and diving with it.

The breeding season over, the birds do not return to the rocks until the next spring.

Common Guillemot.

Lomvia troile.

Head, neck, and upper parts blackish brown; under parts white. Length, eighteen inches.

The common guillemot is the most abundant of the four species of auks which inhabit the British Islands. Less handsome and striking in appearance than the razorbill, in its habits it is just as interesting. It is found in the breeding season on all parts of our coasts where extensive rocky cliffs and headlands exist, and it has not been driven away by persecution. At some points on the coast, as at Bempton Cliffs and Flamborough Head, and at the Farne Islands, and other localities farther north, the guillemots are still exceedingly numerous ; south of Yorkshire they have greatly diminished in numbers, and several of the old breeding-stations have been abandoned.

On the sea their habits are similar to those of the razorbill : they swim, dive, and fly in strings in the same manner. In appearance the two species differ considerably. The guillemot has a dusky brown or mouse-coloured upper plumage, and a straight, sharp beak, very different to the massive weapon of the razorbill.

Early in spring the guillemots begin to gather from the neighbouring seas at their old breeding-stations on the summits and sides of cliffs that face the ocean. Of all birds that breed in communities, they are the most social, or, at all events, crowd closest together. Where they breed on the side of the cliff, as at Flamborough, they may be seen standing in close rows and groups on every ledge or jutting rock large enough to afford them a footing. A strange and fascinating spectacle is presented when the cliff is looked at from below, and the guillemots are seen in thousands, row above row, lessening in size by distance until, near the summit of the vast precipice, they appear no bigger than dippers ; all standing erect, their backs to the dark stone wall, and their shiny, white breasts to the sea. It is also strange to see them gathered on the flat, table-like tops of the ' Pinnacles,' a group of isolated, precipitous rocks at the Farnes ; for here the space they have is not sufficient to properly accommodate the vast number of birds that resort to it. Their appearance forcibly reminds the spectator of a human crowd on some fête day in a populous city ; but the bird-crowd does not move or sway : each guillemot keeps its place, for it is standing over its own egg, which must be kept warm at any cost. In spite of this fixity they are all very alert and lively, turning their beaks about this way and that, and, when alarmed, all bobbing and bowing their heads as if to salute the intruder. Although silent birds when on the sea, the guillemots become loquacious at their breeding-grounds. They are very excitable, and when two or three neighbours quarrel, as they frequently do, or a bird returned from the sea drops on to a ledge where others are standing, or when male and female meet again after a separation of a few hours, there is a great deal of noise. They utter a hoarse, long-drawn cry, like the beginning of a dog's howl before he has cleared his voice ; also a succession of laughter-like notes, and other sounds resembling the cries, guttural and clear, of the black-headed gull; and, sometimes, short, barking notes like those of geese and sheldrakes.

Like most short-winged, heavy-bodied birds, they fly straight to their point, rushing violently through the air with rapidly-beating wings. It is amusing to watch a bird flying in from the sea, and attempting to alight on a ledge of rock already crowded ; one or two birds at the spot the new-comer attempts to drop on threaten to strike with their beaks. This demonstration prevents him from coming down among them ; and, being incapable of gliding off to one side to drop on to some other spot, or of suspending himself in the air for a few moments, he is compelled to drop down without touching the ledge, sweep round, and go straight out to sea again, and after flying a distance of three or four hundred yards, or farther, to circle round and come back to the ledge a second time. The frustrated bird is often seen to fly right away out of sight.

The single egg of the guillemot is deposited on the naked rock, without any nest, often dangerously near the edge. The sitting-birds are very careful when leaving the rock to push the eggs from under them ; but when suddenly startled, as by the report of a gun fired from a ship or boat for the amusement of cockney excursionists, the eggs may be thrown off the ledge, and in some instances have been seen to fall in a shower down the cliff-side. The guillemot lays a handsome pear-shaped egg, very large for the bird. No other bird lays eggs so various in colour ; so greatly do they vary that two eggs cannot be found quite alike, even among hundreds. The ground-colour in different specimens is white, cream, stone-colour, pale blue, reddish, and many shades of green, from a strong, bright green to olive-green. The egg is spotted and blotched with brown, black, and deep red, and grey. The guillemot when incubating does not lie on its egg like most birds, but stands with the egg between its legs, which are placed very far back, as in all auks, divers, and grebes. It is a pretty and amusing sight to watch the guillemot, when returning to her egg after a short absence, walk on to it, and adjust and readjust it a score of times, using her beak and chin for the purpose, before she is satisfied that it is effectually covered. Incubation lasts a month, and only one young bird is reared in the season ; if the first egg is taken she will lay a second, and sometimes a third.

BB

In strange contrast to the guttural croaking and barking cries of the adults is the language of the young bird. Its hunger-note is a far-reaching, sandpiper-like cry, clear, tremulous, and musical. In imitation of this sound the young bird is called a *willock*; and it is supposed that the name of guillemot, which is of French origin, is also derived from the young bird's cry.

Black Guillemot.

Uria grylle.

Plumage sooty black, except a patch on the wing-coverts, which is white with a black bar; bill black; legs vermilion-red. Length, fourteen inches.

The black guillemot is much less abundant than the last species. On the south and east coasts it is extremely rare; its principal breeding-stations are on the west coast of Scotland; and it also breeds on the north and west coasts of Ireland. It differs greatly from the common guillemot in size, being scarcely more than half as large as that species; also in colouring, the whole plumage, except a broad white patch on the wing, being glossy black, the legs and feet bright red. It breeds in the same situations as the common guillemot, but is not so gregarious; and in its nesting-habits it resembles the razorbill, laying its eggs in a hole or cranny in the rocks, or beneath a rock on the soil. Two eggs are laid, in ground-colour white, or pale stone, or pale green, spotted and blotched with brown and grey. The young are covered with a greyish black down, and their first

FIG. 119.—LITTLE AUK. ⅛ natural size.

plumage is mottled black and white.

The black guillemot frequents the seas in the vicinity of its breeding-station throughout the year.

Brünnich's guillemot (*Lomvia bruennichi*) is a very rare straggler from the arctic regions to the northern islands and coasts of Scotland.

The little auk (*Margulus alle*) is an irregular visitor, sometimes in considerable numbers, to the British coasts, especially in the north. It is a circumpolar species, and straggles southwards in winter, but seldom approaches the British Islands, except in very severe weather.

Puffin.

Fratercula arctica.

FIG. 120.—PUFFIN. ⅙ natural size.

Crown, collar, and upper parts black, all the rest white; bill, bluish at the base, yellow in the middle, bright red at the tip; legs and feet orange-red. Length, twelve inches.

Among British birds, whether sea or land, the puffin is the most singular in appearance—a small auk, compact in build, conspicuous in black and white plumage, broad collar, white, owlish face, and great beak, short and adze-shaped, but massive as a toucan's. The brilliant colours of this beak, too—red with orange bars—give it a curious resemblance to the enormous organ of the tropical bird. One may look at the puffin almost daily, as he stands on the rocks, always with something of surprise at his strikingly handsome yet grotesque appearance. The fanciful idea suggests itself that the bird is a masquerader; that the visible, brilliantly coloured beak has been artificially made, and put on over the natural beak, just as in the case of a human masquerader a large, gaily coloured, artificial nose is sometimes placed over the natural organ. And the puffin's beak is, in fact, something of a mask, or superimposed ornament; and after the breeding season its surface peels off in horny plates, and is shed like the deciduous bark of certain trees. The bird's beak in winter is moderate in size and dull-coloured.

The puffin is a spring visitor to our coasts, and after rearing their young the birds scatter over the sea and journey southwards. The puffins found on the east coasts of England and Scotland during the winter months are probably migrants from more northern latitudes. Puffins are found in summer in most localities on our coasts where razorbills and guillemots collect; on the south coast they are rare, but increase as we go north, until at St. Kilda they are found gathered in incalculable numbers. As a cliff-breeder the puffin deposits its egg in a hole or cranny in the rocks like the razorbill, but never on an exposed ledge, as the guillemot always, and the razorbill sometimes, does. Sometimes they take forcible possession of rabbit-burrows among sandhills, driving the owners out; but they prefer making their own burrows in a soft peaty soil, such as they find at St. Kilda and in many other localities. In March or April they return from their wanderings on the sea and begin the great business of the year. Where they are in large numbers and make their burrows near each other the soft soil is so undermined by them that it is difficult to walk over the ground without breaking through the turf and sinking almost knee-deep in their holes at every few steps. When engaged in digging the birds are so intent on their work that they may be approached very closely, and sometimes even taken with the hand. The burrow is three or four feet in length, sometimes more, and at the extremity a single egg is laid, oval in form, large for the bird's size, and white, faintly spotted and streaked with grey. The young bird is covered with black down, and has a comparatively small beak, of a dark colour. He is a squat, lumpish creature, owlish in appearance. When fishing to supply its young the parent puffin has the curious habit and faculty of keeping the small fishes it catches in its beak, where they may be seen as the bird swims on the sea, their tails and a portion of their bodies protruding at the sides of the beak and mouth. How it manages to hold several little fishes in this way and go on diving and catching others is a puzzle. On arriving at the burrow the fishes are placed on the floor inside, or at the entrance, where the young bird sits waiting for its parent, and are then picked up one by one and put into the open, hungry mouth.

INDEX.

Wheelbird, 181
Whimbrel, 313
Whinchat, 54
Whiskered tern, 323
White-bellied swift, **179**
White-eyed duck, 246
White-fronted goose, 230
White-spotted bluethroat, 59
White's thrush, 52
White stork, 226
Whitetail, 54
White-tailed eagle, 205
Whitethroat, 64
— greater, 65
— lesser, 66
White wagtail, **108**
White-winged black tern, 323
— crossbill, 145
— lark, 178
Whooper swan, 234
Wigeon, 237
— American, 238
Wild duck, 239
— swan, 234
Willow-warbler, 76
Willow-wren, 76
Wilson's petrel, 336
Windhover, 212
Woodchat, 116

Woodcock, 296
Woodlark, 176
Wood-owl, 198
Woodpecker, barred, **183**
— green, 184
— lesser spotted, 183
— spotted, 181
Wood-pigeon, 258
Wood-sandpiper, 316
Wood-wren, 78
Wren, 101
— furze, 70
— golden-crested, 72
— red-craking night, 84
— willow, 76
— wood, 78
Wryneck, 186

XEMA sabinii, 330

YAFFLE, 185
Yellow-billed cuckoo, 193
Yellow-browed warbler, 79
Yellow bunting, 148
Yellowhammer, 149
Yellow wagtail, 107
— yoldring, 149

Printed at THE BALLANTYNE PRESS
SPOTTISWOODE, BALLANTYNE & CO. LTD.
Colchester, London & Eton, England